CONTENTS

The official directory of the Diocese of Westminster

Westminster Year Book 2006

54th edition

ISSN 1468-8549

www.westminsteryearbook.org.uk

The Diocese comprises the London Boroughs north of the Thames and west of Waltham Forest and Newham, the districts of Staines and Sunbury-on-Thames and the County of Hertfordshire.

Patrons of the Diocese
Our Blessed Lady Immaculate, Dec 8; and St Joseph, Mar 19.
St Peter, Prince of the Apostles, June 29; and St Edward, Oct 13.
Consecrated to the Sacred Heart of Jesus, 17 June 1873.

Diocesan Website **www.rcdow.org.uk**

Westminster Year Book, Archbishop's House, Ambrosden Avenue, SW1P 1QJ
Tel: 020 7798 9092 (voice mail) E-mail: wyb@rcdow.org.uk

Editor **Fr Stuart Wilson** Deputy Editor **Fr Christopher Bedford**
Production/Advertising **Roland Hayes** Liturgical Calendar **Fr Richard Andrew**
Cover design: **Joe Kennedy**

Printers **Newnorth Print Ltd www.newnorth.co.uk**

Compilation completed 25 October 2005

Unless stated otherwise all **e-mail addresses** in this Year Book are formed as follows:
Individuals: ***firstname+surname*@rcdow.org.uk** eg: **stuartwilson@rcdow.org.uk**
Parishes: ***parish*@rcdow.org.uk** eg: **abbotslangley@rcdow.org.uk**

FROM THE CARDINAL

The Challenges of Change

The past year has been an eventful one. 2005 saw the death of Pope John Paul I I and the election of his successor, Benedict XV I, and these coincided with the launch of the long-awaited 'Green Paper' on the future of our Diocese.

At Your Word, Lord', our spiritual renewal programme, came to an end with a call for Catholics to put into social action the fruits of their two and-a-half year journey.

We saw the retirement of Bishop Jim O'Brien after 28 years of marvellous service, but will soon, I hope, be announcing his successor.

Next year is about harvesting these changes. The 'White Paper', which I expect to publish in January, will map out the future of the Diocese and suggest how we can best meet our new opportunities.

As a Diocese, we are changing, and becoming more diverse. Our congregations seem to be steadily expanding while our resources are not always in the right place, or do not meet our current needs. We need a new emphasis on mission and formation.

The small faith-sharing groups in our parishes are asking to continue, and to be supported. It is especially important at a time of change to be able to pause and take stock.

I am convinced that we have a much stronger sense of who we are as a Diocese; our bonds of communion are stronger than ever.

We need to celebrate this. Which is why, in July 2006, we hope to have a diocesan festival, 'Open the Doors', and to celebrate the gifts of the Holy Spirit in the parishes and communities of our Diocese.

It is a time of new beginnings. I hope very much we will look back at this time as a Year of Favour.

Yours devotedly in Christ,

Cardinal Cormac Murphy O'Connor

FROM THE EDITOR

As Editor of the Westminster Year Book, it is my job to ensure that the information contained in the book is gathered together in time for the publication deadline. Added to this, I also have the responsibility of making sure that this information is accurate as inaccuracies are soon reported! I could not complete these aspects of the work without the collaboration of so many people – the unseen agents of the Westminster Year Book. Without this working together the Yearbook would simply be a dream and not the solid piece of diocesan work that you are now holding in your hand.

Sometimes people use the word Diocese in different ways. Occasionally it is used to describe the faceless people who fit the question "What is the Diocese thinking? Sometimes people credit the idea of Diocese to those who work at the centre. With respect to all of them, Directors, Heads of Departments, Vicars General, Auxiliary Bishops and even the Cardinal are not the Diocese on their own. It is everyone, every parishioner, every priest, every volunteer worker, every lay minister, who, together, with our Cardinal makes the Diocese. The Year Book is for each and every one.

For the editor, bringing together so many different interests and keeping them is some kind of unity is not easy. In today's individualist society there is a pressure to resist uniformity. Of course unity is different from uniformity, but even unity needs a few rules, a few boundaries in style and contribution if the book is to hold together Some request different names for their parishes, some want to be free of rcdow.org.uk, some want different titles to the norm , some want different parish lay outs. I suspect I didn't please everyone – let's hope I pleased someone.

The Yearbook serves the Diocese in two ways. First it makes a statement. It is a who's who and a what's what. Secondly it is a means of communication. Much of the detailed work in editing is concerned with making sure phone numbers and emails correct. My own view is that this Yearbook needs more not less phone numbers and email addresses so that our communication is two way. Central departments are tackling the challenge to be more communicative and with the coming of our new Diocesan Communications Officer that will continue to develop. Communication is a two way thing and maybe my last comment would be a request to parishes on behalf of so many of my correspondents. "Please don't leave the answer phone on all the time."

Stuart Wilson.

Fr Stuart Wilson

7 Ways to Transform Lives: The Cardinal Hume Centre's 20th Anniversary

This is a landmark year for the Cardinal Hume Centre. It has been 20 years since the Centre first began helping young homeless people and families to transform their lives. For many of the people who live at or visit the Centre this is a lifetime, and during their lifetime they may have experienced homelessness, poverty and abuse. But they have their whole lives ahead of them, and by working with staff at the Centre young people can learn to cope with their previous experiences and gain the skills and confidence they need to look to the future. The 20th anniversary also marks a turning point for the Cardinal Hume Centre, which has grown and developed over the years to meet changing demands. The most dramatic change has taken place in the past 2 years and has been only recently completed. The refurbishment and extension of the entire Centre building has allowed services to expand and even more young people and families to access support in a specially designed space.

The Centre was founded in 1986 by Cardinal Hume in response to the desperate need of young homeless people and families in crisis. As the only charitable organisation to bear his name, we are incredibly proud to continue the work of a man who had an unfailing commitment to enabling young people to fulfil their potential. Since opening the Centre has grown to encompass two Hostels, a Drop-in Centre, a Family Centre, Education and Training Programmes, a Move On Team and a Surgery. Through these 7 services the Centre helps people to transform their lives.

The Centre Hostel has 32 bedrooms and enables young people between the ages of 16 and 21 to work towards independent living. Staff at the Hostel understand that each young person who comes to stay has their own set of experiences and needs. On arrival each resident is allocated a key worker with whom they meet regularly to address the issues that have affected them and to provide support and guidance to meet their individual specific requirements. They are able to live at the Hostel for up to a year, during which they work to improve their self-confidence, basic life skills and employability.

The Horseferry Road Project is the Centre's second hostel, which provides accommodation for 8 residents up to the age of 35 who have completed a

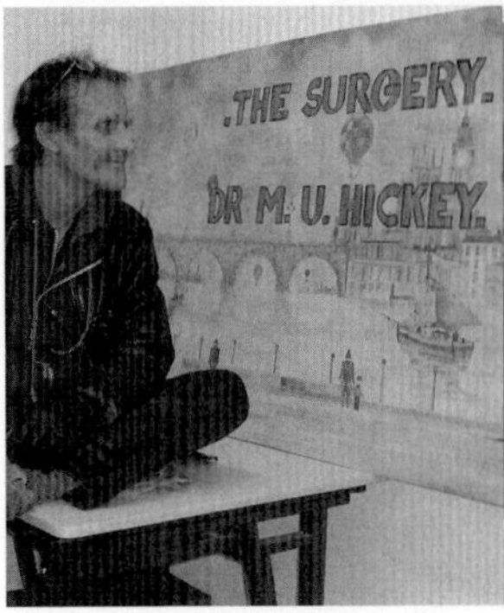

rehabilitation programme for drug or alcohol dependency. Again residents stay for up to a year. They have already taken huge steps towards recovery and with the support and guidance of trained staff, they are able to prepare themselves for independent living. The Move On Team work with residents from both hostels throughout their stay to find future accommodation for the time when they are ready to leave the Centre. The Team also provide ongoing support to ex-residents as they build a life for themselves after leaving.

With a limited number of beds in the two hostels it is vital that the Centre finds a way to support the vast number of young homeless people that need help. The Drop-in Centre does exactly that. Vulnerable young people aged between 16 and 25 years old are able to literally drop-in for support and advice. The young people who visit the Drop-in are either homeless or living in insecure accommodation. In the morning staff help with their immediate practical needs by making appropriate referrals to night shelters and other emergency and long-term accommodation, as well as offering facilities such as laundry and showers. In the afternoon, the young people are able to work on developing skills such as healthy eating, cooking on a budget, and managing money. There is also a weekly drug clinic and 1-1 counselling sessions. Finally, out reach in local schools is a key area of work, enabling students to learn about the reality of homelessness and prevent the young people of today becoming the homeless of tomorrow.

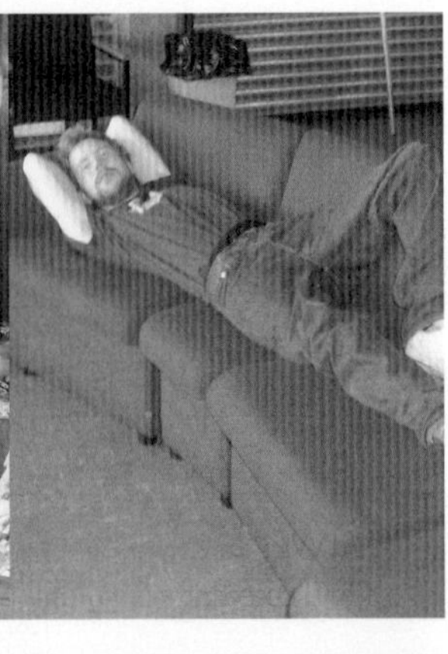

The Family Centre supports families with pre-school children in the local community who are living in temporary, insecure or inappropriate accommodation, providing a friendly atmosphere where parents can bring their small children to play and meet others in similar circumstances. While their children play, parents can seek advice and support from staff on a range of issues from benefits to healthcare, child education to parenting, and there is also the opportunity to attend educational courses. The Family Centre is a place which helps to lift the feeling of isolation and which gives families hope for the future.

The Education, Training and Employment Programme continues to play a fundamental part in all of the Centre's services, embracing the theme of lifelong learning and development. Clients from all backgrounds, from both the Centre and other projects across London, are given the opportunity to improve their English language skills, receive accredited computer training from basic to advanced levels and gain support in finding employment or training. A dedicated Skills Development Co-ordinator also works across all the Centre's projects to ensure that young people and families are given the opportunity to achieve their long-tem goals. Finally, a full time Surgery dedicated to helping homeless and vulnerable people is accessible to all the people who come to the Centre as well as homeless people throughout London.

Amazing achievements occur everyday at the Centre, and this has been the case for the past 20 years. None of the help, support and opportunities provided to young homeless people and families would have been possible without the dedication of our supporters. I hope that you will be able to celebrate with us at various events throughout the year, marking 20 years of transforming lives.

BENEDICT XVI

BISHOP OF ROME, VICAR OF JESUS CHRIST
Successor of St Peter Prince of the Apostles, Supreme Pastor of the Universal Church
Patriarch of the West, Primate of Italy,
Archbishop and Metropolitan of the Province of Rome
Sovereign of the State of the Vatican City, Servant of the Servants of God

His Holiness Pope Benedict XVI (Joseph Ratzinger) Born in Marktl am Inn, Germany, 16 April 1927.
Ordained priest 29 June 1951.
Ordained Archbishop of Munich 28 May 1977.
Created Cardinal 27 June 1977.
Elected Pope 19 April 2005.
Inaugurated 24 April 2005.

BISHOPS IN ENGLAND AND WALES

Archbishops are addressed as Most Reverend,
Bishops as Right Reverend
The dates are of Episcopal Ordination and Translation

PROVINCE OF WESTMINSTER

WESTMINSTER Cormac Murphy-O'Connor (1977; 2000)
Archbishop's House, Ambrosden Avenue, Westminster, London SW1P 1QJ
Auxiliary Bishops George Stack (2001), Alan Hopes (2003), Bernard Longley (2003)
Retired Bishop James O'Brien (1977),
BRENTWOOD Thomas McMahon (1980)
Bishop's House, Stock, Ingatestone, Essex CM4 9BU
EAST ANGLIA Michael Evans (2003)
The White House, 21 Upgate, Poringland, Norwich NR14 7SH
NORTHAMPTON Peter Doyle (2005)
Bishop's House, Marriott Street, Northampton NN2 6AW
Retired Bishop Leo McCartie (1977; 1990)
NOTTINGHAM Malcolm McMahon OP (2000)
Bishop's House, 27 Cavendish Road East, The Park, Nottingham NG7 1BB
Retired Bishop James McGuinness (1972; 1974)

PROVINCE OF BIRMINGHAM

BIRMINGHAM Vincent Nichols (1992; 2000)
Archbishop's House, 8 Shadwell Street, Birmingham B4 6EY
Archbishop Emeritus Maurice Couve de Murville (1982)
Auxiliary Bishop Philip Pargeter (1990)
CLIFTON Declan Lang (2001)
St Ambrose, Leigh Woods, Bristol BS8 3PW
Retired Bishop Mervyn Alexander (1972; 1974)
SHREWSBURY Brian Noble (1995)
Bishop's House, Laburnum Cottage, 97 Barnston Road, Barnston, Wirral L61 1BW

PROVINCE OF CARDIFF

CARDIFF Peter Smith (1995; 2001) *Archbishop's House, 43 Cathedral Rd, Cardiff CF1 9HD*
Archbishop Emeritus John Ward OFM Cap (1980; 1983)
MENEVIA Mark Jabalé OSB (2000) *Bryn Rhos, 79 Walter Road, Swansea SA1 4PS*
Retired Bishop Daniel J Mullins (1970, 1987)
WREXHAM Edwin Regan (1994), *Bishop's House, Sontley Road, Wrexham, Clywd LL13 7EW*

PROVINCE OF LIVERPOOL

LIVERPOOL Patrick Kelly (1984; 1996),
Archbishop's House, Lowood, Carnatic Road, Liverpool L18 8BY
Auxiliary Bishop Vincent Malone (1989) Tom Williams (2003)
HALLAM John Rawsthorne (1981; 1997), *75 Norfolk Road, Sheffield S2 2SZ*
HEXHAM & NEWCASTLE Kevin Dunn (2004),
Bishop's House, East Denton Hall, 800 West Road, Newcastle-upon-Tyne NE5 2BJ
Retired Bishops Ambrose Griffiths OSB (1992); Hugh Lindsay (1969; 1974)
LANCASTER Patrick O'Donoghue(1993; 2001)
Cathedral House, Balmoral Road, Lancaster LA1 3BT
LEEDS Arthur Roche (2001, 2002)
Bishop's House, 13 North Grange Road, Leeds LS6 2BR
Retired Bishop David Konstant (1977; 1985)
MIDDLESBROUGH John Crowley (1986;1993)
Bishop's House, 16 Cambridge Road, Middlesbrough, Cleveland TS5 5NN
Retired Bishop Augustine Harris (1966; 1978)
SALFORD Terence Brain (1991; 1997)
Wardley Hall, Worsley, Manchester M28 5ND

PROVINCE OF SOUTHWARK

SOUTHWARK Kevin McDonald (2001, 2003)
Archbishop's House, St George's Road, SE1 6HX
Archbishop Emeritus Michael G Bowen (1970, 1977)
Auxiliary Bishop John Hine (2001)
Retired Bishops Charles Joseph Henderson (1972), John Jukes OFM Conv (1980), Howard Tripp(1980),
ARUNDEL & BRIGHTON Kieran Conry (2001)
High Oaks, Old Brighton Road North, Pease Pottage, West Sussex RH11 9HA
PLYMOUTH Christopher Budd (1986)
Bishop's House, 31 Wyndham Street West, Plymouth, Devon PL1 5RZ
PORTSMOUTH Crispian Hollis (1987, 1988)
Bishop's House, Edinburgh Road, Portsmouth PO1 3HG

THE CARDINAL ARCHBISHOP

His Eminence Cormac Murphy-O'Connor Ph.L, STL
Born Reading 24 August 1932
Ordained priest 28 October 1956
Elected to the Diocese of
Arundel and Brighton 17 November 1977
Ordained Bishop by Archbishop Michael Bowen
21 December 1977
Became Tenth Archbishop of Westminster 22 March 2000.
Created Cardinal Priest of Santa Maria Sopra Minerva
21 February 2001

ARCHBISHOP'S HOUSE (Residence of the Cardinal Archbishop)
Ambrosden Avenue SW1P 1QJ
Tel: 020 7798 9033 Fax: 020 7798 9077
E-mail: archbishop@rcdow.org.uk
Website: www.rcdow.org.uk/archbishop/

Office of the Private Secretary
Private Secretary Fr Mark O'Toole
Tel: 020 7798 9041 E-mail: markotoole@rcdow.org.uk
PA to the Cardinal's Private Office Sue Hayden
Tel: 020 7931 6007 E-mail: suehayden@rcdow.org.uk

Personal Secretary to the Cardinal Sister Damian McGrath RSM
Tel: 020 7798 9039 E-mail: srdamian@rcdow.org.uk

Office for Public Affairs
Director Austen Ivereigh
Tel: 020 7798 9045 E-mail: austenivereigh@rcdow.org.uk
PA to the Director Susan Claridge
Tel: 020 7798 9030 E-mail: susanclaridge@rcdow.org.uk

Director of Diocesan Communications Eddie Tulasiewicz
Tel: 020 7798 9031 E-mail: eddiet@rcdow.org.uk

Sisters responsible for the Household
Augustinian Sisters (OSA) Sr Clement, Sr Barbara, Sr Pius Tel: 020 7798 9398

Reception
Gillian Reid, Michael Holmes Tel: 020 7798 9033
E-mail: abh@rcdow.org.uk

AUXILIARY BISHOPS

Right Rev George Stack
Titular Bishop of Gemellae in Numidia
Born 9 May 1946 Cork; ordained priest 21 May 1972;
ordained bishop by Cardinal Murphy-O'Connor 10 May 2001.
Archbishop's House, Ambrosden Avenue SW1P 1QJ Tel: 020 7798 9060
Secretary Linda Murphy **Tel: 020 7798 9381**
Residence **14 Egerton Gardens NW4 4BA Tel: 020 8202 8024**

Right Rev Alan Hopes
Titular Bishop of Cuncacestre
Born 17 March 1944 Oxford; ordained priest 4 December 1995,
ordained bishop 24 January 2003 by Cardinal Murphy-O'Connor.
Archbishop's House, Ambrosden Avenue SW1P 1QJ
Tel: 020 7798 9043
Secretary Ellen Dunleavy. **Tel: 020 7798 9023**
Residence **16 Abingdon Road W8 6AF Tel: 020 7376 1661**

Right Rev Bernard Longley
Titular Bishop of Zarna
Born 5 April 1955 Manchester; ordained priest 12 December 1981,
ordained bishop 24 January 2003 by Cardinal Murphy-O'Connor.
Archbishop's House, Ambrosden Avenue SW1P 1QJ
Tel: 020 7931 6061
Secretary Julie McMahon
Tel: 020 7798 9381
Residence **64 Lichfield Road E3 5AL Tel: 020 8980 6925**

RETIRED AUXILIARY BISHOP
Right Rev James O'Brien
Titular Bishop of Manaccenser
Born Wood Green, London, 5 August 1930; ordained priest 12 June 1954;
ordained bishop by Cardinal Hume, 21 September 1977.
Residence **The Gate House, All Saints Pastoral Centre, London Colney, Herts AL2 1AG**

E-mail: first name+surname@rcdow.org.uk (unless stated otherwise)

ARCHBISHOP'S COUNCIL ARCHBISHOP'S HOUSE SW1P 1QJ

Tel: 020 7798 9033 Fax: 020 7798 9077

The Cardinal, Auxiliary Bishops, Vicars General, Private Secretary, Financial Secretary

ADMINISTRATION

VICARS GENERAL
Bishop Alan Hopes **Tel: 020 7798 9043** **Secretary** Ellen Dunleavy. **Tel: 020 7798 9023**
Mgr John Arnold **Tel: 020 7931 6062** **PA** Linda Murphy

CHANCELLOR **Tel: 020 7931 6062** Mgr John Arnold
Assistant Miss Brenda Roberts **Tel: 020 7798 9037** Chancery Office open Mon - Fri

EPISCOPAL VICAR FOR EASTERN CATHOLIC CHURCHES Canon Vincent Berry
St Mary's Rectory, Draycott Terrace SW3 2QR Tel: 020 7589 5487

VICARS FOR RELIGIOUS
Fr Michael Campbell OSA **Tel: 020 8748 3788 (Episcopal Vicar)**
55 Fulham Palace Road W6 8AU
Sr Louise Swanston **47 Cornwall Crescent W11 1PJ Tel: 020 7792 8260**
Sr Mary Paul Ewen SSCJ **6 Oakleigh Park South N20 9JU Tel: 020 8445 9299**

CHILD PROTECTION CO-ORDINATOR Mgr Canon Harry Turner
Tel: 01582 712245 Fax: 01582 460601
CHILD PROTECTION OFFICER Mr Peter Turner
73 St Charles Square W10 6EJ Tel: 020 8969 5305 Fax: 020 8960 1464
E-mail: pturner@cathchild.org.uk Website: www.rcdow.org.uk/childprotection

METROPOLITAN TRIBUNAL **Vaughan House, 46 Francis Street SW1P 1QN**
Tel: 020 7798 9003 Judicial Vicar Mgr Ralph Brown ProtAp, JCD, KCHS
Personal Assistant Mrs Maureen Scammell **Tel: 020 7798 9078**
Assistant Judicial Vicars Canon Michael Brockie JCL; Fr John Conneely JCL
Canonical Assistants Fr Nicholas Kavanagh; Mrs Alicia Sloan JCL.
Tribunal Assistants Mr Matthew Gillespie; Miss Patricia McGloin; Miss Maria Phelan;
Miss Marilyn Smith **Tribunal Archives** Mrs Mary Moss

DIOCESAN ARCHIVES **16a Abingdon Road W8 6AF Tel: 020 7938 3580**
E-mail: archivist@rcdow.org.uk
Archivist Fr Nicholas Schofield

DATA PROTECTION OFFICER Fr John Conneely **Tel: 020 7485 2727** (Camden Town)

MASTER OF CEREMONIES Canon Daniel Cronin LL.M, KCHS **Tel: 020 7435 6678**
Assistants Fr Peter Grant, Fr Kevin Jordan, Fr Michael O'Boy, Fr Anthony O'Gorman

COUNCIL OF CENSORSHIP **Secretary** Fr Anton Cowan,
St Paul's Church, 17 Churchfield Path, Cheshunt, Herts EN8 9EG Tel: 01992 629878
for applications and information concerning the Nihil obstat & Imprimatur

CONSULTATIVE BODIES

METROPOLITAN CATHEDRAL CHAPTER (est 19 June 1852) Code, cc 377, 463, 503-10
The Chapter assembles at Archbishop's House for a meeting once a month, generally on the first Tuesday, after which Vespers and Capitular Mass are celebrated in the Cathedral for the intentions of the whole diocese.
Provost Canon Michael Brockie; **Secretary**; Canon Vincent Berry;
Treasurer Canon Patrick Davies; **Canon Penitentiary** Canon Edward Matthews;
Master of Ceremonies Canon Daniel Cronin; Canon John McDonald;
Canon Bernard Scholes; Canon Gerard Burke; Canon Matthew Kennelly;
Canon Michael Munnelly; Canon Paul McGinn; Mgr Canon Harry Turner;
Canon John Formby; Canon Charles Acton; Canon Philip Cross; Canon Patrick Browne;
Mgr Canon Thomas Egan; Canon Robert Plourde.
Canons Emeriti
Provost Emeritus Mgr Canon Frederick Miles;
Mgr Canon Adrian Arrowsmith; Canon Peter Gilburt; Canon Peter Moore;
Canon Peter Phillips; Canon Frederick Smyth; Canon Louis Thomas;
Canon Charles McGowan;
Honorary Canons Canon Richard Marriott; Canon Reginald Fuller

COLLEGE OF CONSULTORS (Code, c502) functions entrusted to Cathedral Chapter.

FINANCE COMMITTEE (Code, c492)
Chair Bishop George Stack Mgr John Arnold; Cllr Angela Hooper; Miss Leslie Ferrar; Mr Ken Minton; Mr Dominic Moseley; **in attendance** Mr John Gibbs

FINANCE BOARD
Chair Bishop George Stack; Bishop Bernard Longley; Bishop Alan Hopes; Mgr John Arnold; Mgr Canon Thomas Egan; **in attendance** Mr John Gibbs .

COUNCIL OF PRIESTS (Code, cc495-501)
President The Cardinal; **Chair** Fr Stuart Wilson; **Secretary** Fr Norbert Fernandes

LITURGY COMMISSION - charged by the Cardinal to assist him in promoting liturgical renewal and on-going liturgical formation in the diocese. It is to establish policy for and approving any Church ordering and has oversight of principal diocesan liturgies.
Chair Fr Allen Morris, **Liturgy Commission, 39 Eccleston Square SW1V 1PL**
Vice Chair (vacant), Chair of Art and Architecture Committee Fr Alan Fudge
Chair of Ministerial Formation Committee Fr Aidan Rossiter CJ
Chair of Music Committee Ian Coleman
Chair of Spirituality Committee Mary Crowley
Editor of Westminster Worship John Green
Other Members Canon Vincent Berry, Sr Pauline Clarke, Sr Sheila MacNamara, Fr Michael O'Boy, Jane Porter

ADMINISTRATION DEPARTMENTS

Vaughan House, 46 Francis Street SW1P 1QN Tel: 020 7798 9009 Fax: 020 7798 9011
Receptionist Tim Brophy All E-mails: first name+surname@rcdow.org.uk

FINANCE
Financial Secretary John W B Gibbs KSG, FCA Tel: 020 7798 9036 Fax: 020 7828 3768
PA/Parish Support Team Alice Walford Tel: 020 7798 9160

FINANCE OFFICE

Financial Controller	Cyril Wood FCA	Tel: 020 7798 9174
Assistants	Zoe Decouto	Tel: 020 7798 9169
	Sandy Hirani	Tel: 020 7798 9171
Cathedral & Choir School	Eva Brister	Tel: 020 7798 9170
Office		Tel: 020 7798 9002

FUNDRAISING & LEGACIES Patrick Bolger Tel: 020 7798 9177

HUMAN RESOURCES

Manager	Monica Turner	Tel: 020 7798 9166
PA	Julie Dauncey	Tel: 020 7798 9167
Payroll	Marian Aitkins	Tel: 020 7798 9172
Clerical Assistant	Angela Keyes	Tel: 020 7798 9162
Office		Tel: 020 7798 9001

INFORMATION TECHNOLOGY Rod de Silva Tel: 020 7798 9165

PLANNED GIVING & GIFT AID

Manager	Charles Donnington	Tel: 020 7798 9375
Co-ordinators	Mary Harrington	Tel: 020 7798 9159
	Anne Rimell	Tel: 020 7798 9161
Office		Tel: 020 7798 9004

PRINT ROOM David Darby Tel: 020 7798 9380

PROPERTY
Estates Surveyor Stephen J Peter, BSc (Econ), FRICS Tel: 020 7798 9158
Parish Building Surveyor Christopher P Fanning, MBEng, MGB *based at*
St Joseph's, Watford Way NW4 4TY Tel: 020 8202 2695 Fax: 020 8202 1459
Mobile: 07885 768889 PA Debbie O'Connor
Archives Marie Ryan Tel: 020 8201 5349

SCHOOLS BUILDING FINANCE

Fundraising	John Lee	Tel: 020 7798 9168
Clerical Assistant	Marisa Borgerth	Tel: 020 7798 9176

CLERGY AND CONSECRATED LIFE

Archbishop's House, Ambrosden Avenue SW1P 1QJ Tel: 020 7798 9023
Fax: 020 7931 6058
E-mail: first name+surname@rcdow.org.uk

Chair of Department & Vicar General for Clergy Bishop Alan Hopes
Secretary Ellen Dunleavy **Tel: 020 7798 9023**

VOCATIONS DIRECTOR

Fr Chris Vipers **Tel: 020 7798 9083**
247 High Road W4 4PU Fax: 020 8987 8332
Website: www.rcdow.org.uk/vocations

THE SEMINARY Allen Hall, 28 Beaufort Street SW3 5AA

Tel: 020 7349 5600 *See page 40 for details*
Rector Canon Paul McGinn **Administrator** Mr Gerald Daly BA

PASTORAL CARE & ONGOING FORMATION OF CLERGY

Amicus Clero Fr Martin Hayes **Tel: 020 7349 5782 Mobile: 07712 837423**
Allen Hall, 28 Beaufort Street SW3 5AA E-mail: martinhayes@rcdow.org.uk

WESTMINSTER ECCLESIASTICAL EDUCATION FUND (WEEF)

Chair Mgr John Arnold **Tel: 020 7931 6062**
Archbishop's House, Ambrosden Avenue SW1P 1QJ

NATIONAL CONFERENCE OF PRIESTS

Elected representatives Mgr Canon Adrian Arrowsmith, Fr Digby Samuels, Fr Stephen Wang

COMMITTEE FOR THE WELFARE OF SICK AND RETIRED PRIESTS

Chair Bishop Alan Hopes;
Vice Chair Fr Brian Ward; Fr James Garvey; Fr Eugene Fitzpatrick; Fr Duncan Adamson; Fr John Cunningham; Fr Pat Cassidy
Healthcare Visitor Sr Clement Doran RGN, RMN **Tel: 020 7798 9398**

DECEASED CLERGY ASSOCIATION

Archbishop's House, Ambrosden Avenue SW1P 1QJ
Registrar Mgr Ralph Brown ProtAp

PERMANENT DIACONATE

Director of Diaconate Programme Canon Patrick Browne
Tel: 020 7834 6965
47 Cumberland Street SW1V 4LY

ECUMENISM, INTERFAITH AND JUSTICE & PEACE

Chair of Department Vacant
E-mail: first name+surname@rcdow.org.uk (unless stated otherwise)

ECUMENISM

Vice Chair Mgr James Overton **(Ashford)**
Secretary Fr Michael Seed, sa, **c/o Clergy House, 42 Francis Street SW1P 1QW**
Tel: 020 7931 6063 Fax: 020 7798 9090
Ecumenical Officers
For County of Hertfordshire
The Hertfordshire Commission for Ecumenism; Fr Brian Reynolds **Tel: 01582 832114**
For the Deaneries of Hammersmith, Hounslow, Kensington and Chelsea, Marylebone, North Kensington, Upper Thames and Westminster
Br Volodimir Bezulowsky sw **Tel: 020 8993 8113 E-mail: volodia@doctors.org.uk**
For the Deaneries of Brent, Ealing, Harrow and Hillingdon
Br Volodimir Bezulowsky sw **Tel: 020 8993 8113 E-mail: volodia@doctors.org.uk**
For the Deaneries of Barnet, Camden, Enfield and Haringey
Awaiting appointment
For the Deaneries of Hackney, Islington, Tower Hamlets
Fr Digby Samuels **(Wapping)**
Churches Together in England (CTE) Britain & Ireland (CTBI) Canon Robert Plourde **(Pinner)**

INTERFAITH

Westminster Interfaith Offices 23 Kensington Square W8 5HN
Director Alfred Agius **17 Garrison Close, Hounslow TW4 5EZ Tel/Fax: 020 8570 8639**
Co-ordinators

Sr Elizabeth O'Donoghue HC	**Tel: 020 7272 8048**
Sr Simon Catlin ra	**Tel: 020 7515 8944**
Miss Margaret Slynn	**Tel: 01442 269440**
Sr Hilda Denyer ra	**Tel: 020 7361 4700**

Catholic-Jewish Relations
Vice Chair Sr Clare Jardine SND
Secretary Mr Peter Keenan, **Tel: 020 7727 3597/020 8422 8084**

JUSTICE & PEACE COMMISSION

24 Golden Square W1F 9JR
Tel: 020 7437 1525 Fax: 020 7025 1598
Co-ordinator Canon Patrick Davies
Information & Communication Worker Elizabeth Steward
Commission Members Mr Lee Caddick, Sr Elizabeth Donohue, Ms Annette Figueiredo, Sr Christine Frost, Mrs Sheila Gallagher, Mrs Clare Hickey, Mr Dermott McNulty, Ms Valerie Simcock, Mrs Adelheid Smith, Mr Chris Smith

EDUCATION AND FORMATION

Chair of Department Bishop George Stack

THE DIOCESAN EDUCATION COMMISSION

is appointed by the Archbishop as a decision making body which acts in his name. It is responsible to him in all areas relating to education, catechesis and adult formation set out in canon law and English law.

It is responsible to the Diocesan Trustees for the financial aspects of providing and maintaining Catholic education in the Diocese. Through its Chair, the Education Commission liaises with the Archbishop and his Auxiliary Bishops, the Diocesan Trustees, schools and parishes mainly through the Director of Education and the staff of the Education Service.

Members of the Commission
Chair Bishop George Stack;
Sr Dorothy Bell OBE, Canon Bernard Scholes, Fr John Ablewhite, Fr Tim O'Connor, Mrs Sue Flockton, Mrs Pamela Singh OBE, Mrs Margaret Smart OBE, Mrs Mary Waplington, Mr Alan Scouller, Mr Nicolas Vecchione
In attendance Director of Education **Secretary** Greeny Longville

THE EDUCATION SERVICE

works to the Diocesan Education Commission in providing professional support for Catholic education at all levels, including Parish Catechetics, Adult Formation, Religious Education, Support for Head Teachers and Governing Bodies.

Vaughan House, 46 Francis Street SW1P 1QN
Tel: 020 7798 9005 Fax: 020 7798 9013

E-mail: first name+surname@rcdow.org.uk
Website: http://www.rcdow.org.uk/education (where all e-mail addresses are listed)

Director of Education (Diocesan Schools Commissioner)
Paul Barber
PA to the Director Greeny Longville

Deputy Director
Maureen Roe

Chief Inspector
Rita Price

Operations Manager
Mike Pittendreigh

SCHOOL SUPPORT TEAM
Vaughan House, 46 Francis Street SW1P 1QN
Tel: 020 7798 9005 Fax: 020 7798 9013

Team Leaders
Primary Sr Sheila McNamara
Secondary Peter Ward

Advisers for Catholic Education (Primary)
Kathleen Gilbert, Yvonne Govan (two vacancies)
Advisers for Catholic Education (Secondary)
Anthony Clark, Kitt Elliott (one vacancy)

Capital Strategy Manager (School Buildings)
Sally Livesey

PARISH CATECHETICAL SUPPORT TEAM
Westminster House, Watford Way, Hendon NW4 4TY
Tel: 020 8202 3611 Fax: 020 8203 8278

Team Leader Anthony Curran — **Tel: 020 8457 6535**

Catechetical Advisers
Mary Crowley — **Tel: 020 8457 6533**
Judy Makin — **Tel: 020 8457 6534**
Diana Klein — **Tel: 020 8906 3841**

OFFICE SUPPORT TEAM
Secretaries
Carol Campbell **(Vaughan House)** — **Tel: 020 7798 9005 Fax: 020 7798 9013**
Maria Leondiou **(Hendon)** — **Tel: 020 8202 3611 Fax: 020 8203 8278**

Conference Secretary
Margaret Theissi **(Hendon)** — **Tel: 020 8202 2371**

Foundation Governor Co-ordinator
Monica Fuller **(Vaughan House)** — **Tel: 020 7798 9005**

CCRS, Youth Contact, Marriage and Family LIfe
Moira Wilson **(Hendon)** — **Tel: 020 8202 3611**

School Chaplains Director Mgr Vladimir Felzmann
All Saints Pastoral Centre, London Colney, Herts AL2 1AF
Tel: 01727 829206 Fax: 01727 822880 E-mail: vladimirf@compuserve.com

PASTORAL AFFAIRS

Vaughan House, 46 Francis Street SW1P 1QN **Website: www.wdpastoral.co.uk**
Chair of Department Bishop Bernard Longley
Director Edmund Adamus **Tel:020 7798 9363**

The Westminster Deaf Service; The Service for People with Physical Disabilities; St Joseph's Pastoral Care Centre, Hendon; The Mission to Travelling People; Pastoral Care of Young People; HIV/Aids support; Interfaith Refugee Network; Ethnic Chaplains, Prison Chaplains; Hospital Chaplains; University Chaplains; London Churches Group for Social Action;
Faith Sector Emergency Planning - London Resilience Office;
Marriage preparation/Marriage enrichment resources and information.

DIOCESAN PASTORAL BOARD MEMBERS

Bishop Bernard Longley **Chair;** Margaret Ann Fisken **Vice-Chair;**
Helen Baly; Mark Brenninkmeyer; Sr Brigid Collins RSM; Margaret Dixon; John Dumbrell; Sr Sheila Sumner OSM; Catherine Howarth; Marcia Jaques; Fr Jim Kennedy; Bwalya Kangwa. **In attendance** Edmund Adamus; John Gibbs

CHAPLAIN TO YOUNG PEOPLE Fr Antonio Ritaccio

Tel: 07813 066 462 Corpus Christi Presbytery, Maiden Lane WC2E 7NA

DEAF SERVICE

Tel: 020 7798 9026 (voice phone) **020 7798 9150** (text phone) **SMS 07940 280 404**
A Diocesan agency working with Deaf and Hard of Hearing people of all ages, to facilitate and enable them to participate fully in the life of the Church, sharing their own gifts.
Deaf Counselling Service offering counselling to Deaf and hard of hearing people and their relatives in sign language or English. Mini-loop system available.
Director Awaiting appointment **Pastoral Worker** Lara Kasza (Acting Director)
Admin Support Sarah Metcalfe
Deafblind Fr Cyril Axelrod CssR **E-mail:cyril@axelrod1.freeserve.com**
Hard of hearing support group Sr Kate O'Neill **E-mail: k_oneill2002@yahoo.co.uk**

SERVICES FOR PEOPLE WITH DISABILITIES **Co-ordinator** Fr Tad Tokarski SJ

48 Links Side Enfield, Middx EN2 7QU Tel/Fax: 020 8366 9843

CAMID (Christian Action for the Ministry & Integration of physically Disabled people)

Chair Cissy Sheldon **10 Melody Court, 43 Wellesley Road W4 3AD Tel: 020 8995 4977**
Priest Adviser Fr Austin Garvey **211 Old Marylebone Road NW1 5QT Tel: 020 7723 7757**

CATHOLIC HIV/AIDS MINISTRY CATHAM **Pastoral Worker** Sr Catherine McErlean DC

Corpus Christi Presbytery, Maiden Lane WC2E 7NA Tel: 020 7836 4092

ALL SAINTS PASTORAL CENTRE

Shenley Lane, London Colney, Herts AL2 1AF
Tel: 01727 822010
Fax: 01727 822880 E-mail: conf.office@allsaintspc.org.uk

Director Mgr Vladimir Felzmann
Tel: 01727 829206 E-mail: vladimirf@rcdow.org.uk
Administrator Alan Johnstone **Tel 01727 829203**
Conference Office Tel 01727 829306
For bookings, information, planning of retreats, seminars, days of recollection etc, please telephone 9am to 5pm.
In residence: Mgr Canon Adrian Arrowsmith **Tel: 01727 829202**
Bookshop McCrimmonds at All Saints (open daily 11-5pm) **Tel: 01727 827612**

WESTMINSTER YOUNG PEOPLE SERVICE Tel: 01727 828888 Fax: 01727 822927
SPEC Centre (Retreat & Resource Centre for ages 16 to 30)
LOFT @ SPEC (Spiritual Field Course Centre for 7-15 year olds)
Co-Directors Sandra & David Satchell
E-mail: spec@rcdow.org.uk Website: www.spec-centre.org.uk
SPECeast 2 Chandler Street E1W 2QT **Tel: 020 7680 7600 Fax: 020 680 7601**
E-mail: info@speceast.org.uk Website: www.speceast.org.uk Director Cleo Jones

ST JOSEPH'S PASTORAL CENTRE - LEARNING DISABILITIES

St Joseph's Pastoral Centre, St Joseph's Grove, The Burroughs NW4 4TY
Tel: 020 8202 3999
Fax: 020 8202 1418
E-mail: enquiries@stjoseph.org.uk Website: www.stjoseph.org.uk
A diocesan agency supporting adults with learning disabilities, their families and friends.

Director Helen O'Brien
Project Manager Ann Walawalkar
Outreach Co-ordinator Sue Pratt
Admin Manager Nigel Coleman
Fundraising Manager Sylvia Lehrian-Spellins

Area Co-ordinators

Central London	Mary Gilmartin	**020 8743 0472**
East London	Gerald McEnery	**020 7254 8562**
North London	Libby Biberian	**07960 226421**

SAINT JOSEPH'S PASTORAL MUSICIANS' CHOIR
Perform contemporary and traditional sacred music liturgically and in concerts. Rehearsals second Saturday 10am to 1 pm at **Saint Joseph's Pastoral Centre, The Burroughs, NW4 4TY Musical Director** Robert St John
Information from Ann Macdonald **Tel 01923 779442**

THE CATHOLIC CHILDRENS SOCIETY

Crusade of Rescue founded 1859
73 St Charles Square W10 6EJ Web site: www.cathchild.org.uk
Tel: 020 8969 5305. Fax: 020 8960 1464 E-mail: info@cathchild.org.uk
Director Jim Richards, MA, DASS, DSA
Deputy Director Rosemary Keenan BA, DSA, DASS, CQSW, MA, PhD

ADOPTION AGENCY covering the dioceses of Westminster and Brentwood, finding families, both Catholic and non-Catholic for children in local authority care.
Tel: 020 8969 5305

Help to unsupported mothers with babies and pregnant women. A range of counselling and practical services to assist mothers to decide whether to care for their children themselves or to place them for adoption. **Tel: 020 8969 5305**

COUNSELLING AND THERAPY SERVICES
Bishop Harvey Family Service, 6 Egerton Gardens NW4 4BA
Tel: 020 8202 5115 Fax: 020 8202 0969
Individual child and adolescent psychotherapy service
Referrals from parents, schools and parishes. Also available for telephone consultation with priests and teachers. **Contact** Patsy Ryz

St Vincent's Family Centre, 118 Mayfield Gardens W7 3RD Tel: 020 8578 6378
Fax: 020 8813 0238 Family and marital therapy and individual counselling service.
Contact Leigh Moriarty

SCHOOL COUNSELLING SERVICE **Contact** Juliet Goodman **Tel: 020 8969 5305**
Trained counsellors provide services to pupils in primary and secondary schools.

FAMILY CENTRE BASED SERVICES
Nurseries, playgroups, after school groups advice and information.
St Francis' Family Centre, Flora Close *(off Ricardo Street)* **E14 6EQ.**
Contact Margaret Wilkinson **Tel: 020 7987 8257 Fax: 020 7538 4872**
St Margaret's Family Centre, 73 St Charles Square W10 6EJ
Contact Janice Thompson **Tel: 020 8969 5305**
St Mark's Park Stay & Play contact Val Patel or Fay Brooks **Tel: 020 8968 4339 (12-4pm)**

SERVICES TO HOMELESS FAMILIES
Central London Homelessness Team Tel: 020 8969 5305
St Albans Project Manager Caroline McCaffrey **Tel: 01727 822610**
Westway Travellers Project
Contact Toni Liburd **Tel: 020 8960 5651**

THE CARDINAL HUME CENTRE

3-7 Arneway Street, Horseferry Road SW1P 2BG Tel: 020 7222 1602
E-mail: info@cardinalhumecentre.org.uk Website: www.cardinalhumecentre.org.uk
'Transforming Lives'
Director Cathy Corcoran OBE **Chair** Sr Sheila Sumner OSM
Central Services Manager Rachel Cross
Head of Fundraising & Communications Claire Moore

SERVICES
Hostel providing support in single room accommodation for recently homeless young people (16-21 years) **Manager** Gerry Donnelly
Hostel for alcohol/substance abusers in recovery. **Manager** Martin Lilley
Drop-in for homeless young people (16-25) open each weekday **Manager** Fiona Russell
Family Day Centre for families and children in temporary accommodation
Manager Carol Skipper
Doctor's surgery for homeless people
Doctor Sr Mary Hickey
Education and Training Project offering personal tuiton for all homeless peope who wish to improve their basic skills **Manager** Sonia Thomas
Charity Shop selling clothes and bric-a-brac **Contact** Ted Neville Tel: 020 7227 1659

THE PASSAGE

Helping homeless people. St Vincent's, Carlisle Place SW1P 1NL Tel: 020 7592 1850
Fax: 020 7592 1870 E-mail: info@passage.org.uk Website: www.passage.org.uk
Director Sr Ellen Flynn DC

DIOCESAN PILGRIMAGE TO LOURDES

Director Fr Chris Vipers Tel: 020 7798 9083 Fax: 020 8987 8332 247 High Rd W4 4PU
Administrator Gerald Daly Tel: 020 7349 5606 Allen Hall 28 Beaufort Street SW3 5AA

WESTMINSTER RECORD

Diocesan newspaper, published monthly (second Sunday).
Editor Fr Kit Cunningham, IC; Tel: 020 7405 1061 Fax: 020 7405 7440
14 Ely Place, Holborn Circus EC1N 6RY

WESTMINSTER YEAR BOOK

Editor Fr Stuart Wilson, Archbishop's House SW1P 1QJ Tel: 020 7798 9092
E-mail: wyb@rcdow.org.uk
Website: www.westminsteryearbook.org.uk

In September 2005 Bishop James O'Brien retired

Canon Pat Davies has kindly offered the following tribute.

Bishop James O'Brien has been Bishop in Hertfordshire for over 28 years. Having reached the age of 75, he now moves into retirement with a big thank you from all who have known and worked with him.

James O'Brien was born on 5th August 1930 in Wood Green. He was educated at St. Ignatius College and at St. Edmund's, Ware, the diocesan seminary. He was ordained priest on 12th June 1954 and served eight years at curate at St. Lawrence's, Feltham, which included ministering to the local Borstal. Fr. O'Brien was then seconded to the Catholic Mission Society for the years 1962 to 1968 and for the last two years he was Director of the Catholic Enquiry Centre. Cardinal Heenan asked Fr. O'Brien to become Rector of St. Edmund's College, Ware, in 1968. He oversaw the relocation of the seminary to Allen Hall, Chelsea in 1975, and remained Rector there until 1977 when he was appointed Auxiliary Bishop of Westminster with special responsibility for Hertfordshire. As with all Bishops, he also undertook various national responsibilities. He was Chair of the Committee for International Justice and Peace and travelled extensively abroad both for the Bishops and for CAFOD. He represented our Conference at Archbishop Romero's funeral in 1980. Subsequently, Bishop Jim headed up the Committee for Ministerial Formation.

Back in the diocese, Bishop Jim is well known for his commitment to ecumenism. Like Bishop Butler before him, he developed a very good relationship with the Bishop of St. Albans: weekly celebration of Mass in St. Albans Abbey is a lasting testimony to his work for ecumenism.

Under Archbishop Cormac, Bishop Jim was given responsibility for the Department for Ecumenism, Interfaith and Justice and Peace and this new appointment drew on his skills and experience in these fields.

One of the best bits of advice that Bishop Jim was regularly in the habit of passing on to people was "don't take life too seriously" and this was as true for himself and for others. Bishop Jim is a great family man and is in regular touch with his sisters and his nephews. Insofar as hobbies and past-times are concerned, Bishop Jim is a great walker and is often to be seen out walking his dog, Ben. On top of that he is a keen bee-keeper – a hobby he will now have more time for in his retirement. We wish him a long and happy retirement and we thank him for all he has done for us.

DEANERIES

The name of the Auxiliary bishop with particular responsibility is given in brackets

1. BARNET (Bishop George Stack)
Barnet, Burnt Oak, Cricklewood, Edgware, Finchley East, Finchley Church End, Finchley North, Golders Green, Grahame Park, Hendon, Hendon West, Mill Hill, New Barnet, Whetstone
Dean Fr Michael Kennedy **(Cricklewood) Tel: 020 8452 2475**

2. BRENT (Bishop George Stack)
Dollis Hill, Kensal Rise, Kenton, Kingsbury Green, Neasden, Stonebridge, Sudbury, Wembley, Wembley Park, Wembley/Preston Road, Willesden, Willesden Green.
Dean Fr David Williamson **(Kingsbury Green) Tel: 020 8204 2834**

3. CAMDEN (Bishop Bernard Longley)
Camden Town, Hampstead, Haverstock Hill, Kentish Town, Kilburn, Kilburn West, Laxton Place, Somers Town, Swiss Cottage.
Dean Fr Dermot Morrin OP **(Haverstock Hill) Tel: 020 7482 9210**

4. EALING (Bishop Alan Hopes)
Acton, Acton East, Acton West, Ealing, Greenford, Hanwell, Northfields, Perivale, Polish Church, Southall
Dean Canon Bernard Scholes **(Hanwell) Tel: 020 8567 4056**

5. ENFIELD (Bishop George Stack)
Cockfosters, Edmonton, Enfield, New Southgate, Palmers Green, Ponders End.
Dean Mgr Canon Thomas Egan **(New Southgate) Tel: 020 8368 1638**

6. HACKNEY (Bishop Bernard Longley)
Clapton, Clapton Park, Hackney, Homerton, Hoxton, Kingsland, Manor House, Stoke Newington.
Dean Fr Christopher Colven **(Kingsland) Tel: 020 7254 4378**

7. HAMMERSMITH & FULHAM (Bishop Alan Hopes)
Brook Green, Fulham, Hammersmith, Parsons Green, Polish Church, Shepherd's Bush, Stephendale Road, White City.
Dean Fr Norbert Fernandes **(Fulham) Tel: 020 7385 4040**

8. HARINGEY (Bishop George Stack)
Harringay, Muswell Hill, Stamford Hill, Stroud Green, Tottenham, West Green, Wood Green.
Dean Fr Tim Curtis **(Stamford Hill) Tel: 020 8800 2121**

9. HARROW (Bishop George Stack)
Harrow-on-the-Hill, Harrow North, Harrow South, Headstone Lane, Pinner, Stanmore, Wealdstone.
Dean Canon Robert Plourde (Pinner) Tel: 020 8866 0098

10. HATFIELD (Bishop)
Cuffley, Hatfield, Hatfield South, Potters Bar, Welwyn Garden City, Welwyn Garden City Digswell, Welwyn Garden City East.
Dean Fr Timothy O'Connor (Potters Bar) Tel: 01707 654359

11. HILLINGDON (Bishop Alan Hopes)
Eastcote, Harefield, Hayes, Hillingdon, London Airport, Northwood, Ruislip, Ruislip South, Uxbridge, West Drayton, Yeading; US Navy (West Ruislip).
Dean Fr Michael Johnston (Ruislip) Tel: 01895 632 739

12. HOUNSLOW (Bishop Alan Hopes)
Brentford, Chiswick, Cranford, Feltham, Grove Park, Gunnersbury, Heston, Hounslow, Isleworth, Osterley.
Dean Fr Antony Convery (Hounslow) Tel: 020 8570 1693

13. ISLINGTON (Bishop Bernard Longley)
Bunhill Row, Clerkenwell, Copenhagen Street, Highbury, Highgate, Holloway, Islington, Polish Church, Tollington Park, Upper Holloway.
Dean Fr Jim Kennedy (Copenhagen Street) Tel: 020 7837 4841

14. KENSINGTON AND CHELSEA (Bishop Alan Hopes)
Chelsea 1, Chelsea 2, Fulham Road, Kensington 1, Kensington 2, Oratory.
Dean Canon Vincent Berry (Chelsea 1) Tel: 020 7589 5487

15. LEA VALLEY (Bishop)
Bishop's Stortford, Buntingford, Cheshunt, Hertford, Hoddesdon, Much Hadham, Old Hall Green & Puckeridge, Sawbridgeworth, Waltham Cross, Ware.
Dean Fr Brian Ward (Ware) Tel: 01920 462140

16. MARYLEBONE (Bishop Bernard Longley)
Farm Street, Marylebone, Ogle Street, St John's Wood, Spanish Place, University Chaplaincy.
Dean Fr Terry Phipps (Spanish Place) Tel: 020 7935 0943

17. NORTH KENSINGTON (Bishop Alan Hopes)
Bayswater, Harrow Road, Kensal New Town, Notting Hill, Paddington, Queensway, St Charles Square.
Dean Fr Stephen Bartlett (Paddington) Tel: 020 7286 2672

18. ST ALBANS (Bishop)
Berkhamsted, Borehamwood, Borehamwood North, Harpenden, Hemel Hempstead Boxmoor, Hemel Hempstead East, Hemel Hempstead North, Hemel Hempstead West, London Colney, Radlett, Redbourn, St Albans, St Albans South, Shenley, Tring, Wheathampstead.
Dean Mgr Canon Harry Turner **(Harpenden)** **Tel: 01582 712245**

19. STEVENAGE (Bishop)
Baldock, Hitchin, Knebworth, Letchworth, Royston, Stevenage Bedwell & Pin Green, Stevenage Old Town & Symonds Green, Stevenage Shephall.
Dean Fr Michael Lambert AA **(Hitchin)** **Tel: 01462 459126**

20. TOWER HAMLETS (Bishop Bernard Longley)
Bethnal Green, Bow, Bow Common, Commercial Road, German Church, Limehouse, Lithuanian Church, Mile End, Millwall, Poplar, Tower Hill, Underwood Road, Vietnamese Church, Wapping.
Dean Fr Digby Samuels **(Wapping)** **Tel: 020 7481 2202**

21. UPPER THAMES (Bishop Alan Hopes)
Ashford, Hampton-on-Thames, Hampton Hill, St Margaret's, Shepperton, Staines, Stanwell, Sunbury-on-Thames, Teddington, Twickenham, Whitton.
Dean Fr Seamus O'Boyle **(Whitton)** **Tel: 020 8894 9923**

22. WATFORD (Bishop)
Abbots Langley, Bushey, Carpenders Park, Chipperfield, Chorleywood, Croxley Green, Garston, Mill End, Rickmansworth, Watford, Watford North.
Dean Fr James Duffy **(Rickmansworth)** **Tel: 01923 773387**

23. WESTMINSTER (Bishop Bernard Longley)
(City) Ely Place, Italian Church, Lincoln's Inn Fields, Moorfields;
(West End) Cathedral, French Church, Maiden Lane, Pimlico, Soho, Warwick Street.
Dean Canon Patrick Browne **(Pimlico)** **Tel: 020 7834 6965**

HOSPITALS IN THE DIOCESE

Westminster Diocese Health-care Chaplaincy Co-ordinator
Fr Peter Scott **Tel: 020 7349 5609**
PLEASE SEE IMPORTANT NOTE AT THE END OF THIS SECTION

ASHFORD 01784 884488 *Ashford*
Fr Ken Rimini 01784 255973
BARNET General 020 8216 4000 *Barnet*
Bishops Wood 01923 835814 *Northwood*
Brompton 020 7352 8121 *Oratory*
BUPA Bushey 020 8950 9090 *Bushey*
BUPA Harpenden 01582 763191 *Harpenden*
CENTRAL Middlesex 020 8864 3232
Fr Paul McDermott; Sr Barbara Patterson
Charing Cross 020 8846 1042 *Fr Nigel Griffin*
Charter Clinic 020 7351 1272 *Chelsea 1*
Charter Nightingale 020 7258 3828
Marylebone
Chelsea & Westminster *Servites*
Chase Farm 020 8366 6600 *Enfield*
Clayponds 020 8560 4011 *Brentford*
Clementine Churchill 020 8422 3464 *Sudbury*
Colindale 020 8200 1555 *Kingsbury Green*
Cromwell 020 7370 4233 *Kensington (2)*
DANESBURY 01438 714447 *Welwyn Garden City (Digswell)*
EALING 020 8967 5000/5130
Sr Marie McGrogan, Hanwell
Eden Hall *Swiss Cottage*
Edgware Community 020 8952 2381
Mr Lionel Carriere 0798 557 0199
Elizabeth Garrett Anderson
Fr Peter Harries OP 020 7961 5734
Mrs Angela McCann-Keetley
FINCHLEY Memorial 020 8349 3121
Finchley Church End
Fitzroy-Nuffield 020 7723 1288 *Spanish Place*
GARDEN Hospital 020 8203 0111
Hendon
Garden House 01462 679540 *Letchworth*
Great Ormond Street 020 7405 9200
Lincolns Inn Fields; Sr Catherine Gilligan
HAMMERSMITH 020 8383 4574
Fr Nigel Griffin; Sr Carmel Keegan
Harefield 01895 823737 *Harefield*
Harley Street Clinic 020 7935 7700
Spanish Place
Harpenden Memorial 01442 213141 *Harpenden*
Heart Hospital
Fr Peter Harries OP 020 7961 5734
Hemel General 0845 241 2255
Mrs Lynn Bassett, 01727 897254 *Boxmoor*
Herts and Essex General 01279 655191
Bishop's Stortford
Hillingdon 01895 238282 *Hillingdon*
Fr Christopher Gawecki 01895 279638
Hitchin 01462 422444 *Hitchin*
Homerton 020 8510 5555
Fr William Rose OSCam 020 8986 5181
Hornsey Central 020 8340 6244
Fr Voytek Przjalkowski
KING Edward VII Hospital for Officers
020 7486 4411 *Spanish Place*
LISTER 020 7730 3417 *Chelsea 1*
Lister (Stevenage) 01438 781038
Sr Marian Davey 01462 485249
London Chest 020 8980 4433 *Bethnal Green*
London Clinic 020 7935 4444 *Spanish Place*
MANOR House 020 8455 6601
Golders Green
Middlesex 020 7961 5734
Fr Peter Harries OP; Sr Pauline Forde DC
Mildmay 020 7613 6300
Sr Mary Horan
Mile End (Bancroft Road) 020 7377 7000 *Mile End*
Moorfields Eye 020 7253 3411 *Bunhill Row*
Mount Vernon 0845 241 1299
Lynn Bassett 01727 897254 *Northwood*

NATIONAL for Neurology & Neurosurgery
020 7837 3611
Fr Peter Harries OP 020 7636 8333
Normansfield 020 8977 7583 *Teddington*
North London Hospice 020 8343 8841
Whetstone
North London Nuffield 020 8366 2122 *Enfield*
North Middlesex 020 8887 2000 *Edmonton*
Northwick Park 020 8864 3232
Fr Paul McDermott, Sr Barbara Patterson
Northwood & Pinner Community
01923 824182 *Northwood*
POTTERS Bar 01707 653286 *Potters Bar*
Princess Grace 020 7486 1234 *Spanish Place*
Princess Louise 020 8969 0133 *St Charles Sq*
QUEEN Charlotte's & Chelsea
020 8343 4574
Fr Nigel Griffin; Sr Carmel Keegan
Queen Elizabeth II 01707 328111
Sr Marian Davey 01462 485249
Queen Mary's House (RFH) 020 7794 0500
Haverstock Hill
Queen Victoria Memorial 01438 714488
Welwyn Garden City (Digswell)
RAVENSCOURT Park
Fr Nigel Griffin 020 8846 1042
Royal Free 020 7794 0500 *Haverstock Hill*
Royal Hospital Infirmary 020 7730 0161
Chelsea (1)
Royal London & St Bartholomew's
020 7377 7000 *Fr Philip Miller*
020 7377 7385 *(direct);*
020 7531 6956 *(home)*
Royal London Homoeopathic
Fr Peter Harries OP 020 7691 5734
Royal Marsden 020 7352 8171 *Kensington (2)*
Royal National Orthopaedic 020 8954 2300
Stanmore
Royal National Throat, Nose & Ear
020 7837 8855 *Clerkenwell*
Royston Cottage 01763 242134 *Royston*

ST ALBANS CITY 0845 241 2323
Mrs Lynn Bassett, 01727 897254
St Andrew's 020 7476 4000 *Bow*
St Bernard's (Southall) 020 8574 2444 *Hanwell*
St Charles 020 8969 2488 *St Charles Sq*
SS John and Elizabeth 020 7286 5126
Canon John McDonald
St Joseph's Hospice 020 8525 6000
Fr Brian Griffiths OSCam 020 8986 5181
St Luke's Woodside 020 8883 8311 *Muswell*
St Mark (Northwick Park) 020 864 3232
Fr Paul McDermott, Sr Barbara Patterson
St Mary's Paddington 020 7886 6666
Fr Anthony Brunning 020 7886 1508
TEDDINGTON Memorial
020 8977 2212 *Hampton Hill*
UNIVERSITY College 020 7691 5734
Fr Peter Harries OP 020 7636 8333
Mrs Angela McCann-Keetley; Sr Pauline Forde
WATFORD General 0845 241 2300
Mrs Lynn Bassett, 01727 897254
Wellington 020 7586 5959 *St John's Wood*
Wembley 020 8903 1323 *Sudbury*
West Middlesex 020 8321 5447
Sr Marie McGrogan
Western Ophthalmic 020 7886 6666
Marylebone
Whittington 020 7272 3070
Fr Voytek Przjalkowski 020 7288 5337
Willesden General 020 8459 1292
Willesden Green

Hospital tel number in italics followed either by parish from which served or specially appointed Chaplain

IN LIGHT OF DATA PROTECTION ACT 1998 PLEASE INDICATE ON ENTERING HOSPITAL THAT YOUR DETAILS MAY BE PASSED TO THE RC CHAPLAIN. ALSO STATE THAT YOU WOULD LIKE RC CHAPLAIN TO VISIT YOU.

ETHNIC CHAPLAINCIES

Particular responsibility — Bishop Alan Hopes and Bishop Bernard Longley

African See Societies and Organisations
Albanian Fr Gary Walsh **47 Cumberland Street SW1V 4LY Tel: 0779 1054 137**
Belarussian See Eastern Catholic Churches
Brazilian Fr Frederico Ribeiro **St Anne's Church, Underwood Rd E1 5AW Tel: 020 7247 7833**
Chinese Fr Eddie Woo, M.Af **4 Lady Margaret Road NW5 4XT Tel: 020 7485 4023**
Croatian Fr Drago Berisic **17 Boutflower Rd SW11 1RE Tel: 020 7223 3530** (Southwark)
Czech/Slovak Fr Jozef Vojtek **22 Ladbroke Square W11 3NA Tel: 020 7727 7849**
Eritrean/Ethiopian See Eastern Catholic Churches across page
Filipino Sr Amada Martin SSC **8 Ridgdale Street E3 2PW Tel: 020 8980 3017**
French See Parish Directory - French Church
German See Parish Directory - German Church
Ghanaian Fr James Ennin MIC **212 Sangley Rd SE6 2JS Tel: 020 8355 8360 Fax: 020 8698 5037**
E-mail: james.enin@ntlworld.com (Southwark)
Goan Fr Oliver Antao, SFX **St Thomas School, Commonside East, Mitcham CR4 1YG**
Hungarian Mgr George Tutto **141 Gunnersbury Avenue W3 8LE Tel: 020 8992 2054**
Iraq See Eastern Catholic Churches across page
Irish Sr Lucy Troy, PBVM **50/52 Camden Square NW1 9XB Tel: 020 7482 5528**
Irish Elderly Fr Nigel Charles **50/52 Camden Square NW1 9XB Tel: 020 7482 5528**
Irish Prisoners Fr Gerry McFlynn **50/52 Camden Square NW1 9XB Tel: 020 7482 4148**
Italian Mgr Agostino Gonella, Fr Paolo Tornambi **197 Durants Rd, Enfield EN3 7DE Tel: 020 8804 2307**
See also Parish Directory - Italian Church
Kerala See Eastern Catholic Churches across page
Korean Fr John Baptist Ho Chui Cha **2 Ullswater Crescent SW15 3RQ** (Southwark)
Latin-American Fr Angelo San Eufrasio, Fr Carmelo Arroyo, Fr Francisco Umedia OAR
363 Kennington Lane SE11 5QY Tel: 020 7735 1862 (Southwark)
Lebanese See Eastern Catholic Churches across page
Lithuanian See Parish Directory - Lithuanian Church
Maltese Fr Stephen Scibberas OFM **1 Balniel Gate SW1V 3SD Tel/Fax 020 7834 9512**
Fr Victor Camilleri OFM **(East London) 47 Adler Street E1 1EE**
Melkite See Eastern Catholic Churches across page
Nigerian Fr Albert Ofere **100 Ballspond Road N1 4AG**
Polish Mgr Tadeusz Kukla, **2 Devonia Road N1 8JJ Tel: 020 7226 3439**
see also Parish Directory Polish Churches
Portuguese Mgr Jose Vaz Pinto **6 Minerva Close SW9 6NZ. Tel: 020 7267 9612** (Southwark)
Slovene Fr Stanislav Cikanek **62 Offley Road SW9 0LS Tel: 020 7735 6655** (Southwark)
Spanish Fr Ernesto Atanes Fr Segundo Peña, CM **47 Palace Court W2 4LS Tel: 020 7229 8815**
Sri Lankan - Sinhalese Fr Anthony Ponweera
Clergy House, Peter Avenue NW10 2DD Tel: 020 8451 4677
Sri Lankan - Tamil Fr Eugene Francis **304 Garrett Lane SW18 4EH Tel 020 8870 6257** (Southwark)
Vietnamese Fr Paul Huynh Chanh **117 Bow Common Lane E3 4AU Tel: 020 7987 3477**

EASTERN CATHOLIC CHURCHES

Ukrainian Catholic Church: Exarchate of Great Britain
Apostolic Exarch Bishop Paul Chomnycky OSBM
Cathedral of the Holy Family in Exile, 22 Binney St W1K 5BQ
Tel: 020 7629 1534 see also Parish Directory - Ukrainian Church

Belarussian Mitred Archpriest Alexander Nadson
Marian House, Holden Road N12 8HY Tel: 020 8445 5358

Chaldean (Iraq) Fr Habib Jaujou **38 Cavendish Avenue W13 0JQ Tel: 020 8997 6370**

Gheez Rite (Eritrea) Fr Kidane Lebasi **24 Golden Square W1F 9JR. Tel: 020 7437 1525;**
Fr Ephrem Andon **Presbytery, Commonwealth Avenue W12 7QR**
Tel: 020 8743 8334

(Ethiopia) Fr Bogale Tiruneh Tafesse
Parish House, Moorhouse Road W2 5DJ Tel: 020 7229 0487

Maronite Catholic Church Fr Augustin Aoun, Fr Dany Akiki, LMO
6 Dobson Close, NW6 4RS Tel: 020 7586 1801

Melkite Catholic Church Fr Shafiq Abouzayd **46 Sunderland Avenue, Oxford OX2 8DU**
Fr Robert Gibbons **40 Nethercote Rd, Tackley, Oxford OX5 3AT Tel: 01869 331186**
Fr John Salter **1 Bishop Street N1 8PH Tel: 020 7359 0250**
Rev Deacon Richard Downer **3 Palmer Close, Redhill RH1 4BU Tel: 01737 778863**

Syrian Catholic Church (Iraq) Fr Nizar Sengan

Syro-Malabar Church (Kerala) Fr John Biju **373 Bowes Road N11 1AA Tel: 020 8368 1638**

LITURGICAL CELEBRATIONS IN THE LATIN RITE IN FOREIGN LANGUAGES

Albanian	Second Sunday 3pm	Holy Apostles, Pimlico
Cantonese	Sunday 2.15pm	St Patrick's, Soho Square
Croatian	Sunday 4pm	Sacred Heart Church, Horseferry Road
Czech & Slovak	Sunday 1pm	Our Lady of Salette, Melior Street SE1
	Sunday 8pm	Velehrad, 22 Ladbroke Square
	Mon, Wed, Thurs 5.30pm	Velehrad, 22 Ladbroke Square
	Tue & Fri 8pm	Velehrad, 22 Ladbroke Square
	Sat 12.30pm	Velehrad, 22 Ladbroke Square
French	See Parish Directory French Church	
German	See Parish Directory German Church	
Ghanaian	4th Sunday 2pm	Transfiguration, Kensal Rise
	5th Sunday 1pm	St Francis de Sales, Tottenham
Hungarian	1st Sunday 3pm	Mindszenty Hse, 5 Arundel Gdns W11
Iraqi	See Liturgical celebrations in other Rites - Chaldean & Syriac	
Irish	Saturday 7pm, Sunday 10am	Irish Centre. Camden Square
Italian	See Parish Directory Italian Church and	
	Sunday 12.30pm	Mary, Mother of God, Ponders End
	Sunday 4pm	St Augustine, Hoddesdon
	Sunday 5pm	Our Lady & St Joseph, Waltham Cross

Japanese	3rd Sunday 12 noon	House Chapel, Farm Street
Konkani	4th Sunday 3pm	St Christopher's, Cranford
Latin American	See below - **Spanish**	
Lebanese (Maronite)	See Maronite Catholic Church	
Lithuanian	See Parish Directory Lithuanian Church	
Maltese	Call sisters if you wish to attend **Convent of Franciscan Sisters, 9 St George's Drive Tel: 020 7834 4020**	
Polish	See Parish Directory Polish Church	
Portuguese:	**for Brazilians** Sunday (Eve 7pm), 12, 4, 7pm	St Anne's, Underwood Road
	for Portuguese Sundays 5pm	Our Lady of Hal, Camden Town
Slovene	Sunday 11am	62 Offley Road SW9
Spanish	**for Spaniards**	
	Sunday 10am	47 Palace Court W2
	Sunday 11.15am	Servite Church, Fulham Rd
	Sunday 12.30pm	Holy Apostles, Pimlico
	Sunaday 1.15pm	Our Lady Help of Christians, Kentish Town
	Sunday 6 pm	47 Palace Court W2
Spanish	**for Latin Americans**	
	Sunday 1pm	Our Lady, Kensal New Town
	Sunday 4.30pm	St Ignatius, Stamford Hill
	Sunday 6pm	St Patrick's, Soho Square
	Sunday 6.15pm	Convent of Mary Immaculate, Southwell Gardens SW7
Tamil	1st Sun 4.30pm	St Bernard's, Northolt
Vietnamese	Sunday 12 noon & 3pm	Holy Name, Bow Common

LITURGICAL CELEBRATIONS IN OTHER RITES

Byzantine-Slavonic	(Belarus)	Sunday 10.30am Matins 9am; Weekday Matins 7.15am Vespers 6pm	Marian House, Holden Road N12
Chaldean Rite	(Iraq)	Sunday 12.15pm	St Anne, Laxton Place NW1
Gheez Rite	(Eritrea)	Sunday 1pm	St Francis of Assisi, Notting Hill
	(Ethiopia)	Sunday 1pm	Our Lady, Queen of Heaven, Queensway
Maronite Rite	(For Lebanese)	Sunday 12 noon	Our Lady of Sorrows, Cirencester St W2
	(For Cypriots)	Sunday 10.30am	Convent of Providence, Palmers Green
Melkite Rite		Sunday 11.30am	St Barnabas Anglican Church, Pimlico Road,
Syriac Rite (Iraq)		Sunday 1pm	Holy Trinity, Brook Green
Syro-Malabar Catholic Church		2nd Sunday	Our Lady of Lourdes, New Southgate
		Last Sunday 5pm	Our Lady of Sorrows, Paddington
Ukrainian Rite		Sunday 10.30am	Ukranian Cathedral Binney St W1

Co-ordination of foreign language chaplaincies and supply of foreign language Mass sheets
Fr Austin Garvey **211 Old Marylebone Road, NW1 5QT Tel: 020 7723 7757**

THE DIOCESAN SEMINARY

ALLEN HALL ♿

28 Beaufort Street, SW3 5AA *Tel: 020 7349 5600 Fax: 7349 5601*
E-mail: allenhall@rcdow.org.uk (Douai 1568; Old Hall Green 1793; Chelsea 1975)
Rector Canon Paul McGinn *Tel: 020 7349 5605* **PA** Helena Duckett *Tel: 020 7349 5786*
Vice Rector Fr Anthony Dwyer *Tel: 020 7349 5627*

FORMATION TEAM

Canon Charles Acton STL	Dean of Studies	*Tel: 020 7349 5611*
Fr Dermot Power BA, BD, STL, STD	Spiritual Director	*Tel: 020 7349 5602*
Sr Bernadette Hunston SCJA, BA, MTh	Spirituality	*Tel: 020 7349 5622*
Fr Peter Scott STB	Pastoral Director	*Tel: 020 7349 5609*
Fr Stephen Wang PhL, STL, PhD	Formation Advisor	*Tel: 020 7349 5608*
Fr Francesco Donega STB, SLL	Formation Advisor	*Tel: 020 7723 9364*

ACADEMIC STAFF

Canon Charles Acton STL	Dean of Theology, Systematic Theology
Fr Francis Selman MA, MTh, PhD	Dean of Philosophy
Mgr Keith Baltrop MA, STL	Evangelisation & Mission
Fr John Conneely JCL	Canon Law
Fr Francesco Donega STB, SLL	Liturgy, Systematic Theology
Fr Peter Harris BEd, MTh	Church History
Fr John Hemer MHM, STB, LSS	Scripture, Biblical Greek
Dr Bernard Hoose BA (Phil) STB, STL, STD	Fundamental Moral Theology
Mgr Mark Langham MA, STL	Latin
Fr Anthony Meredith SJ MA DPhil	Patristics
Miss Letitia Nicoll LGSM, DipCE, FESB	Vocal Communications
Fr Joseph O'Hanlon BA, BD,MTh, LSS PhD	Scripture, Greek
Fr John O'Leary STB, PhL	Philosophy
Fr Dermot Power BA, BD, STL, STD	Dogmatic Theology, Spirituality
Fr Aidan Rossiter CJ, BSc, STB, MA	Liturgy, Music
Sr Margaret Taylor FMM, MA, SRN, SCN,HV.FWT	Spirituality, Psychology
Fr Stephen Wang PhL, STL, PhD	Philosophy, Systematic Theology
Mrs Liz Wilson STB	Catechetics

Pastoral Supervisor	Sr Petronia Williams OSM, DipEd	
Administrator	Mr Gerald Daly BA	*Tel: 020 7349 5606*
Administrative Assistant	Miss Mary Aldridge	*Tel: 020 7349 5600*
Librarians	Fr Francis Selman, MA, MTh, PhD	
	Sr Madeleine de Cruz, FMDM, SRN, SCM, RNT, FFNRCSI, MA	

SOME USEFUL ADDRESSES

Apostolic Nunciature
Apostolic Nuncio His Excellency Archbishop Faustino Sainz Muñoz
54 Parkside, Wimbledon, SW19 5NF Tel: 020 8944 7189 Fax: 020 8947 2494

Bishops' Conference of England and Wales
39 Eccleston Square, SW1V 1BX
Tel: 020 7630 8220 Fax: 020 7630 5166

Caritas-social action – an agency of the Bishops' Conference with responsibility for carrying out the social mission of the Church 39 Eccleston Square SW1V 1BX
Tel: 020 7901 4875 caritas@cbcew.org.uk

Catholic Central Library and Information Centre at Farnborough Abbey, Hampshire
Librarian Mrs Joan Bond
E-mail: librarian@catholic-library.org.uk Website: www.catholic-library.org.uk

Catholic Communications Centre 39 Eccleston Square, SW1V 1BX Tel: 020 7233 8196

Catholic Agency to Support Evangelisation (CASE) and Catholic Enquiry Office
Tel: 020 8458 3316/020 8455 9871 Fax: 020 8905 5780
114 West Heath Road, NW3 7TX E- mail: cms@cms.org.uk

Catholic Media Office 39 Eccleston Square, SW1V 1BX Tel: 020 7901 4800
E-mail: cmo@cbcew.org.uk

Catholic Office for the Protection of Children and Vulnerable Adults (COPCA)
12 St Paul's Square, Birmingham B3 1RB Tel: 0121 233 1963

Churches Together in England 101 Queen Victoria Street, EC4V 4EN Tel: 020 7332 8230

Jesuit Refugee Service 6 Melior Street SE1 3QP Tel: 020 7357 0974 E-mail: uk@jrs.net

National Retreat Association Central Hall, 256 Bermondsey Street, SE1 3UJ Tel 020 7357 7736

Society for the Protection of Unborn Children (SPUC) Phyllis Bowman House,
5/6 St Matthew Street Westminster, SW1P 2JT Tel: 020 7222 5845

In the Parish Directory section (except for academic institutions) priests are listed by name only.
Degrees and other biographical details will be found in the alphabetical list of clergy.
Unless otherwise indicated, postal addresses in this Year Book are London.

PARISH DIRECTORY

1. Within the Diocese the parishes are grouped in deaneries. The deaneries, with their component parishes, are listed on the pages at the end of the section Diocese of Westminster.

2. + Indicates a church registered for marriages.

3. Each parish entry gives the name of the parish, the title of the church, the postal address and telephone, the road in which it is situated, and its Deanery reference (in italic bold type). Dates in parentheses refer to the founding of the mission, the building of the church and its consecration.

4. Unless otherwise indicated, the first name is that of the Parish Priest.

5. In the list of services the following abbreviations are used:

B	Benediction	HC	Holy Communion
Conf	Reconciliation	HH	Holy Hour
CW	Liturgy of Word for Children	M	Mass
EP	Evening Prayer	MP	Morning Prayer
Exp	Exposition	R	Rosary

6. The first Mass of Sunday celebrated on Saturday evening, or the first Mass of a Holyday celebrated on the evening of the preceding day, is indicated thus:
Sun, M (Sat 6pm), 8, 9, ... Hds, M (Eve 8pm), 10, 12 .....
Different timetables will apply at Christmas, Easter and public holidays. Enquire at the church.

7. When no Ecumenical or Justice and Peace Contact is given or telephone specified please ring the parish office.

8. Religious houses and other Catholic establishments in each parish are given in bold type. Public in titutions listed (e.g. hospitals) are served by priests of the parish unless otherwise stated.

9. Facilities for physically disabled and/or hearing impaired people are indicated after the name of the church by the following symbols:

A	Access only (ramps, etc)
♿	Full facilities (access plus disabled access lavatory);
👂	Loop System for hearing-aid users;
S	Mass celebrated regularly in Word and Sign, and/or Confession in Sign Language. Enquire for details and times.

WESTMINSTER CATHEDRAL METROPOLITAN CATHEDRAL OF THE MOST PRECIOUS BLOOD

Cathedral Clergy House, 42 Francis Street SW1P 1QW
Enquiries **Tel 020 7798 9055** Times of services **020 7798 9097** **Fax: 020 7798 9090**
E-mail: westminstercathedral@rcdow.org.uk Website: www.westminstercathedral.org.uk
E-mail: all e-mail addresses are formed: **first name+surname@rcdow.org.uk**

Underground: Victoria Station ***(Westminster Deanery)*** (1903; consecrated 28 June 1910)
Cathedral open:
Mon-Fri 7am-7pm; Sat 8am-7pm Sun & Holydays 7am-7.45pm; Public Holidays 8 - 5.30pm

Administrator Mgr Mark Langham **PA** Ms Elizabeth Arnot **Tel: 020 7798 9062**

College of Cathedral Chaplains
Sub-Administrator Fr Michael O'Boy **Tel: 020 7798 9374**
Registrar Fr Michael Archer, **Tel 020 7798 9376**; **Cathedral Communications** Fr Timothy Dean, **Tel: 020 7798 9372**; Fr Michael Seed SA, **Tel: 020 7798 9463**; Fr Denis Sarsfield, **Tel: 020 7798 9068**; Fr Slawomir Witon, **Tel: 020 7798 9180**; Fr Dwayne Bednar (Diocese of Lublin, Poland) **Tel: 020 7798 9048**; **Parish Sister** Sr Bridget Cullen DC, **Tel: 020 7798 9419**
Retired Priests in Residence Mgr David Norris; Fr Michael Durand

Centre for Spirituality Tel: 020 7798 9055

Music Department
Master of Music Mr Martin Baker
PA Awaiting appointment **Tel: 020 7798 9057 Fax: 020 7798 9091**
Assistant Mr Matthew Martin **Organ Scholar** Mr Christopher Eastwood

Mass
Sunday 8am, 9am (Family, 2nd S), 10.30am (sung), 12noon, 5.30pm, 7pm.
Mon-Fri 7am, 8am, 10.30am (Latin), 12.30pm, 1.05pm, 5.30pm (sung).
Saturday 8am, 9am, 10.30am (sung), 12.30pm, 6pm (First Mass of Sunday)
Holydays (Eve 5.30pm), 7am, 8am, 10.30am, 12.30pm, 1.05pm, 5.30pm
Public Holidays 8am, 10.30am, 12.30pm

Divine Office
Morning Prayer Sun 10am, Mon-Fri 7.40am, Sat 10am
Evening Prayer Sun 3.30pm; Mon-Fri 5pm, Sat 5.30pm;
Evening Prayer II of weekday Solemnities 4.45pm
Public Holidays Morning Prayer 10am. No Evening Prayer.

Sacrament of Reconciliation
Saturday 10.30am to 6.30pm;
Sunday 11am to 1pm, 4.30pm to 7pm;
Mon-Fri 11.30am to 6pm. Public Holidays 11am to 1pm.

Cathedral Choir School, Ambrosden Avenue SW1P 1QH Tel: 020 7798 9081
Head John Browne **Chaplain** Fr Tim Dean

Cathedral Head of Development Mr Charles Donington **Tel: 020 7798 9375**

Cathedral Manager Mr Barry Palmer. Hall booking enquiries **Tel: 020 7798 9064**
E-mail: hallbookings@westminstercathedral.org.uk

Clerk of Works Mr Paul Gilpin **Tel: 020 7798 9054**
E-mail: paulgilpin@rcdow.org.uk

Friends of Westminster Cathedral Mrs Mary Skehan, **Organising Seretary**
Tel: 020 7798 9059 E-mail: friends@westminstercathedral.org.uk

Cathedral Gift Shop Manager: Ms Evelyn Casey **Tel: 020 7798 9028**

St Paul's Bookshop Managing Director: Fr Sebastian Karamvelil SSP
Morpeth Terrace SW1P 1EP Tel: 020 7828 5582 Fax: 020 7828 3329

Chapel-of-Ease: Sacred Heart Church, Horseferry Road SW1P 2EF Sun, M 11am
Enquiries to Cathedral Administrator **Tel: 020 7798 9055**

Cardinal Hume Centre, 3-7 Arneway Street, SW1P 2BG Tel: 020 7222 1602
Director Ms Cathy Corcoran

The Passage, St Vincent's, Carlisle Place SW1P 1NL Tel: 020 7592 1850
Website: www.passage.org.uk
Director Sister Ellen Flynn DC

Franciscan Friars of the Atonement (SA), 47 Francis Street SW1P 1QR Tel: 020 7828 4163
Brother Gerard Hand **Guardian;** Fr Michael Seed;

Daughters of Charity (SVP), St Vincent's, Carlisle Place SW1P 1NL. Tel: 020 7834 4004
E-mail: dc@sv-cp.freeserve.co.uk
Also **94a Horseferry Road SW1P 2EE Tel: 020 7222 6485**
E-mail: mail@dc-horseferry.fsnet.co.uk

Franciscan Sisters of Our Lady of Victories Cathedral Clergy House Tel: 020 7798 9067
Sr Angelina Amaral; Sr Maria Augusta; Sr Maria Do Ceu; Sr Angelina Moniz;

ABBOTS LANGLEY + ST SAVIOUR THE CRESCENT

The Presbytery, 96 The Crescent, Abbots Langley, Watford, Herts WD5 0DT
Tel: 01923 265646 Fax: 01923 291146 *(Watford Deanery)* (1928; 1963)
E-mail: abbotslangley@rcdow.org.uk
Salvatorians (SDS) Fr Henry Nevin **Pastoral Assistant** Mr Steven Hurrell
Services Sun M (Sat 6pm), 9, 11, 6pm. Hds, M (6pm Eve) 10, 8pm. Wkds, M Mon-Fri 10 (Wed HC); Conf: Sat 11 to 11.30, 5.15 to 5.45.
Ecumenical Contact Paul Goggins **Tel: 01923 264562 Justice and Peace Contact** Parish Priest

ACTON + OUR LADY OF LOURDES

5 Berrymead Gardens W3 8AA Tel: 020 8992 2014 Fax: 020 8993 9940
E-mail: acton@rcdow.org.uk Web site: http://www.acton-olol.com/
On High Street, between Town Hall and Horn Lane. ***(Ealing Deanery)*** (1878; 1902; cons May 17, 1961)
Sacred Hearts Community (SSCC)
Fr Christopher McAneny (Parish Priest); Fr Fintan Crotty; Fr Kieran Murtagh
Services Sun, M (Sat 7pm), 9, 10.30, 12, 6pm; HH 7pm. Hds, M 7, 10, 8pm.
Wkds, M 7, 10; (Wed and Fri 10, 7pm; Sat 10, 12) Conf: Sat 10.30, 12.30, 6 to 7pm.
Ecumenical Contact Freda Murphy **Tel: 020 8993 2525**
Justice & Peace Contact Sr Deidre Duffy CSJP **Tel: 020 8752 1608**
Emmaus House (Acton Homeless Concern), 1 Berrymead Gardens W3 Tel: 020 8992 5768
Damien Centre (Acton Homeless Concern), 3-5 Church Road W3 Tel: 020 8993 6096
Medical Mission Sisters (SCMM), 41 Chatsworth Gardens W3 9LP Tel: 020 8992 6444
IBVM 4 Buxton Gardens W3 9LQ Tel: 020 8993 6931
Sr Gilberte Regnard; Sr Josette Zammit-Mangion; Sr M Magdalen O'Neill
Religious Sisters of Charity 9 Rosemont Road W3 9LU, Tel: 020 8992 4461
Srs Jacinta Rankin; Nuala Gaffney; Joan Barry; Carmel Keegan; Madelaine McCann

ACTON EAST + ST AIDAN OF LINDISFARNE

24 Sunningdale Avenue W3 7NS Tel: 020 8743 5732 E-mail:actoneast@rcdow.org.uk
Church on Old Oak Common Lane just off Western Avenue (A40) at Savoy Circus, 1 min East Acton stn
(Ealing Deanery) (1922; 1961; cons 31 Oct 1972) ***In pastoral care of White City***
Administrator Fr Danny Horan **Office** (Mon, Wed 10.30-12.30pm) **Tel: 020 8743 6733**
Services Sun M (Sat 6.30pm), 9, 11 (Sung) Hds, M 10am, 7.30pm. Wkds, M 10am Conf: Sat 5.30 to 6.15pm. Exp Sat during conf. B at 6.15pm
Ecum Contact Donald Allwright **020 8992 7616 Justice/Peace** Sr Breda Madigan **020 8248 9458**
Hammersmith & Queen Charlotte's Hospitals
Chaplain Fr Nigel Griffin **Tel: 020 8383 4574** M Sun11.30am, Tue 12.30pm St Luke's Chapel
Infant Jesus Sisters, 16 East Acton Lane W3 7EG Tel: 020 8248 9458
Sr Kitty Ellard; Sr Breda Madigan also **30 Sunningdale Ave W3 7NS Tel: 020 8743 0116**
Sisters of Mercy, 39 Ashfield Road W3 7JF Tel: 020 8740 6168.
HMP Wormwood Scrubs Chaplain Ms Helen Baly **Tel: 020 8588 3618 See Prison Service)**

ACTON WEST + THE HOLY FAMILY ♿ A

The Presbytery, Vale Lane W3 0DY Tel: 020 8992 1308 Fax: 020 8896 9393
In residential area; travel to North Ealing or West Acton stn ***(Ealing Deanery)*** (1967)
Fr John Wiley
Services Sun M (Sat 6pm), 9, 11. Hds M 10, 7.30pm
Wkds, M Mon-Fri 10. Conf: Sat 5-5.30
Ecumenical Contact Parish Priest
Justice and Peace Contact Parish Priest
Sacred Hearts Community (SS.CC), 372 Uxbridge Road W5 3LH Tel: 020 8992 5941
Fr Kenneth Barnes
Franciscan Missionaries of Mary, 26 Inglis Road W5 3RL Tel: 020 8992 0802.

ARNOS GROVE, N11 SEE NEW SOUTHGATE

ASHFORD + ST MICHAEL ♿ A

112 Clarendon Road, Ashford, Middx TW15 2QD
Tel: 01784 252230 Fax: 01784 247090
E-mail: ashford@rcdow.org.uk Website:www.stmichaels-ashford.org.uk
Corner of Fordbridge Road & Clarendon Road, behind the War Memorial ***(Upper Thames Deanery)***
(1906;1928)
Mgr James Overton
Services Sun, M (Sat 6pm), 9.30, 11.30, 6pm Hds, M 9.30, 8pm.
Wkds, M 9.30 (Mon, Tues, Thur, Fri, Sat) Conf: Sat 10.30 to 11am
Ecumenical Contact Anne Shenton **Tel: 01784 456774**
HMP Bronzefield Chaplain Mrs Kathleen Coates **Tel: 01784 425690 See Prison Service**

BALDOCK + HOLY TRINITY AND ST AUGUSTINE OF CANTERBURY ♿ A

Holy Trinity Church, London Road, Baldock, Herts SG7 6LQ
Tel: 01462 893127 E-mail: baldock@rcdow.org.uk
Website: www.rcdow.org.uk/baldock/
(Stevenage Deanery) (1913; 1926; new church 1977; cons 17 Dec 1977)
Fr Norman Wrigley (Retired)
Services Sun, M (Sat 6.30pm), 8.30, 10.30am (Sung)
Latin M 1st Sun 3pm
Hds M 10am, 7.30pm
Wkds M as announced Conf Sat 6pm
Ecumenical Contact Parish Priest
Justice and Peace Contact Parish Priest
Sisters of Providence, Limekiln Lane, Baldock, Herts SG7 6PG
Tel: 01462 892236.

BOREHAMWOOD + ST TERESA OF THE CHILD JESUS ☑ A

291 Shenley Road, Borehamwood, Herts WD6 1TG Tel: 020 8953 1294
Opposite Hertsmere Civic Offices ***(St Albans Deanery)*** (1925; 1962; cons 27 Sept 1978)
Fr Peter Lyness
Parish RE Co-ordinator Sr Rita Gauthier **Tel: 020 8445 4655**
Services Sun, M (Sat 6pm), 9.30 (CW), 11 (Sung). Hds, M 9.30, 7.30 pm.
Wkds, M as announced Conf: Sat 11.30-11.45, 5.15-5.45pm.R Fri 7.30pm; Sat 11.45am
Ecumenical Contact Nicholas Todd **Tel: 020 8953 2758 Justice & Peace Contact** Parish Priest
Comboni Missionaries (MCCJ), The Priory, Barnet Lane, Elstree, Herts WD6 3QU
Tel: 020 8953 8065 Fr Teckie Hagos Woldeghebriel

BOREHAMWOOD NORTH + SS JOHN FISHER AND THOMAS MORE ☑ A

The Presbytery, 28 Rossington Avenue, Borehamwood, Herts WD6 4LA
Tel: 020 8953 0715 *(St Albans Deanery)* (1955; 1958 cons 27.10.1992)
Administrator Fr Frans Azzopardi
Services Sun M (Sat 6pm), 10.30, 6.30pm. Wkds, M as announced.
Conf: Sat 10.30am. Rosary Tue 10.30am. Exp & B Fri 10.30am
Scalabrini Fathers, Villa Scalabrini, Green St, Shenley Tel: 020 8207 5713 Fr Alberto Vico
Daughters of Our Lady Mercy, Villa Scalabrini, Green St, Shenley Tel: 020 8905 2597

BOW + OUR LADY AND ST CATHERINE OF SIENA A

177 Bow Road E3 2SG Tel/Fax: 020 8980 3961 E-mail: bow@rcdow.org.uk
Fr Donald Graham *(Tower Hamlets Deanery)* (1868; 1870)
Services Sun, M (Sat 6pm), 9.30 (Sung), 11.30 (Family) Hds, M 10, 6pm.
Wkds, M Mon, Tue, Wed 10; Fri 12noon. Conf: Sat 5 - 5.30pm
Ecumenical Contact Parish Priest **Justice & Peace Contact** Sr Maria Fay **Tel: 020 8980 0044**
Columban Sisters, Filipino Chaplaincy, 8 Ridgdale Street E3 2TW Tel: 020 8980 3017
Website: www.columbansisters.org
Sisters of Charity of Jesus and Mary, 23 Bow Road E3 2AD Tel: 020 8983 4335
Sr Mary Thornton; Sr Molly Swain; Sr Camillus Gallagher
Sisters of Mercy, 152 Bruce Road E3 3EU Tel: 020 8980 0044
Sr Maria Fay; Sr Bernadette McCaffrey
St Andrew's Hospital

BOW COMMON + THE HOLY NAME AND OUR LADY OF THE SACRED HEART ☑

117 Bow Common Lane E3 4AU Tel: 020 7987 3477 Email: **limehouse@rcdow.org.uk**
(Tower Hamlets Deanery) (1892; 1894; cons June 30, 1894)
Served from Limehouse by Fr Aidan Rossiter CJ **Services** Sun, M 9.30
Vietnamese Chaplaincy Tel: 020 7987 3477 Fr Paul Huynh Chanh

BOXMOOR (SEE HEMEL HEMPSTEAD)

BRENTFORD + ST JOHN THE EVANGELIST ☑ A

44 Boston Park Road, Brentford, Middx TW8 9JF
Tel: 020 8560 1671 Fax: 020 8232 8003 E-mail: brentford@rcdow.org.uk
North side of Great West Road (A4); approach via Windmill Rd ***(Hounslow Deanery)*** (1856; cons1866)
Fr Gerard Quinn
Services Sun, M (Sat 6.30pm), 9.30, 11.30am, 6.30pm.
Hds M 9.30am, 7.30pm, Wkds, M as announced
Conf: Sat 5.30 - 6.15pm
Ecumenical Contact Sr Rose Lucy **Tel: 020 8560 7124**
Justice & Peace Contact Parish Priest
Servants of the Mother of God, St Mary's Convent, 2 The Butts, Brentford TW8 8BQ
Tel: 020 8847 4800 Chaplain Fr Patrick Miscampbell
Maryville Care Home Tel: 020 8560 7124
Sisters of the Sacred Heart of Mary, 64 Little Ealing Lane W5 4XF Tel: 020 8567 5245 & 020 8567 7199 Community Tel: 020 8567 3148 Provincialate
Clayponds Hospital

BROOK GREEN + HOLY TRINITY ☑ A

41 Brook Green W6 7BL Tel: 020 7603 3832 Fax: 020 7603 0511
E-mail: brookgreen@rcdow.org.uk ***(Hammersmith & Fulham Deanery)*** (1851;1853; cons 2.6.1866)
Off Hammersmith Rd (north side) between Hammersmith Broadway & Olympia.
Fr Terry Tastard; Fr Michael Dunne
Catechetical Co-ordinator Sr Jenefer Glencross OSU
Services Sun, M (Sat 6pm), 8.30, 10, (Family), 11.30 (Sung), Syriac Rite 1pm, 6pm.
Hds, M 9.30, 12.30, 6pm.
Wkds, M 9.30, 6pm; MP 9.15, EP 5.45pm. Conf: Sat 10-10.30, 5.15-5.45pm, Exp Sat 7pm
Ecumenical Contacts Sr Lilian Amato **Tel: 020 7603 2787 &** Neville Collins **020 8741 3814**
Justice and Peace Contact Parish Priest
Sisters of Nazareth, Nazareth House, Hammersmith Road W6 8DB
Tel: 020 8748 3549
Society of the Sacred Heart, Provincial House, 3 Bute Gardens W6 7DR Tel: 020 8748 9353; 9 Bute Gardens, W6 7DR Tel: 020 8741 8457; 9a Bute Gardens W6 7DR Tel: 020 8748 1439
121 Blythe Road W14 0HL Tel: 020 7603 2787 Sr Lilian Amato, Sr Christine Head, Sr Bernadette Sacce, Sr Elizabeth Smith
Spanish Sisters of Santa Ana, 93 Addison Gardens W14 Tel: 020 7603 0018
Sr Isabel Herrera; Sr Lucila Mendez; Sr Salva Piera
Austrian Catholic Centre, 29 Brook Green W6 Tel: 020 7603 2697
St Joseph's House, 42 Brook Green W6 7BW Tel: 020 7603 9817

BUNHILL ROW + ST JOSEPH

St Joseph's Presbytery, 15 Lamb's Passage, off Bunhill Row EC1Y 8LE
Tel: 020 7628 0326
E-mail:bunhillrow@rcdow.org.uk www.rcdow.org.uk/bunhillrow/
In small street linking Bunhill Row to Errol St; 3 min from entrance to Barbican Centre, beside City University Business School; nearest tubes Barbican, Moorgate, Old St ***(Islington Deanery)*** (1856; 1901)
Priest-in-charge Fr Bruno Healy
Services Sun M (Sat 6pm), 10.30. Hds, M 12.05, 6pm. Wkds, M Tues-Fri 12.05pm
Conf: Sat 4.30 to 5.30pm and after lunchtime M
Quiet Garden Tues-Sat 8-6pm
Ecumenical Contact and **Justice & Peace Contact** Parish Priest
Moorfields Eye Hospital

BUNTINGFORD + ST RICHARD OF CHICHESTER

3 Station Road, Buntingford, Herts SG9 9HT
Tel: 01763 271471
E-mail: buntingford@rcdow.org.uk ***(Lea Valley Deanery)*** (1912; 1914; cons June 5, 1940)
Fr Ian Dickie
Services Sun, M 9.30am, 6.30pm. Hds, M 10, 8pm.
Wkds, as announced. Conf: Sat 10.30-11.15.
Ecumenical Contact Mike Smith **Tel: 01763 272890**
Justice & Peace Contact Parish Priest
Mass Centre, The Annunciation, Furneux Pelham. Sun, M (Sat 6pm). Hds as announced

BURNT OAK + THE ANNUNCIATION A

4 Thirleby Road, Burnt Oak, Edgware, Middx HA8 0HQ
Tel: 020 8959 1971
Fax: 020 8959 1903 E-mail: burntoak@rcdow.org.uk
Off Gervase Road, close to Burnt Oak stn ***(Barnet Deanery)*** (1928)
Fr Eugene J Fitzpatrick
Services Sun, M (Sat 6.30pm), 9, 10.30, 12.
Hds, M 9, 2pm (Annunciation Junior School), 7pm.
Wkds, M Mon to Thurs 9; MP 8.40am R after M Mon, Tue, Thurs
Conf: Sat 10.30-11am & 5.45-6.15pm. Exp Wed 9.30am-6pm (except summer school holidays)
Ecumenical Contact Sheila Benson
Justice & Peace Contact Parish Priest
Holy Ghost Fathers (CSSp), 18 Limesdale Gardens, Edgware HA8 5JA Tel: 020 8200 5091
Fr Eamonn Mulcahy' Fr Alan Collins; Fr John McFadden **Superior**
Edgware Community Hospital
Chaplain Lionel Carriere **Tel: 020 8732 6869**

BUSHEY AND OXHEY + THE SACRED HEART OF JESUS AND ST JOHN THE EVANGELIST

Presbytery, London Road, Bushey, Watford, Herts WD23 1BA Tel/Fax: 020 8950 2077
E-mail: busheyandoxhey@rcdow.org.uk Website: www.rcdow,org.uk/bushey/
Ten minutes walk up Chalk Hill from Oxhey BR Stn ***(Watford Deanery)*** (1863; 1959; cons Sept. 20, 1977)
Fr Michael Markey **Catechetical Co-ordinator** Miss R Gonsalves.
Services Sun, M (Sat 6pm), 8.30, 10.30 (Sung), 6pm. Hds, M (Eve 7.30pm), 10, 8pm.
Wkds, M 9. Conf: Sat 11 to 11.30, 5 to 5.30pm and at call.
Ecumenical Contact Anthony Kilkerr **020 8950 9242 Justice & Peace** David Furber **020 8950 1422**
BUPA Hospital; Heath House; Birchville Court.
Dominican Sisters, Rosary Priory, Elstree Rd, Bushey, Watford, Herts WD23 3RJ
Tel: 020 8950 1148 Chaplain Fr Michael Platts OP

CAMDEN TOWN + OUR LADY OF HAL

165 Arlington Road NW1 7EX Tel: 020 7485 2727 Fax: 020 7485 1213
E-mail: camdentown@rcdow.org.uk Website: www.ourladyofhal.net
(Camden Deanery) (1921; 1933)
Fr Dominic McKenna **Administrator** Fr John Conneely also in residence Fr Jim Duffy
Residence for Retired Priests: Fr Pat Nolan, Fr Cyril Axelrod, Fr Colin McLean
Parish Sisters Sr Angela, Sr Maura and Sr Rita
Services Sun, M (Sat 7.30pm), 8.30, 10, 12, 5 (Portuguese), 7.30pm;
Hds, M 9.30, 12, 7.30pm. Wkds, M 9.30, 12 (Sat 12, 7.30pm). Sat HH & B 6-7pm.
Conf: Sat 11 to 11.30, 6.30 to 7pm.
Ecumenical Contact Parish Priest **Justice and Peace Contact** Parish Priest
Portuguese Centre, 165 Arlington Road NW1 7EX Tel: 020 7587 0881
Mgr Jose Vaz Pinto.
Helpers of the Holy Souls Tel: 020 7485 1745
Alexian Brothers 28 Delancey Street NW1 7NH Tel: 020 7482 4199
Irish Centre: See Kentish Town.

CARPENDERS PARK + ST JOSEPH A

St Joseph's Church, Oxhey Drive, South Oxhey, Watford, Herts WD19 7SW
Tel: 020 8428 2774 Fax: 020 8421 5840
Off Prestwick Road (shopping centre), close to Carpenders Park stn - on South Oxhey side of railway line
(Watford Deanery) (1952; 1960; cons 1981)
Fr Aidan Sharratt
Services Sun, M (Sat 6.30pm), 8.30, 10.30am
Hds, M 9.15, 7.30pm.
Conf: Sat 5 to 5.30pm
Ecumenical Contact Ronald Deller **Tel: 020 8428 0246**
Justice & Peace Contact Parish Priest
The Fairways Old People's Home, Pinewood Lodge Old People's Home

CHELSEA 1 + ST MARY CADOGAN STREET ☎

St Mary's Rectory, Draycott Terrace SW3 2QR Tel: 020 7589 5487
Fax: 020 7581 5727 E-mail: chelsea1@rcdow.org.uk Website: www.stmarycadogan.co.uk
Corner of Cadogan St /Draycott Terrace, ***(Kensington & Chelsea Deanery)***
(1798; 1811; 1879; cons 12 June 1882)
Canon Vincent Berry; Fr Hilary Crewe
Services Sun, M (Sat 6.30pm), 10 (Family), 11.30am (sung Latin), 6.30pm.
Hds, M (Eve 6.30pm), 7.30, 12, 6.30pm.
Wkds, M 7.30am (Tue, Wed, Thurs); 12 noon (Mon, Wed, Fri); Sat 10am;
6.30pm (Mon, Tue, Thurs, Fri); Conf: Sat 11 - 11.30, 5.30 - 6.15pm. Exp Fri 7pm - 10pm
Ecumenical Contact Parish Priest **Justice and Peace Contact** Parish Priest
Royal Hospital, Chelsea (Sun, M 9.30); **Charter Clinic; Lister Hospital.**
Daughters of the Cross, St Wilfrid's Convent, 29 Tite Street SW3 4JX
Tel: 020 7351 5339 Fax: 020 7376 5339 (Convent and Home);
Tel: 020 7351 2117 Fax: 020 7351 4634 Provincialate
Sr Veronica Hagan **Provincial**; Sr Veronica Bolam **Superior**; Sr Margaret McMullan;
Sr Thomas More; Sr Mary Basil; Sr Nilda Pettenuzzo; Sr Elena Pettenuzzo; Sr Catherine
Sweeney; Sr Peggy O'Gorman; Sr Kathleen McKenna
Chaplain Fr William Wilby **Tel: 020 7351 5339 ext 381**
Dawliffe Hall, 1-2 Chelsea Embankment SW3 4LG Tel: 020 7352 1545
Pastoral care entrusted to Prelature of Opus Dei

CHELSEA 2 + OUR MOST HOLY REDEEMER AND ST THOMAS MORE ☎

7 Cheyne Row SW3 5HS Tel: 020 7352 0777 Fax: 020 7352 4223
E-mail:chelsea2@rcdow.org.uk Website: www.holyredeemerchelsea.com
North of Albert Bridge, off Oakley St ***(Kensington & Chelsea Deanery)*** (1892; 1895; cons 21.6 1905)
Canon Michael Brockie
Services Sun, M (Sat 6.30pm), 10 (Family), 11 (Latin Sung), 12.15, 6.30pm.
Hds, M 8, 10, 6.30pm. Wkds, M Mon - Fri 8am; Sat 10am
Conf: Sat 10.30 to 11, 5.30 to 6.15pm. MP 7.30 Mon - Fri; 9.30am Sat & Sun
Ecumenical Contact Parish Priest **Justice and Peace Contact** Parish Priest
Thamesbrook Nursing Home
Diocesan Seminary, Allen Hall. See Index.

CHESHUNT + ST PAUL ☎ A

17 Churchfield Path, off Church Lane, Cheshunt, Herts EN8 9EG
Tel: 01992 629878 Fax: 01992 621741 ***(Lea Valley Deanery)*** (1998)
Fr Anton Cowan also Secretary of Diocesan Council of Censorship
Services Sun M (Sat 5pm) 9, 11, Hds M 9.30am & 8pm; Wks M 9.30am (except Thurs)
Exp Fri 9am; Conf: Sat 4.15-4.45pm.
Ecumenical Contact Parish Priest **Justice & Peace Contact** Parish Priest

CHIPPERFIELD + OUR LADY, MOTHER OF THE SAVIOUR A

Catholic Church, Dunny Lane, Chipperfield, Herts WD4 9DB
Tel: 01923 265327 E-mail: chipperfield@rcdow.org.uk *(Watford Deanery)* (1989)
Salvatorians (SDS) Fr Desmond Cantwell, Fr Ian Dalgliesh
Also serves Kings Langley, Bovingdon, Sarratt
Services Sun, M (Sat 6pm) 9, 11. Hds, M 7.30pm. Wkds, M as announced.
Ecumenical Contact Michael Tiernan **Tel: 01923 267914 Justice & Peace Contact** Parish Priest

CHISWICK + OUR LADY OF GRACE AND ST EDWARD

247 High Road W4 4PU Tel: 020 8994 2877 Fax: 020 8987 8332.
E-mail: chiswick@rcdow.org.uk Website: www.rcdow.org.uk/chiswick/
Also serves Gunnersbury Main road, corner of Dukes Ave ***(Hounslow Deanery)*** (1852; 1886; cons 10 Oct 1904)
Mgr James Curry; Fr Michael Daley; Rev Ragnor Salvesen (Deacon)
Also in residence Fr Chris Vipers **(Vocations Director) Tel: 020 7798 9083**
Services Sun, M (Sat 6.30pm), 8.30, 9.45 (Family), 11, 12.15, 6.30pm. Hds, M 10, 12.30, 7.30pm. Wkds, M 10, 12.30. Conf: Sat 11-12, 5 - 6pm & at call. Exp Mon - Sat 1pm - 6pm
Ecumenical Contact Cathy Pearce **Tel: 020 8994 6277 Justice & Peace** Hugh Caldin **Tel: 020 8994 6368**
Religious Sisters of Charity, Provincial House, 55 Barrowgate Road W4 4QT
Tel: 020 8995 1963 Fax: 020 8742 2175 Sr Jacinta Boland; Sr Geraldine O'Connor
Missionary Sisters of Mary Immaculate (PIME), Regina Pacis Convent,
10 Chiswick Lane W4 Tel: 020 8994 2053 House of Studies and Kindergarten.
Comboni Missionary Sisters, 2 Chiswick Lane W4 2JE Tel: 020 8994 0449
Fax: 020 8747 3896 House for Student Sisters & Elderly Sisters

CHORLEYWOOD - ST JOHN FISHER

Hill Cottage, Shire Lane, Chorleywood, Rickmansworth, Herts WD3 5NH
Tel/Fax: 01923 283616 E-mail:chorleywood@rcdow.org.uk
Close to shopping centre & station ***(Watford Deanery)*** (1955)
Fr Peter F Stevens.
Services Sun, M (Sat 6pm), 8.30, 10.30. Hds, M 10, 8pm.
Wkds, M Mon to Fri 9.30 (Wed 7.30pm). Conf: Sat 11.30am, 5.30pm.
Ecumenical Contact Francis O'Loughlin **Tel: 01923 283976 Justice & Peace Contact** Parish Priest

CLAPTON + ST SCHOLASTICA A

17 Kenninghall Road E5 8BS Tel: 020 8985 2178
E-mail: clapton@rcdow.org.uk *(Hackney Deanery)* (1862; 1962; cons 15.2.87)
Fr Christopher Tuckwell; Fr Hector Rouco Gutierrez
Services Sun, M (Sat 6pm), 10, 11.45, 6pm. Hds, M 9.30, 7.30. Wkds, M Mon to Fri 9.15, Sat 12 noon MP 8.50am Conf: Sat 11 to 11.45am & on request. Exp Fri 6-7pm
Ecumenical Contact Parish Priest **Justice and Peace Contact** Parish Priest
Servite Sisters, Flat 1 Brownsea Court 160 Clarence Rd, E5 8EF Tel: 020 8985 3489

CLAPTON PARK + ST JUDE ☎

131 Glenarm Road E5 0NB Tel: 020 8525 1929 Fax: 020 8985 9208
E-mail: claptonpark@rcdow.org.uk *Off Chatsworth Rd. Blurton Rd* ***(Hackney Deanery)*** (1964)
Administrator Fr Neil Hannigan
Services Sun, M (Sat 6.30pm), 9.30 (sung), 11.30 (sung), 6pm. Hds, M 10am, 7pm.
Wkds, M Thu 9am, other days 10am. Conf: Sat 6 to 6.15 & at request.
Justice & Peace Contact Sr Mary Radcliffe **Tel: 020 8986 4435**
Homerton University Hospital NHS Trust Tel: 020 8986 5181 Sun, M 11(Camillians)
Columban Sisters, 148 Glenarm Road E5 0NB Tel: 020 8986 4435
Sisters of Mercy, 4 Hilsea Street E5 0SG Tel: 020 8986 3196

CLERKENWELL + SS PETER AND PAUL ☎ A

5 Amwell Street, Rosebery Avenue EC1R 1UL Tel: 020 7837 2094 Fax: 020 7837 2724
E-mail: clerkenwell@rcdow.org.uk ***(Islington Deanery)*** (1842; 1847)
Pallottine Fathers (SCA) Fr George Ranahan
Services Sun, M (Sat 6.30pm) 10, 12. Hds, M 12, 7.30. Wkds, M 12. Conf: Sat 11.30, 6 - 6.15
Ecumenical Contact Parish Priest **Justice and Peace Contact** Parish Priest
Pallottine Missionary Sisters, 35 Wilmington Square WC1X 0EG Tel: 020 7837 3010
Fax: 020 7837 7539.
Royal National Throat, Nose & Ear Hospital

CLERKENWELL + ST PETER (SEE ITALIAN CHURCH)

COCKFOSTERS + CHRIST THE KING ☎ ♿

Monastery of Christ the King, 29 Bramley Road N14 4HE Tel: 020 8449 6648 (Parish)
020 8440 7769 (Monastery) Fax: 020 8440 2296 E-mail:cockfosters@rcdow.org.uk
On main road, a few yards west of Oakwood stn (LT), junc Peace Close ***(Enfield Deanery)*** (1936; 1940)
Benedictines: Congregation of Monte Oliveto (OSB) Dom Costanzo M Scaglia **Prior;**
Dom Paschal M Pennington **Sub Prior/PP;** Dom Benedict M Heron **Tel: 020 8441 4719;**
Dom Willibrord M Schlatmann; Dom Laurence M Freeman; Dom Philip M Temple;
Dom Bernard M Akoeso; Dom Felician M Roux; Dom Andrew M Galazka
Divine Office MP 7.40; Midday 12.35; EP Sun 5, Mon to Fri 6.40, Sat 6.30
Other Services Sun, M (Sat 5.30pm), 8.30 (CW), 10 (CW), 12,
6.30pm (with Group 2nd, 4th & 5th Sun). Hds, M 8, 11, 7.30pm. Wkds M 8, 11
Conf (Spanish, Italian): Sat 10.30 to 11, after 5.30 M; at call.
Ecumenical Contact Parish Secretary **Justice and Peace Contact** Parish Secretary
Homes for Aged: Servite House, Sir Thomas Lipton's, Trentfield, The Chine, Elizabeth Lodge.
Benedictine Centre for Spirituality Tel: 020 8449 2499 Guest House Tel: 020 8441 8337
Cenacle, Sisters of Our Lady of, 10 The Orchard, Bramley Road N14 4HB
Tel: 020 8440 4087

COMMERCIAL ROAD + ST MARY AND ST MICHAEL

2 Lukin Street, Commercial Road E1 0AA Tel: 020 7790 5911 Fax: 020 7265 9795
E-mail: commercialroad@rcdow.org.uk *200 yards east Watney Market* ***(Tower Hamlets Deanery)***
Fr Francis van Son (1856; cons 4.12.29)
Services Sun, M (Sat 7pm), 9, 11. Hds M 9.30, 12.30pm, 7pm.
Wkds M 9.30am in church on Mon, Wed, Fri; other days in convent. Conf: Sat 6 - 6.30pm
Ecumenical Contact Mrs E Pickin **Justice and Peace Contact** Parish Priest
Sisters of Mercy, 88 Hardinge Street E1 0EB Tel: 020 7790 1459 M. Mon-Fri 8am, Sat 8.30am
Srs: M Sylvester Gill; Rufina Malone; M Malachy Haugh; Bridget Quinlivan; M Lawrence Collins; Mary Elizabeth O'Connor; Mary Josephine Browne; Mary Teresita Heenan; Mary Enda Foley; Mary Regina Malone; Anna Moloney

COPENHAGEN STREET + THE BLESSED SACRAMENT A

157 Copenhagen Street N1 0SR Tel: 020 7837 4841 Fax: 020 7837 7591
E-mail: blesac@rcdow.org.uk www.rcdow.org.uk/copenhagenstreet/
Fr Jim Kennedy *Off Caledonian Road, half mile north of Kings Cross stn* ***(Islington Deanery)*** (1916)
Secretary Teresa Finnigan Tues-Fri 11-1pm (Office also open Wed/Thurs 7.30-8.30pm)
Services Sun, M (Sat 7pm), 9, 11(Sung CW), 6.30pm (Sung) Hds, M 8, 10 (School) 12.30, 7pm.
Wkds, Mon, Wed, Fri 7pm; Tue, Thu, 12.30pm; Sat 10.30am. Conf: Sat 6 to 6.30pm.
Ecumenical Contact Parish Priest **Justice and Peace Contact** Parish Priest

CRANFORD + OUR LADY AND ST CHRISTOPHER

32 High Street, Cranford, Hounslow, Middx TW5 9RG Tel: 020 8759 2160
E-mail: cranford@rcdow.org.uk
Next to Holy Angels Church, opposite The Avenue ***(Hounslow Deanery)*** (1967; 1970, cons 1979)
Fr Paschal Ryan
Services Sun, M (Sat 6pm), 8.30, 10.30am Hds, M 9.30, 7.30pm.
Wkds, M 9.30am Conf: Sat 5.15 -5.45pm & at call.

CRICKLEWOOD + ST AGNES

35 Cricklewood Lane NW2 1HR Tel: 020 8452 2475 Fax: 020 8208 3924
E-mail: cricklewood@rcdow.org.uk
On A407, midway between A41 and Cricklewood Broadway (A5) ***(Barnet Deanery)*** (1883; 1930)
Fr Michael Kennedy; Fr Andrew O'Connell
Services Sun, M (Sat 6.30pm), 9, 10.30, 12, 6.30pm Hds, M 9, 11, 7.30pm
Wkds, M 9.15 (Mon-Fri) Sat 10am. Conf: Sat 10.30am & 5.30pm
Ecumenical Contact Parish Priest **Justice and Peace Contact** Jonathan Alder
Sisters of St Joseph of Peace, 157 Walm Lane NW2 3AY Tel: 020 8450 8859
Sisters of Mercy, 149 Walm Lane NW2 3AU Tel: 020 8450 7472
Dominican Sisters St Rose's Convent, 160 Anson Road NW2 6BH Tel: 020 8830 7465

CROXLEY GREEN + ST BEDE A

185 Baldwins Lane, Croxley Green, Rickmansworth, Herts WD3 3LL
Tel: 01923 231969
Fax: 01923 211089 E-mail: croxleygreenbede@rcdow.org.uk
(Watford Deanery) (1958; cons 1975)

Canon Philip Cross
Services Sun, M (Sat 6pm), 10, 6pm. Hds, M 10, 7.30pm.
Wds, M 10am (Tues Euch Service)
Conf: Sat 10.30 & 12 noon
Ecumenical Contact Mrs U. Bartlett **Tel: 01923 445163**
Justice and Peace Contact Miss Louise McKenna **Tel: 01923 226034**

CUFFLEY + ST MARTIN DE PORRES A

4 Church Close, Cuffley, Herts EN6 4LS
Tel: 01707 873308
Fax: 01707 876549 E-mail: cuffley@rcdow.org.uk
(Hatfield Deanery)

Administrator Fr Patrick Carroll
Services Sun, M (Sat 5.30pm) 9, 11 Hds, M 9.30, 8pm.
Wkds M as announced
Conf 10.30am
Ecumenical Contact Parish Priest
Justice and Peace Contact Mike & Liz Hegarty

DOLLIS HILL + ST MARY AND ST ANDREW ♿

216 Dollis Hill Lane NW2 6HE
Tel: 020 8452 6158 Fax: 020 8450 3350
E-mail: dollishill@rcdow.org.uk Website: www. stmaryandstandrew.co.uk
(Brent Deanery) (1915; 1933)

Canon Matthew Kennelly
Also in residence Fr John D O'Neill (retired)
Services Sun, M (Sat 7pm), 8.30, 10.30 (Family), 12 (sung), 6.30pm.
Hds, M 10, 8pm or as announced
Wkds, M 9.30am (Mon - Fri) and Tues 7pm, Fri 7.30pm, Sat 10am.
R. after each M. Exp Fri 10-7.15pm. B Fri 7.15pm, Sat 6.45pm.
Conf: Sat 12.30 to 1, 6 to 6.30pm. MP Mon-Fri 9. Exp Sat 5.45-6.45pm
Ecumenical Contact Parish Priest
Justice & Peace Contact Cathy Collins **Tel: 020 8452 6158**
Sisters of St Louis, 119 Dollis Hill Lane NW2 6HS
Tel: 020 8208 0696

EALING + ABBEY CHURCH OF ST BENEDICT

Ealing Abbey, Charlbury Grove W5 2DY Parish Tel: 020 8862 2160
Parish Fax: 020 8862 2166 Parish E-mail: st_benedict@freenet.co.uk
Monastery Tel: 020 8862 2100 Fax: 020 8862 2206
E-mail: ealingmonk@aol.com Web site: www. members.aol.com/ealingmonk
1/4 mile north of station & shops; local bus via Eaton Rise to Marchwood Cres. ***(Ealing Deanery)*** (1897; 1899)
Benedictines (English Congregation) (OSB): Fr Peter Burns (Parish Priest); Abbot Francis Rossiter (Prior); Fr Timothy Gorham
Other priests in the community: Abbot Martin Shipperlee (Abbot of Ealing); Abbot Laurence Soper; Fr Bernard Orchard; Fr Kevin Horsey; Fr Gregory Chillman; Fr Stanislaus Hobbs; Fr Dunstan Watkins; Fr Edmund Flood; Fr Vincent Cooper; Fr David Pearce (Novice Master); Fr Andrew Hughes; Fr Thomas Stapleford; Fr Alban Nunn; Fr James Leachman;
Divine Office Matins 6 (Sat 6.30; Sun Vigil on Sat 7.30pm); Lauds 7.35; Conventual M 7 (Sat 9.15, Sun 10.30); Vespers 6.30 (Sat 5.30; Sun 6 with Exp); Compline 8pm (except Sat & Sun).
Services Sun, M (Sat 6pm), 8, 9, 10.15 (Family M, in Parish Centre), 10.30 (Sung), 12, 7pm. Hds, M 7, 9.15, 6pm, 8pm. Wkds, M 7, 9.15, 6pm. Exp Thur 8.15-9pm; Fri 9.45am-12.30pm Conf: Sat 10 to 11, 4 to 5pm, 7 to 7.30pm; Thu 8 to 8.30pm. R Mon - Sat 9.40am.
Ecumenical Contact Veronica Lawlor **Tel: 020 8998 1283 Justice & Peace** Liz Croft
The Benedictine Study and Arts Centre, 74 Castlebar Road W5 2DD
Tel: 020 8862 2156 Fax: 020 8862 2206 E-mail: ann-marie@bsac.ac.uk
Capitanio Sisters, Nile Lodge, Queen's Walk W5 1TJ Tel: 020 8997 3933
Little Company of Mary, 12 Blakesley Avenue W5 2DW Tel: 020 8997 1833
Dominican Sisters, 7-8 Montpelier Avenue W5 2XP Tel: 020 8997 8850
Medical Missionaries of Mary, 2 Denbigh Road W13 8PX Tel: 020 8998 1725
Sr Maureen Clarke; Sr Anne Curtin; Sr Barbara Faulkner; Sr Mary Howard
Sisters of Charity (of St Jeanne Antide), 6 Woodfield Road W5 1SJ Tel: 020 8998 9549
Brothers of St Gabriel, 11 Longfield Road W5 2DH Tel: 020 8998 9182
Br John Hegarty
Sisters of the Holy Cross, 82 The Avenue W13 8LB Tel: 020 8997 2858
Missionaries of Africa (White Fathers) (MAfr), 15 Corfton Road W5 2HP
Tel: 020 8997 8751 Fr John Millane (Superior), Fr Gerard Burton, Fr Stephen Collins
Also **46 Woodville Gardens W5 2LQ Tel: 020 8998 8552**
Fr Damian Watine (Superior); Fr John Sandom; Fr Felix Phiri
Missionary Sisters of Our Lady of Africa, 5 Charlbury Grove W5 2DY
Regional Superior Tel: 020 8998 5017 Fax: 020 8997 1828
Regional Treasurer Tel: 020 8998 5014
Sisters of the Resurrection, 18 Carlton Road W5 2AW Tel: 020 8810 6241
Sr M Goretti Feeheny; Sr M Pauline Hebron; Sr M Janina Kwoczka; Sr Faustina Lagodzinska; Sr Catherine Nastala; Sr Teresita Williams
Also **84 Gordon Road W5 2AR Tel: 020 8998 8954** Sr M Angela Coyne; Sr Teresa Czarniecka; Sr M Kathleen Delaney; Sr Elizabeth Geraghty; Sr M Regina Grin

EASTCOTE + ST THOMAS MORE ♿ 🎧

32 Field End Road, Eastcote, Pinner, Middx HA5 2QT
Tel: 020 8866 6581 Fax: 020 8429 2346 E-mail: eastcote@rcdow.org.uk
On main rd, north of station & shops, just beyond Bridle Rd junction ***(Hillingdon Deanery)*** (1935; 1977; cons 6.2.78)
Administrator Fr Michael Connor
Services Sun, M (Sat 6.30pm), 9.30 (Family), 11.30, 6pm. Hds, M (Eve 7pm) 9.30 & 7.30 Wkds, M 9.30am (Mon, Tues, Thurs, Fri, Sat), Thurs 7.30pm. Conf: Sat 10.00 to 10.30am; Exp Sat 10 - 10.35 (B)
Ecumenical Contact Jane Inglese **Tel: 020 8868 8576** **Justice & Peace Contact** Parish Priest

EDGWARE + ST ANTHONY OF PADUA 🎧 A

5 Garratt Road, Edgware, Middx HA8 9AN
Tel: 020 8952 0663 Office: 020 8951 5769
E-mail: edgware1@rcdow.org.uk Website: www.stanthonyschurch.org.uk
(Barnet Deanery) (1913;1931;1958)
Fr Patrick Sammon **Catechetical Co-ordinator** Sister Barbara Nolan OP
Services Sun M (Sat 6.30pm), 10, 12, 6.30pm. Hds, M, 10, 12, 8pm. Wkds, M 10 as announced, Tues 7.30pm followed by Nov to St Anthony & B (8pm first & last Fri) Exp Mon-Sat 6am to 10pm, Sun 7am to 10pm. Medjugorje Prayer Group for families of people with addictions every second Thursday Conf: Sat 10.30 - 11.30, & after evening M
Daughters of Mary, Mother of Mercy, 16 St Margaret's Road HA8 9UP
Tel: 020 8958 8316
Dominican Sisters, 267 Hale Lane, Edgware, Middx HA8 8NW Tel: 020 8958 5622

Chapel of Ease: St Matthias *In Broadfields Avenue (North side of A41); opp Hartland Drive*
194 Broadfields Avenue, Edgware, Middx HA8 8TF
Tel: 020 8958 8871 E-mail: edgwarebroadfields@rcdow.org.uk
Services Sun, M (Sat 6pm), 10.30 (Sung) Hds, M 10, 7.30pm. Wkds, M Mon & Fri 7.30pm; Tues & Wed 10. Conf: Sat 5.15 - 5.45 Exp Sat 5.15 B at 5.45pm

EDMONTON + THE MOST PRECIOUS BLOOD AND ST EDMUND, KM ♿ 🎧

115 Hertford Road N9 7EN Tel: 020 8803 6631 Fax: 020 8345 6495
E-mail: edmonton@rcdow.org.uk Website: www.rcdow.org.uk/edmonton/
Corner of Croyland Road, 1/4 mile north of Edmonton Green ***(Enfield Deanery)*** (1903; cons 17.5.07)
Fr Sean Carroll; Fr David Barrow **Catechetical Co-ordinator** Kathy Vacca
Services Sun, M (Sat 7pm), 8, 9.15, 10.30, 12, 6.30pm.
Hds, M 9.15, 12, 7.30pm. Wkds, M as announced. Conf: Sat 11 to 11.45, 6pm to 6.45pm
Ecumenical Contact Parish Priest **Justice and Peace Contact** Lauri Clarke
Sisters of Handmaids of Holy Child Jesus Tel: 020 8803 3839
North Middlesex Hospital Chaplain Fr Sean Carroll

ELY PLACE + ST ETHELDREDA

14 Ely Place, Holborn Circus EC1N 6RY
Tel: 020 7405 1061
Fax: 020 7405 7440 E-mail: elyplace@rcdow.org.uk
(Westminster Deanery) (1252-1290; 1297; crypt re-opened 1876; upper church re-opened 1879)
Institute of Charity (IC) Fr Christopher Cunningham (Rector)
Services Sun, M 9, 11 (sung Latin). Hds, M 8, 12.10pm, 1pm, 6pm (Sung Latin).
Wkds, M Mon-Fri 8, 1pm; Sat 9.30.
Conf daily 1.20pm and at call.
Ecumenical Contact Parish Priest **Justice and Peace Contact** Parish Priest
Rosminian Sisters, 13 Ely Place, Holborn Circus EC1N 6RY Tel: 020 7405 1588

ENFIELD + OUR LADY OF MOUNT CARMEL AND ST GEORGE S

45 London Road, Enfield EN2 6DS
Tel: 020 8363 2569
Fax: 020 8342 0159 E-mail: enfield@rcdow.org.uk
Main road, near Enfield Town stn ***(Enfield Deanery)*** (1862; 1958; cons16 07. 67)
Fr Richard Andrew; Fr Gerard Skinner; Rev Agustin Conesa (Deacon)
Catechetical Co-ordinator Mrs Sybil Lee.
Services Sun, M - all sung (Sat 7pm), 8, 9.15 (CW), 10.30,12, 6.30pm
Hds, M 12.30, 8pm (Sung) Wkds, M Mon-Fri 12.30pm, Sat 9.30am,
Convent Mon/Tues 7.30am St George's School (term) Fri 8.25am
Conf Sat 10-11, 6.15-6.45
Exp Sat 10-11am B 11am, 1st Fri 9.30am - 9pm. Rosary Mon-Fri 12.10pm

Chapel of Ease: Our Lady of Walsingham and the English Martyrs, Holtwhites Hill
Tel: 020 8367 8479
Services Sun, M - both sung 9, 10.30am. Hds, M (Eve 7.30pm) 10 Wkds, M Wed, Thu 10

Ecumenical Contacts ***Enfield Town & Forty Hill*** Joe Grachvogel; ***Bush Hill Park*** Malcolm Green; ***North West Enfield*** Paul Tanner **Justice and Peace Contact** Tony Sheen

Sisters of the Holy Family of Nazareth, 52 London Road, Enfield EN2 6EN
Tel: 020 8363 4483
Sr Danuta Kowalewska, Sr Jadwiga Delikowska, Sr Stefana Dmitrzak, Sr James O'Hora,
Sr Grace Keane, Sr Bozena Medeksza, Sr Angela Nowak, Sr Virginia Davolls,
Sr Bernard Lyons, Sr Frances Cullen, Sr Mercedes Maliszewski
Chase Farm Hospital, North London Nuffield Hospital, King's Oak Hospital
Enfield Community Care Centre

EUSTON, NW1 SEE SOMERS TOWN

FARM STREET + THE IMMACULATE CONCEPTION A

114 Mount Street W1K 3AH
Tel: 020 7493 7811
Fax: 020 7495 6685
E-mail: farmstreet@rcdow.org.uk Website: www.farmstreet.org.uk
Opposite Carlos Place (south side Grosvenor Square) and at Farm Street off Berkeley Square
(Marylebone Deanery) (1849)

Jesuits (SJ) Fr William Pearsall **Parish Priest**; Fr James Campbell; Fr Anthony Meredith
Also in residence: Fr Hugh Duffy **Superior**; Fr William Broderick; Fr Ralph Eastwell;
Fr Francis Edwards; Fr John Edwards; Fr Vincent Hawe; Fr Michael Holman;
Fr Geoffrey Holt; Fr Francis Laishley; Fr John Lang; Fr William MacCurtain;
Fr Thomas McCoog; Fr John Mahoney; Fr Paul O'Reilly; Fr Anthony Parish;
Fr Joseph Raybould; Fr John Russell; Fr David Stewart; Bro William Jordan; Bro John Parsons;
Bro James Harkess
Services Sun, M (Sat 6pm), 8, 9.30 (Family), 11 (sung Latin), 12.30, 4.15, 6.15pm.
Hds, M (Eve 6pm), 8, 12.05, 1.05, 6pm.
Wkds, M 8, 12.05, 1.05, 6pm (Sat 8, 11).
Conf (Fr, It, Germ, Span, available): Wkds for 10 min bef each M & at call
Sat: as weekdays Sun bef each M. Exp: Mon-Fri 12.30-1pm.
Ecumenical Contact Parish Priest
Justice and Peace Contact Parish Priest
Jesuits (SJ) Provincial Curia, 114 Mount Street W1K 3AH
Tel: 020 7499 0285 Fax: 020 7408 7111
Fr Michael Holman **Provincial**; Fr Dermot Preston; Fr Kevin Fox; Fr Paul Hamill

FELTHAM + ST LAWRENCE

St Lawrence's Presbytery, The Green, Feltham, Middx TW13 4AF
Tel: 020 8890 2367
E-mail: feltham@rcdow.org.uk
Website: www.rcdow.org.uk/feltham/
Set back on east side of High Street, not far from station ***(Hounslow Deanery)*** (1910; 1934)
Canon Gerard Burke; Fr Stephen Coker
Services Sun, M (Sat 6pm), 9, 11, 6pm.
Hds, M 9.30, 12.15, 8pm. Wkds, M 9.30.
Conf: Sat 11 to 11.45; 5 to 5.45pm.
Ecumenical Contact Parish Priest
Justice and Peace Contact Parish Priest
Sisters of Mercy, 35 Ruscombe Way, Feltham, Middx TW14 9NY
Tel: 020 8751 0862
HMYOI and Remand Centre Tel: 020 8844 5326
Chaplains Fr Roger Reader; Sr Monica Killeen **(See Prison Service)**

FINCHLEY CHURCH END + ST PHILIP THE APOSTLE

The Priest's House, Gravel Hill N3 3RJ
Tel: 020 8346 2459 Fax: 020 8349 1392
E-mail: finchleychurchend@rcdow.org.uk Website: www.stphilipsfinchley.org.uk
Regent's Park Rd Nr Finchley Cent stn junct Gravel Hill ***(Barnet Deanery)*** (1918; 1933; cons 3.5.75)
Fr John P. Dermody; also in residence Fr Gerard Balinnya
Services Sun, M (Sat 6.30pm), 8.30, 10 (sung), 12 (Family).
Hds, M 12, 7.30pm.
Wkds, M Mon-Sat 10am (Wed HC). Conf: Sat 10.30-11am, 5.45 to 6.15pm.
MP Mon-Sat am 9.40. Exp Sat 10.30 - 11am
Ecumenical Contact Sylvia Godwin **020 8346 0472**
Justice & Peace Contact Veronica Devine **020 8922 0351**
Finchley Memorial Hospital, Dell Field Court Nursing Home
Consolata Fathers (IMC), 3 Salisbury Avenue N3 3AJ
Tel: 020 8346 5498
Fr Giorgio Battifolo **Superior**; Fr Pietro Schiavinato, Fr Serafino Dal Pont.
Xaverian Missionaries (SX), 260 Nether Street N3 1HT
Tel: 020 8346 0428 Fax: 020 8922 3876
Fr Ennio Casalucci **Superior**; Fr Giovanni Ceresoli; Fr Alessandro Zanchi; Fr Natalio Paganelli; Fr Jorge Jimenez Estrella

FINCHLEY NORTH + ST ALBAN

51 Nether Street N12 7NN Tel: 020 8446 0224 Fax: 020 8343 7400
E-mail: finchleynorth@rcdow.org.uk Website: www.rcdow.org.uk/finchleynorth/
200 yds from Tally Ho Corner. ***(Barnet Deanery)*** (1903; 1909; cons 24 Feb 1995)
Fr Bernard McCumiskey **Key Catechist** Ursula Morrissey
Services Sun, M (Sat 6pm), 9.am, 10.15, 12, 6pm. Hds, M (Eve 6pm), 10, 6pm.
Wkds, M 10, (MP bef M); also 6pm Mon, Wed, Fri. Conf: Sat 10.45 to 11.30, 5 to 5.45pm.
Exp, 1st Fri 10.30 to 12noon; Sat: 10.30 -11.30 R after M daily
Ecumenical Contact John Robertson **Justice and Peace Contact** Parish Priest
Byelorussian Catholic Mission, Marian House, Holden Ave N12 8HY Tel: 020 8445 1938
Mitred Archpriest Alexander Nadson, STL, BSc (Rector), Fr Constantine Maskalik.
Services (Byzantine-Slavonic Rite) Sun, M 10.30. Wkds, M 7. Conf (Byelorussian, Polish, Russian, French, Italian): bef M and at call. Vespers, Sat 5.30pm, eves of Feasts 7pm, other days 7.30pm
The Francis Skaryna Byelorussian Library, 37 Holden Road N12
Librarian Archpriest Alexander Nadson, STL, BSc. **Tel: 020 8445 5358/020 8445 1938**
Sisters of the Poor Child Jesus, 56 Kings Lodge, Kingsway N12 0EW
Tel: 020 8446 6230 Sr Anne
Acacia Lodge, Torrington, Cairn Ryan, Catherine Lodge, Elmhurst, Fernbank, Dr French Memorial, The Grange, Kenwood House, Barnet Temporary Unhoused, Safestart Foundation, The Limes, Wimbush House, Woodlands

FINCHLEY EAST + ST MARY ♿ 🎧

279 High Road N2 8HG Tel: 020 8883 4234 Fax: 020 8365 3738.
E-mail: finchleyeast@rcdow.org.uk
Ten minutes walk from East Finchley tube stn, heading north ***(Barnet Deanery)*** (1898; 1953)
Administrator Fr Anthony Pellegrini **Parish Sister** Sr Avis
Services Sun, M (Sat 6.30pm), 8.30, 10, 11.30.
Hds, M 10, 8pm Wkds, M as announced.
Conf: Sat 10.30, 6pm. Exp Tue & Sat 10.30 to 11.
Ecumenical Contact Parish Priest **Justice and Peace Contact** Parish Priest
Carmelite Friars(OCarm), 63 East End Rd N2 0SE Tel: 020 8346 1458 Fax: 020 8349 8828
E-mail: carmelites.eastfinchley@carmelnet.org Website: www.carmelite.org
Fr Richard Copsey **Prior & Bursar**; Fr Hugh Clarke; Fr Robert Puthussery; Fr Sean Forde
Good Shepherd Sisters, 61 East End Road N2 0SF Tel: 020 8346 8100
Poor Sisters of Nazareth, Nazareth House, 162 East End Road N2 0RU
Tel: 020 8883 1104 Fax: 020 8444 3691 Chaplain Fr Brian Heaney
Daughters of Wisdom (La Sagesse), 1 King Street N2 8EA Tel: 020 8365 2924

FRENCH CHURCH + NOTRE DAME DE FRANCE 🎧 A

5 Leicester Place WC2H 7BX Tel: 020 7437 9363 Fax: 020 7440 2645
E-mail: notredamechurch@btconnect.com Website: www. notredamechurch.co.uk
Off north side of Leicester Sq ***(Westminster Deanery)*** (1865; 1868; 1955)
Marists (SM) Fr Martin McAnaney (Rector); Fr Jean-Marie Bloqueau;
Fr Christian Andraud; Fr Ed Duffy
Services Sun, M (Sat 6pm), 10, 11.30 (all French).
Hds, M 12.15 (English), 6pm (English), 7pm (French) Wkds, M 12.15, 6pm.
Conf: bef M. During holiday periods telephone to check times of services.
Ecumenical Contact Mrs Chantal Brown **Tel: 020 7821 9036 Justice & Peace** Parish Priest

FULHAM + ST THOMAS OF CANTERBURY ♿ 🎧

60 Rylston Road SW6 7HW Tel: 020 7385 4040 Fax: 020 7610 2506
E-mail: fulham@rcdow.org.uk ***(Hammersmith & Fulham Deanery)*** (1847; 1969)
Fr Norbert Fernandes, also in residence Fr Peter Scott; Fr Allen Morris; Fr Stan Zysk SVD
Services Sun, M (Sat 6.30pm), 9, 10.30 (Children), 12, 3pm (Portuguese), 6pm.
Hds, M (Eve 6.30pm), 9.30, 8pm.
Wkds, M Mon, Tue, Wed, Fri 9.30; Thu 6.30pm; Sat 10.
Conf: Sat 10.30 to 11.30, 5.30 to 6.15pm. Exp Sat 5.30-6.15pm. Bene 6.15pm
Ecumenical Contact Parish Priest **Justice and Peace Contact** Parish Priest
Verbum Dei Community, 54 Colehill Lane SW6 5EG Tel: 020 7731 3367

FULHAM SEE ALSO PARSONS GREEN AND STEPHENDALE ROAD

FULHAM ROAD + OUR LADY OF DOLOURS ♿ A

St Mary's Priory, 264 Fulham Road SW10 9EL Tel: 020 7352 6965 Fax: 020 7351 9749
E-mail: fulhamroad@rcdow.org.uk (1864; 1875; cons 04.11.53)
In Fulham Rd, east Redcliffe Gdns/Edith Grove traffic lights ***(Kensington & Chelsea Deanery)***
Servites (OSM) Fr Dermot Mac Neice (Parish Priest); Fr James Mulherin (Assistant priest); Fr Patrick Ryall (Prior Provincial); Fr Paul Addison (Prior); Fr Joseph Colella
Pastoral Assistant Sr Angela Murphy PBVM
Services Sun M (Sat 6.30pm), 8.30, 10 (Family), 11.15 (Spanish), 12.15pm, 7pm
Hds, M (Eve 6.30pm), 10, 7pm. Wkds, M 10, 6.30pm.
Conf daily 6.15 to 6.30pm and at call; Sat 10.45 to 11.15, 6 to 6.30.
Exp Mon-Fri 10.30 to 11.15am (exp Wed); Legion of Mary, Tues 7.15pm.
Ecumenical Contact Daphne Kilner **Justice and Peace Contact** Lottie Henley
Chelsea & Westminster Hospital Chaplain Tel: 020 8746 8083
Sisters Hospitallers of the Sacred Heart (Spanish) 46 Roland Gardens SW7 3PW
Tel: 020 7373 5820 Provincialate Tel: 020 7373 3054
Sisters of the Cross and Passion, 7 Stadium Street SW10 Tel: 020 7352 6013
Sr Barbara McCauley; Sr Marcella Roe; Sr Rita Cahill

GARSTON + OUR LADY AND ST MICHAEL ♿

Catholic Church, Crown Rise, Garston, Watford, Herts WD2 6NE Tel: 01923 673239
Fax: 01923 677869 E-mail: garston@rcdow.org.uk
On A405 North Orbital Road, just south of St Albans Road junction ***(Watford Deanery)*** (1954)
Fr Christopher Hamilton-Gray
Services Sun, M (Sat 6pm), 8.30, 10, 12. Hds, M (Eve 7.30pm), 9.30, 7.30pm.
Wkds, M 9.30, 1st Fri 7.30pm (Sung Tridentine). R 9.50 (Mon-Sat)
Conf: Sat after 9.30 M, 5 to 5.30pm. Fatima Service 1st Sat 9.50am.
Ecumenical Contact Mr John Evans **Justice and Peace Contact** Parish Priest
Garston Manor Rehab Centre, Pembroke House, Langley House, Tenterden House, Allington Court

GERMAN CHURCH + ST BONIFACE

47 Adler Street E1 1EE Tel: 020 7247 9529 Fax: 020 7247 3879
E-mail: germanchurch@rcdow.org.uk ***(Tower Hamlets Deanery)*** (1809; 1875; cons 4.10.25; 1960)
Fr Heinz Medoch (Aachen) Also in residence Fr Victor J Camilleri OFM
Services Sun, M 11 (2nd, 4th & 5th Sun); Conf (German): by appointment.
Ecumenical Contact Parish Priest **Justice and Peace Contact** Parish Priest
Wynfrid House, 20 Mulberry Street E1 1EH
Community Centre with Hostel Facilities **Tel: 020 7247 6110 Fax: 020 7247 0552**
Manageress A E Greaves. **Lioba House, 40 Exeter Road NW2 4SB**
(St Bonifatius Secular Institute) German Catholic Social Centre for Young People
Tel: 020 8452 8566 Fax: 020 8452 4114

GOLDERS GREEN + ST EDWARD THE CONFESSOR

700 Finchley Road NW11 7NE Tel/Fax: 020 8455 1300
E-mail: goldersgreen@rcdow.org.uk Website: rcdow.org.uk/goldersgreen/
On main road just north of Golders Green tube & bus stn ***(Barnet Deanery)*** (1909; 1915; cons Sept 30, 1931)
Fr John Helm
Services Sun, M (Sat 6.30pm), 9, 10.30, 12, 6pm. Hds, M Eve 7.30pm, (Thu 7pm), 12, 7.30pm (Thu 7pm). Wkds, M as announced. Conf: Sat 10.30 to 11, 5pm
Ecumenical Contact Parish Priest **Justice and Peace Contact** Parish Priest
Carmelite Monastery, Bridge Lane NW11 9JT Tel: 020 8455 3113 M 8 daily
E-mail: community@ocdbvm.org.uk Website: www.ocdbvm.org.uk
Catholic Agency to Support Evangelisation Tel: 020 8458 3316 email: jg@cms.org.uk
The Chase Centre, 114 West Heath Road NW3 7TX
To support and resource Catholic communities and individuals in England and Wales to proclaim the Gospel; to promote dialogue between gospel and culture; and to offer information on the Catholic faith to enquirers.
Team Mgr Keith Barltrop **Director**, Fr Philip Knights, Miss Clare Ward, Miss Clare Ford.
Office Administrator Mrs Jolanta Gallo
Also **Catholic Enquiry Office** To offer information on the Catholic faith to enquirers.
National Office for Vocation Tel/Fax: 020 8458 6017 E-mail: enquiries@ukvocation.org
The Chase Centre, 114 West Heath Road NW3 7TX

GRAHAME PARK + ST MARGARET CLITHEROW A

Presbytery, Everglade Strand NW9 5PX Tel: 020 8205 6830
Off Great Strand (near RAF Museum) ***(Barnet Deanery)*** (1970; 1973 cons 14 Nov 1998)
Administrator Fr John Hai Pham
Services Sun, M (Sat 6.30pm), 9, 12. Hds, M 9.15, 11 (term-time), 7pm.
Wkds, M Mon, Fri 7pm; Tue, Wed, Thu 9.15. Conf: Sat 10 to 10.30, 6 to 6.20pm.
Exp Sat 5.15pm to 6.15pm; Novena Mon after M;
Ecumenical Contact Parish Priest **Justice and Peace Contact** Parish Priest
Metropolitan Police Training School Chandos Lodge Old People's Home.

GREENFORD + OUR LADY OF THE VISITATION

358 Greenford Road, Greenford, Middx UB6 9AN Tel: 020 8578 1363 Fax: 020 8813 2238
E-mail: greenford@rcdow.org.uk
Main rd (A4127) south of Ruislip Rd junct ***(Ealing Deanery)*** (1928; 1937)
Pallottine Fathers (SCA) Fr Thomas Daly; Fr Kevin Ward; Fr William Hanly
Catechetical Co-ordinator Henry Chichon
Services Sun, M (Sat 7pm), 8, 9, 10.30, 12, 7pm. Hds, M 8.30, 12, 7.30pm.
Wkds, M Mon-Fri 8.30, 12; Sat 12. Conf: Sat 11 to 12, 6.15pm to 6.45pm.
Ecumenical Contact Bruce McNair **Justice and Peace Contact** Parish Priest

GROVE PARK + ST JOSEPH ♿ ☎

1 Bolton Road W4 3TE Tel: 020 8994 6861 E-mail: grovepark@rcdow.org.uk
South A4, close to Chiswick stn (BR), corner Devonshire Gdns ***(Hounslow Deanery)*** (1964 cons 23.2.73)
Fr John Seabrook
Services Sun, M (Sat 6.30pm), 9, 11 Hds, M (Eve 7.30pm), 10, 7.30pm. Conf: Sat 11-11.30.
Ecumenical Contact Parish Priest **Justice and Peace Contact** Parish Priest

GUNNERSBURY + ST DUNSTAN ♿ ☎

141 Gunnersbury Avenue W3 8LE Tel: 020 8994 2877
E-mail: gunnersbury@rcdow.org.uk
On North Circular Road (A406), 300 yards north of Chiswick roundabout ***(Hounslow Deanery)*** (1931)
In pastoral care of Chiswick
In residence Mgr George Tutto (Hungarian Chaplaincy); Fr Richard Price
Services Sun, M 10. Wkd M, Conf: as announced.
Ecumenical Contact Andrew Lubienski **Tel: 020 8995 1770**
Justice & Peace Parish Priest
Westpark, 1 Leopold Road W5 3PB. Tel: 020 8992 3954
Pastoral care entrusted to the Prelature of Opus Dei. Fr Andrew Byrne
Woodlands, 12 Gunnersbury Avenue W5 3NJ Tel: 020 8992 4025
Pastoral care entrusted to the Prelature of Opus Dei
Hungarian Chaplaincy, 141 Gunnersbury Ave W3 8LE Mgr George Tutto **Tel: 020 8992 2054**
Little Company of Mary, 91 Gunnersbury Ave W5 4LR Tel: 020 8752 1373
Fax: 020 8752 0449 Sr Margaret Watson **Provincial Leader**; Sr Geraldine Macklin

HACKNEY + ST. JOHN THE BAPTIST ♿ ☎

3 King Edward's Road E9 7SF Tel: 020 8985 2496
E-mail: hackney@rcdow.org.uk
King Edward's Rd Off Mare St, north of St Joseph's Hospice
(Hackney Deanery) (1847; 1956; cons 14. 6. 72)
Fr David Evans
Services Sun, M (Sat 6pm), 9.30, 11.30 Hds M 9.30am, 7.30pm
Wkds, M Mon 5.30pm (Hospice), Tues-Fri 12noon; Sat 10; Conf: Sat 10.30
Ecumenical Contact Parish Priest
Justice and Peace Contact Tigger Cullinane
Religious Sisters of Charity, St Joseph's Hospice, Mare Street E8 4SA
Tel: 020 8525 6000
Chaplain Fr Brian Griffiths, OSCam. Sun M 10.30
Sisters of Charity of St Paul, 28 Warneford Street E9 7NG Tel: 020 8986 2346
Sr Bernie Devine; Sr Dolores Bourke
also **4 Queensgate Villas, Victoria Park Road E9 7BU Tel: 020 8986 2386**

HAMMERSMITH + ST AUGUSTINE

55 Fulham Palace Road W6 8AU Tel: 020 8748 3788 E-mail: augparish@aol.com
Sth Hammersmith Broadway, just beyond flyover ***(Hammersmith & Fulham Deanery)*** (1903; 1916; cons 1933)
Augustinians (OSA) Fr Michael Campbell (Prior & Parish Priest);
Fr John Murphy (Sub Prior); Fr George Stibbles; Fr Barry Clifford; Br Gianni Notarianni
Services Sun, M (Sat 6pm), 9, 11am, 12.15, 6.30pm.
Hds, M 8, 10, 12.15, 6.30pm. Wkds, M 8 (not Sat), 10, 12.15
Conf: Sat 10.30-11.30am; 5-6pm
Ecumenical Contact Parish Priest **Justice and Peace Contact** Parish Priest
Charing Cross Hosp M Mon & Wed 1pm **Chaplain** Fr Nigel Griffin **Tel: 020 8846 1042**

HAMPSTEAD + ST MARY

4 Holly Place NW3 6QU Tel: 020 7435 6678 Fax: 020 7435 8436
E-mail: hampstead@rcdow.org.uk
Nr Hampstead stn (LT); via Church Row lower end of Heath St ***(Camden Deanery)*** (1796; 1816; cons1977)
Canon Daniel Cronin
Services Sun, M (Sat 6.30pm), 8.30, 10, 11.30, 6.30pm. Hds, M 10am, 6.30pm.
Wkds, M as announced. Conf: Sat 6 to 6.30pm; and at call
Ecumenical Contact Juliet Hellings **Tel: 020 7435 4815**
Justice & Peace Contact Mrs. Janet Doyle Blunden
Columban Fathers (SSC), 28 Redington Road NW3 7RB
Tel: 020 7794 8131 Fax: 020 7794 7074
E-mail: londonhouse@columbans.co.uk Website: www.columban.com
Fr Richard Martin **Superior**; Fr Frank Nally; Fr Eamonn O'Brien; Fr Frank Regan;
Fr Parig Digan; Fr Thomas Ryan; Fr Cathal Gallagher
Sisters of St Marcellina, Hampstead Towers, 6 Ellerdale Road NW3 6BD
Residential school for foreign girls **Tel: 020 7435 0181**
Sr Giuliana Carrara; Sr Giuseppina Antonini; Sr Maria Luisa Puerari; Sr Paloma Bernal
Sisters of St Dorothy, 99 Frognal NW3 6XR International Students Residence
Tel: 020 7794 6893 (Sisters) 020 7794 8095 (Students)

HAMPTON HILL (AND UPPER TEDDINGTON) + ST FRANCIS DE SALES

16 Wellington Road, Hampton Hill, Middx TW12 1JR
Tel: 020 8977 1415 Fax: 020 8943 9593
E-mail: hamptonhill@rcdow.org.uk
(Upper Thames Deanery) (1920; 1928; 1966; cons 18 Dec 1976)
Fransalians (MSFS) Fr Huebert Francis Miranda; Fr Saji Mathew
Services Sun, M (Sat 6pm), 9, 11. Hds, M (Eve 8pm), 9.30, 8pm.
Wkds, M 9.30. Conf: Sat 10-11am
Ecumenical Contact Anne Starki **Justice and Peace Contact** Bernie McKay
Teddington Memorial Hospital.

HAMPTON-ON-THAMES + ST THEODORE OF CANTERBURY ♿ ☎

110 Station Road, Hampton-on-Thames, Middx TW12 2AS
Tel: 020 8979 3596 Fax: 020 8979 8854
E-mail: hamptononthames@rcdow.org.uk Website: www.rcdow.org.uk/hampton/
(Upper Thames Deanery) (1927; 1986; cons. March 22, 1987)
Fr Bernard Boylan
Services Sun, M (Sat 6.30pm), 8.30, 10.30, 5pm. Hds, M 9.30, 7.30pm.
Wkds, M as announced. Conf: Sat 10 to 10.30, 5.45 to 6.15pm; and at call.
Exp Thurs after am M
Ecumenical Contact Parish Priest **Justice and Peace Contact** Parish Priest
Servants of the Mother of God, 112 Station Road Tel: 020 8255 4997

HANWELL + OUR LADY AND ST JOSEPH ☎ A

52 Uxbridge Road W7 3SU Tel: 020 8567 4056 Fax: 020 8810 0219
E-mail: hanwell@rcdow.org.uk Website: www.rcdow.org.uk/hanwell/
On main road, corner of St George's Road (traffic lights) ***(Ealing Deanery)*** (1853; 1967)
Canon Bernard Scholes; Fr Cristiano Braz
Catechetical Co-ordinator Elizabeth Anderson
Services Sun, M (Sat 6.30pm), 8, 10 (Sung Family), 12, 6pm;
Hds, M (Eve 6pm), 9.15, 12.15, 7.30pm. Wkds, M 9.15, 6pm; Sat 12.15.
Conf: Sat 11.30 to 12, 5.30 to 6pm.
Exp Fri 6.30 - 7.30pm and Sat 5 to 6pm.
Ecumenical Contact Mr Patrick O'Donohoe **Tel: 020 8248 4330**
Justice and Peace Contact Angie Harris **Tel: 020 8567 1177**
Ealing Hospital, Southall: General Wing (M, Fri 2pm); St Bernard's Wing.
Sisters of St Joseph of Peace, St Mary's Convent, 50 Uxbridge Road W7 3PP Tel: 020 8567 8635
Medical Mission Sisters (SCMM), 8 Springfield Road W7 3YP
Tel: 020 8566 0547
also **109 Clitherow Avenue W7 2BL Tel: 020 8567 1504**

HAREFIELD + ST PAUL, MERLE AVENUE ☎ A

1 Dunster Close, Park Lane, Harefield, Middx UB9 6BS Tel: 01895 822365
Off High Street at south end of shopping parade ***(Hillingdon Deanery)*** (1963; 1967)
Fr Cedric Stanley
Catechetical Co-ordinator Joan Cecil
Services Sun, M (Sat 6.30pm), 9, 11.
Hds, M 9.15, 7pm. Wkds, M 9.15. Conf: Sat after 9.15 M & at 6pm
Ecumenical Contact Parish Priest
Justice and Peace Contact Parish Priest
Harefield Hospital; Courtfield; Rylstone; Bardom Court; Harefield Nursing Home; Cedar House; Coppermill Care Home; St Paul's Transplant House

HARPENDEN + OUR LADY OF LOURDES ♿ 🅃

1 Kirkwick Avenue, Harpenden, Herts AL5 2QH Tel: 01582 712245
E-mail: harpenden@rcdow.org.uk Website: www.rcdow.org.uk/harpenden/
Rothamsted Ave. Off High St, up from Church Green ***(St Albans Deanery)*** (1905; 1929; cons 28.5.36)
Mgr Canon Henry Turner **Pastoral Assistant** Eileen Airey OP **Tel: 01582 712814**
Services Sun, M (Sat 6pm), 8.30, 9.45 (Fam), 11.30 (sung).
Hds, M (Eve 8pm), 9.15, 8pm. Wkds, M Mon, Tue, Wed, Fri 9.15; Thu 11; Sat 10
Conf: Sat 10.30-11, 6.45-7.15 N Wed after M
Ecumenical Contact Mrs Julia Roche **Harpenden Memorial & BUPA Hospitals.**
Dominican Sisters, 18 Kirkdale Road, Harpenden, Herts AL5 2PT Tel: 01582 712814

HARRINGAY + ST AUGUSTINE OF CANTERBURY

49 Mattison Road N4 1BG Tel: 020 8348 1378
E-mail: harringay@rcdow.org.uk Website: www.rcdow.org.uk/harringay/
(Haringey Deanery) (1963) *Off Green Lanes, btwn Manor House & Turnpike Lane*
Fr James Noctor
Services Sun, M (Sat 6.30pm), 10.30 (sung). Hds, M 10am.
Wkds, M 10 Mon - Fri; Conf: Sat 6 to 6.25pm, 7.15 to 7.30pm
Sisters of St Louis, 161 Wightman Rd N8 0BB Tel: 020 8341 5606
Sr Louisa Poole; Sr Marie McQuinn; Sr Kathleen Rice

HARROW NORTH + ST JOHN FISHER ♿ 🅃

80 Imperial Close, North Harrow, Middlesex HA2 7LW Tel: 020 8868 7531
E-mail: harrownorth@rcdow.org.uk or johnfisherharrow@rcdow.org.uk
Betw North Harrow/Rayners Lane stations, just south of The Ridgeway junct ***(Harrow Deanery)*** (1939)
Fr Kevin Jordan **Tel: 020 8429 5684** also resident Fr Paul McDermott Tel: 020 8429 5685 (Hospital Chaplain) **Parish Secretary** Mary Evans **Tel: 020 8429 5681**
Catechist Kay O'Connor **Tel: 020 8429 5682 E-mail: kayoconnor@rcdow.org.uk**
Services Sun, M (Sat 6pm), 8.30, 10 (Family), 11.30am Hds, M 9 (school) 10, 7.30pm, Wks M 10 (except Thur 7.30.pm, Sat 9.30am) Conf: Sat 10 to 10.30, 5 to 5.45pm.
Ecumenical Contact Angela Daly **Tel: 020 8866 3318**

HARROW-ON-THE-HILL + OUR LADY AND ST THOMAS OF CANTERBURY ♿ 🅃

22 Roxborough Park, Harrow-on-the-Hill, Middlesex HA1 3BE
Tel: 020 8422 2513 Fax: 020 8869 6896 E-mail: harrowonthehill@rcdow.org.uk
(Harrow Deanery) (1873; 1894)
Fr Guy Sawyer
Services Sun, M (Sat 6pm), 8.30, 10 (Family), 11.15 (Sung), 6.30pm.
Hds, M 9.30, 8pm. Wkds M daily 9.30am
Conf: Sat 11.30 R & B 1st Sun 5.45pm, Exp Thurs 7 - 8pm
Ecumenical Contact Parish Secretary **Justice and Peace Contact** Parish Priest
Sisters of St Louis 85 Bessborough Road, Harrow, Middx HA1 3DB Tel: 020 8422 2158

HARROW SOUTH + (1) ST GABRIEL (& NORTHOLT + (2) ST BERNARD)

390b Northolt Road, South Harrow, Middx HA2 8EX Tel: 020 8864 5455
E-mail: harrowsouth@rcdow.org.uk
On main road, south of South Harrow stn, near junction Park Lane. ***(Harrow Deanery)*** (1933)
Fr Neil Burrows
Catechetical Co-ordinator Mrs Maria O'Connell
Services Sun, M (Sat 6pm), 8.30, 10, 12.
Hds, M 10 Wkds, M Mon & Thur10. Conf: Sat 5.15 to 5.45
Justice and Peace Contact Diana Salisbury
Sisters of St Louis 67 Parkfield Road, South Harrow, Middx HA2 8LA Tel: 020 8248 3838

2 + St Bernard Served from No 1
Mandeville Road, Northolt, Middx UB5 5HE
On main road, between Target roundabout & Northolt stn (1965)
Services Sun, M 9, 11.
Hds, M 7.30pm. Wkds, M Tues & Wed 10

HARROW ROAD + OUR LADY OF LOURDES AND ST VINCENT DE PAUL

337 Harrow Road W9 3RB Tel: 020 7286 2170 Fax: 020 7266 3506
E-mail: harrowroad@rcdow.org.uk
East Gt Western Rd junct; nr Westbourne Park stn. ***(North Kensington Deanery)*** *(1876,1912,1975)*
Fr Francis Antwi-Darkwah
Services Sun, M (Sat 6.30pm), 10, 12, 6.30pm.
Hds, M 10, 7.30pm. Wkds, M 10 (1st Fri also 7.30pm). Conf: Sat 10.30 and at call.
Ecumenical Contact Parish Priest **Justice and Peace Contact** Parish Priest

HARROW WEALD SEE WEALDSTONE HATCH END SEE HEADSTONE LANE

HATFIELD + MARYCHURCH A

26 Salisbury Square, Old Hatfield, Herts AL9 5JD Tel: 01707 262439
E-mail: hatfield@rcdow.org.uk
Just off Great North Rd (A1000), nr BR stn & Hatfield House ***(Hatfield Deanery)*** (1930, 1971)
Fr Gerard King
Services Sun, M (Sat 6pm), 11, 6pm. Hds, M 9.30am, 7.30pm. Wkds, M Mon, Tues, Thu 9.30am; Wed 7.30pm; Fri 12.30pm Conf: Sat 12.30 - 1pm; 5.15pm. Exp Fri 1-1.30pm
Ecumenical Contacts Anne Cashmore **Tel: 01707 260961** (Hatfield);
Tony Wilcock **Tel: 01707 269882** (Welham Green) **Justice and Peace Contact** Parish Priest
Chapel of Ease: St Thomas More, Station Rd, Welham Green
Sun M 9.30 Hds (Eve) 7.30pm

HATFIELD SOUTH + ST PETER ♿ ⓩ

St Peter's Presbytery, Bishop's Rise, Hatfield, Herts AL10 9HN
Tel: 01707 262121
E-mail: hatfieldsouth@rcdow.org.uk
Half-mile from Comet roundabout, via Cavendish Way ***(Hatfield Deanery)*** (1959; 1961)
Fr John Boland
Services Sun, M (Sat 6pm), 9.15, 11 (CW & Folk).
Hds, M 10am, 7.30pm. Wkds, M Mon, Tues, Wed, Fri 10am
Conf: Sat 5-5.45pm Novena Tue after M
Ecumenical Contact Patricia Martin
Justice and Peace Contact Minna Browne
Highview House, 77 Bishop's Rise, Hatfield, Herts AL10 9BZ
Tel: 01707 271785

HAVERSTOCK HILL + ST DOMINIC ⓩ A

St Dominic's Priory, Southampton Rd NW5 4LB
Tel: 020 7482 9210 Fax: 020 7482 9239
E-mail: stdominics@op-london.org Website: www.op-london.org/
Top of Malden Rd, nearest tubes Chalk Farm & Belsize Park.
(Camden Deanery) (1867; 1874; cons Aug 1, 1923)
Dominicans (OP)
Fr Dermot Morrin **(Parish Priest & Prior Tel: 020 7482 9224);**
Fr Allan White **(Provincial Tel/Fax: 020 7485 2760)**
Hospital Chaplain to Royal Free Fr Aelred Connelly **Tel: 020 7482 9230** (M, Sun 10.15)
Hospital Chaplain to UCLH NHS Trust Fr Peter Harries **Tel: 020 7482 9216;**
(Elizabeth Garret Anderson, Heart, National for Neurology & Neurosurgery, Middlesex, UCH)
Fr Columba Ryan; Fr Rudolf Loewenstein; Fr Paul White; Fr Christopher Caruana;
Fr Denis Geraghty; Fr Dominic White; Fr Leo Edgar; Fr Timothy Gardner
Services Sun, M (Sat 6pm), 8.30, 10 (Family), 12 (Solemn), 6pm.
Hds, M (Eve 6pm), 7.30, 9.30, 7.15pm.
Wkds, M 7.30, 9.30, 6pm.
Conf: Fri 6.45-7pm; Sat 10 to 10.30, 5.30 to 6pm
MP, Mon to Fri 7.55, Sat 9.10;
EP, Mon - Fri 6.30pm, Sun 6.50pm; Exp Thurs 6.25-7.50pm
Ecumenical Contact Marion Hill
Justice and Peace Contact Keiran Proffer
Dominican Sisters, 97 Constantine Road NW3 2LP
Tel: 020 7267 1579
Sisters of Providence, Bartrams Hostel, Rowland Hill Street NW3
Tel: 020 7794 4504

HAYES + THE IMMACULATE HEART OF MARY A

Botwell House, Botwell Lane, Hayes, Middx UB3 2AB
Tel: 020 8573 2065 Fax: 020 8561 6748 E-mail: botwell@claret.org.uk
In town centre, just off Coldharbour Lane / Station Road; not far from Hayes stn (BR) ***(Hillingon Deanery)***
(1912; 1954; 1961; cons Oct. 24, 1972).
Claretian Missionaries (CMF)
Fr Martin Stone **Parish Priest**; Fr Philip Blandford **Superior**; Fr Paul Joseph Katanpally;
also in residence: Fr James Kennedy;
Catechetics Director Anna Maria Dupelycz. **Administrator** Michael Bagness.
Services Sun, M (Sat 6.30pm), 8.30, 10 (Sung), 12 (Sung), 5pm.
Hds, M (Eve 7.30pm), 12.15, 7.30pm. Wkds, M Mon - Fri 12.15, 7.30pm; Sat 12.15pm.
Conf: Sat 10.30 - 11.30am, 5.45 - 6.15pm
(Conf can be heard in Spanish, Kannada, Hindi, Tamil and Assamese).
Ecumenical Contacts Bill Murphy **Tel: 020 8573 6063** & Rita Walton **Tel: 020 8573 2065**
Justice and Peace Contact Ann Mullaney **Tel: 020 8573 2065**
Society of the Sacred Heart, St Mary's Convent, 208 Botwell Lane, Hayes UB3 2AJ
Tel: 020 8573 8658 (Emmaus); 020 8561 1935 (Shalom)
Hayes Cottage Hospital

HEADSTONE LANE + ST THERESA OF THE CHILD JESUS

22 Boniface Walk, Harrow, Middx HA3 6PU Tel: 020 8428 3260
Uxbridge Rd, Hatch End, junc Headstone Lane; nr Headstone Lane/Hatch End stns ***(Harrow Deanery)*** (1953)
Administrator Fr Richard Parsons
Services Sun, M (Sat 5pm), 9, 11, 6pm; B 1st Sun 5.30pm.
Hds M 10, 7.30pm. Wkds M 10. Conf: Sat 10.30 and 4.30pm. Exp Tues 10.30-11.30am
Ecumenical Contact Deidre St John **Justice and Peace Contact** Paul Benjamin

HEMEL HEMPSTEAD (BOXMOOR) + SS MARY AND JOSEPH A

186 St John's Road, Boxmoor, Herts HP1 1NR Tel: 01442 391759
E-mail: hemelhempstead@rcdow.org.uk
Website: www.rcdow.org.uk/hemelhempstead/boxmoor/
(St Albans Deanery) (1890; 1938; 1951)
Fr John Byrne (also serves Hemel Hempstead West & Hemel Hempstead North)
Parish Sister Sr Teresa O'Donovan OP **Tel: 01442 264669**
Services Sun, M 9, 11.30am; Hds, M, 10am, 7.30pm.
Wkds M Mon, Wed, Fri 9.30; Thurs 12.30pm (convent).
Conf: Sat 11 to 11.30am
Ecumenical Contact Geoff Doyle **Justice and Peace Contact** Richard Dodd
Hemel Hempstead General Hospital M Tue 1pm (Chapel)
Dominican Sisters,
St Mary's Convent, Green End Road, Boxmoor, Herts HP1 1QW Tel: 01442 255577

HEMEL HEMPSTEAD EAST + OUR LADY QUEEN OF ALL CREATION

The Presbytery, Rant Meadow, Hemel Hempstead, Herts HP3 8PG
Tel: 01442 255471 Fax: 01442 260307 E-mail: hemelhempsteadeast@rcdow.org.uk
(St Albans Deanery) (1955; 1987; cons Nov13, 1987)
On dual carriageway A414 betw M1 (exit 8) & town centre. St Albans Rd
Fr Raymond Legge
Services Sun, M (Sat 5.30pm), 9.30, 11, 6.30pm. Hds, M (Eve 7.30) 9.30, 7.30pm. Wkds, M Mon-Thu 9.15, (FF 7.30pm), Sat 10. Conf: Sat 10.30-11, Exp Sat 10.30-11
Ecumenical Christopher Jones **Tel: 01442 394470** **Justice & Peace** Dr David Toorawa

HEMEL HEMPSTEAD NORTH + HIGHFIELD AND GROVEHILL

299 St Agnell's Lane, Grovehill, Hemel Hempstead, Herts HP2 6EQ Tel: 01442 259141
E-mail: hemelhempsteadnorth@rcdow.org.uk *(St Albans Deanery)*
Administrator Fr Kevin McEwan CSsR
1. Grovehill: Church of the Resurrection
(Shared Church: June 1977), *Henry Wells Square; behind Grovehill shops*
Services Sun, M (Sat 5pm), 9.30. Hds, M 7.30pm. Wkds, M Wed 7.30pm. M in John F Kennedy School Tues 8.30am, Wed 1.30pm. Conf: Sat after evng M. Exp 1st Sat 5.45pm.
Ecumenical Contact Margaret Slynn **Justice and Peace Contact** Parish Priest

2. Highfield: St Paul (Shared Church: 1971) *by old railway cutting*
Services Sun, M 11.30. Hds, M 11. Wkds, M Thu, Fri 9. Conf: Sun after morning M.

HEMEL HEMPSTEAD WEST + ST MARK

186 St John's Road, Boxmoor, Herts HP1 1NR Tel: 01442 391759
off Holybush Lane, rear of J F Kennedy School, Warners End and Fields End ***(St Albans Deanery)*** *(1977)*
In pastoral care of Hemel Hempstead Boxmoor
Services Sun, M (Sat 5.30pm) 10.15am; Hds & Wkds, M as announced; Conf Sat before M
Ecumenical Contact & **Justice and Peace Contact** Camille Fidgett

HENDON + OUR LADY OF DOLOURS A

4 Egerton Gardens NW4 4B Tel: 020 8202 0560 Fax: 020 8201 5707
E-mail: hendon@rcdow.org.uk *(Barnet Deanery)* (1849; 1863; recons 1927; cons 25.03.66
Off The Burroughs (opp Town Hall), close to Watford Way (A41) & Hendon Central stn (LT)
Fr Francis Press
Services Sun, M (Sat 6pm), 10, 12. Hds, M as announced. Wkds, M Mon, Tue 10am, Wed 9am Thu 7.30pm; Fri 12.30pm; Sat 12. Conf: Sat 11 to 11.45, 5 to 5.30pm. HH Sat 11
Ecumenical Contacts Mr & Mrs Havery **Tel: 020 8203 3167** **Justice & Peace** Parish Priest
Poor Handmaids of Jesus Christ, St Joseph's Convent, Westminster House, Watford Way NW4 4TY Tel: 020 8202 7626 **The Garden Hospital**

HENDON WEST + ST PATRICK

167 The Broadway NW9 7EB Tel: 020 8202 5143 Fax: 020 8203 7895
E-mail: hendonwest@rcdow.org.uk
Hendon Broadway On main road (A5), just north of Staples Corner. (Barnet Deanery) (1964)
Administrator Fr John White
Mobile: 07841 528665
Services Sun, M (Sat 7pm), 9.30, 12 noon, 6.30pm. Exp. 1 to 6.30 pm
Hds, M 10, 8pm.
Wkds, M Mon, Fri 7pm; Tue, Wed, Thurs, Sat 10;
Conf Sat 10.30 to 11, 6 to 6.45pm and on call.
Exp Sun 1-6.30pm, OLPS Nov Tue 7 pm; Legion of Mary Tues 7.30pm
Ecumenical Contact Parish Priest **Justice and Peace Contact** Parish Priest
Social Club Tel: 020 8202 2039

HERTFORD + THE IMMACULATE CONCEPTION AND ST JOSEPH A

23 St John's Street, Hertford, Herts SG14 1RX Tel: 01992 582109
E-mail: hertford@rcdow.org.uk
Website: www.rcdow.org.uk/hertford/
Off Railway St, close Hertford East stn. ***(Lea Valley Deanery)*** (Priory 1087-1539; 1848; 1858; cons 16.10.1866)
Fr Gladstone Liddle.
Services Sun, M (Sat 6pm), 8.30, 10.30 (sung; CW), 6pm.
Hds, M 7.30, 10 (school term time), 8pm.
Conf: Sat 10-10.30, 5.15 to 5.45pm Exp Sat 5-5.45pm & 1st Friday 6-10pm
Ecumenical Contacts Glen Sexton & Sheila Smith
Justice & Peace Contact Parish Priest

HESTON + OUR LADY QUEEN OF APOSTLES

15 The Green, Heston Road, Heston, Middx TW5 0RL
Tel: 020 8570 1818 Fax 020 8572 7861
Set back from main rd just south of motorway bridge ***(Hounslow Deanery)***
(1928; 1929; 1964; cons 19.5.74)
Fr Simon Nguyen Duc Tang
Services Sun, M (Sat 7pm), 8, 9.30, 11.30, 5.30pm.
Hds, M (Eve 7pm), 9.30, 11.30, 8pm.
Wkds, M as announced. Conf: Sat 9.45am, 6 to 6.45pm and at call.
R daily after morning M & 6.30pm; Novena Wed 7pm.
Ecumenical Contacts Mrs Shirley Dave **Tel: 020 8572 9005**
& Mrs Catherine Jennings **Tel: 020 8572 7205**
Justice and Peace Contact Martin Birdseye **Tel: 020 8571 1691**
Pope John Centre Tel: 020 8574 3284/020 8574 5411
(Heston Catholic Social Club)

HIGHBURY + ST JOAN OF ARC ☑ A

60 Highbury Park N5 2XH Tel: 020 7226 0257
E-mail: highbury@rcdow.org.uk *(Islington Deanery)* (1920; 1962; cons 2001)
Fr William Skehan; also in residence Fr Voytek Przjalkowski
Services Sun, M (Sat 6.30pm), 9, 11am
Hds, M 7.15, 9.15, 7.30pm.
Wkds, M Mon-Fri 7.15, 9.15; Sat 10. Conf: Sat after M, and at call.
Ecumenical Contact Parish Priest
Justice and Peace Contact Parish Priest
Sisters of St Paul of Chartres, 30 Aberdeen Park N5 2BL Tel: 020 7359 1712
Sisters of Mercy 40 Aberdeen Road N5 2XD Tel: 020 7359 3897
Sr Dolores Hyland; Sr Patricia Mockler; Sr Linda Dearlove; Sr Noreen Cullen

HIGHGATE + ST JOSEPH ☑ ♿

St Joseph's Retreat, Highgate Hill N19 5NE Tel: 020 7272 2320
Fax: 020 7281 9433
E-mail: 'name'@stjospehshighgate.org Website: www.stjosephshighgate.org
Corner Dartmouth Park Hill; Archway stn (LT) ***(Islington Deanery)*** (1858; 1888; cons 28.4.32)
Passionists (CP): Fr Mark White (Parish Priest); Fr Christopher Kelly; Fr Charles Owen;
Community Fr Daniel Donovan; Fr Theodore Davey; Fr Aidan Baker; Fr Timothy Cullen;
Fr Conleth O'Hara; Fr Malachy Steenson;
Bros Bernard Connolly, Francis Welsh, Joseph Ward; Peter Aspin
Pastoral Assistant Shirley Taylor **Administrator** Edmund Tierney
Services Sun, M (Sat 7pm), 8, 10, 12 (folk), 1.30 (Polish), 7pm
Hds, M (Eve 6.30pm), 9.30, 11, 12, (Polish) 6.30 - Times may change, please enquire
Wkds, M Mon-Fri 9.30, 6.30pm; Sat 9.30, 11. Novena after 6.30 M Tue.
Conf: Sat 10-11, 6-6.30pm
Ecumenical Contact Edmund Tierney
Justice and Peace Contact Edmund Tierney
Whittington Hospital & Hornsey Central Hospital
Chaplain Tel: 020 7263 3754
St Joseph's Parish Centre, Highgate Hill N19 Tel: 020 7272 4571
Missionaries of Africa (White Fathers) (MAfr), 42 Stormont Road N6 4NP
Tel: 020 8342 8447 Fax: 020 8347 8147
E-mail: mafrgb@blueyonder.co.uk
Provincial Fr Peter Smith **Tel: 020 8348 7799**
Fr David Goergen **(Treasurer)**; Fr Jack Thora
Augustinian Sisters of Meaux,
'Bethanie' Convent, 54 Highgate Hill N19 5NQ
Tel: 020 7272 3696
Sr Christopher; Sr Helen; Sr Bernardine

HILLINGDON + ST BERNADETTE ☎ A

160 Long Lane, Hillingdon, Middx UB10 0EH Tel: 01895 234577
Fax: 01895 619820 E-mail: hillingdon@rcdow.org.uk
South Long Lane (half mile up from Uxbridge Rd) ***(Hillingdon Deanery)*** (1937; 1961; cons 7.10.78)
Fr James Garvey
Pastoral Assistant Anne Widgington
Services Sun, M (Sat 6pm), 9, 11, 6pm. Hds, M 9.30, 7.30pm. Wkds, M Tue, Thurs, Fri 9 am, Sat 10. MP Wkds 8.45 Conf: (with Exp) Sat 10.30-11, 5.15-5.45pm.
Ecumenical Contact Martin Rowley **Tel: 01895 233190**
Justice & Peace Contact Jill Rhodes **Tel: 01895 234348**
Hillingdon Hospital (Sun & Hds, M 4.30pm).
Sisters of Mercy, St Raphael's Convent, Court Drive, Hillingdon, Middx UB10 0BW
Tel: 01895 233771 Sr Mary Jo Brennan, Sr Mary Ignatius Costello,
Sr Mary Andrew Flaherty; Sr Anne Marie Cleary; Sr Winifred Graham; Sr Marie McGrogan, Sr Teresa Minogue; Sr Mary Martha O'Leary; Sr Mary Roche

HITCHIN + OUR LADY IMMACULATE AND ST ANDREW ♿☎

16 Nightingale Road, Hitchin, Herts SG5 1QS Tel: 01462 459126 Fax: 01462 432043
E-mail: hitchin@rcdow.org.uk Website: www. rcdow.org.uk/hitchin/
Junction with Grove Rd, opp Bancroft Rec Ground ***(Stevenage Deanery)*** (1890; 1902; cons 1977)
Assumptionists (AA) Fr Robert Henshaw (Regional Superior) **Tel: 01462 457673**;
Fr Michael Lambert (Superior & Parish Priest); Fr Christopher Burgess
Pastoral Assistants Eileen Dutt; Jane Gonzalez **Tel: 01462 455577**
Services Sun, M (Sat 6pm) 8.30, 10.30, 5pm Hds, M 7.30, 10 (term time in Our Lady's School, Old Hale Way), 7.30pm. Wkds, M10 daily; and Wed, Fri 7.30pm.
Conf (French): Sat 10.30-11.15
Ecumenical Contact Dr Sylvia Watkins **Tel: 01462 451775**
Justice and Peace Contact One World Group (Via Parish House)
Hitchin Hospital; Cheshire Home

HODDESDON + ST AUGUSTINE ♿☎

Presbytery, High Street, Hoddesdon, Herts EN11 8DS
Tel: 01992 440986 Fax: 01992 440244 E-mail: hoddesdon@rcdow.org.uk
Junction with Charlton Way ***(Lea Valley Deanery)*** (1932; 1962)
Services Sun, M (Sat 6.30pm), 9.15 (CW), 11.15 (CW), 4 (Italian).
Hds, M 9.30, 8pm. Wkds, M Mon, Tue, Wed 9.15 (MP 9); Fri 12 noon; Conf: Sat 5.30 to 6pm.
Ecumenical Contact Tony Stavrou **Tel: 01920 465597**
Justice & Peace Contact Tony Barrell **Tel: 01992 442430**

HOLBORN (CIRCUS), EC1 SEE ELY PLACE; (HIGH), WC1. SEE LINCOLN'S INN FIELDS

HOLLOWAY + SACRED HEART OF JESUS ☏ A

62 Eden Grove N7 8EN Tel: 020 7607 3594 Fax: 020 7607 1867
E-mail: holloway@rcdow.org.uk Website: www.rcdow.org.uk/holloway/
Off Holloway Road opp North London University ***(Islington Deanery)*** (1855; cons May 29, 1928)
Fr Gideon Wagay
Services Sun, M (Sat 6pm), 8.30, 10.15 (Sung), 12 (Folk) .EP & B 6pm
Hds, M 9.15am, 7.30pm. Wkds, M Mon - Sat 9.15am, except Tues 7.30pm,
Conf: Sat 11 - 12noon
Justice & Peace Parish Priest
Sisters of La Sainte Union, 51 Freegrove Road N7 9RG Tel: 020 7609 7160
Holloway and Pentonville (See Prison Service)

HOMERTON + IMMACULATE HEART OF MARY AND ST DOMINIC ☏

Presbytery, Ballance Road E9 5SR Tel: 020 8985 1495
E-mail: homerton@rcdow.org.uk Website: www. rcdow.org.uk/homerton/
Kenworthy Road ***(Hackney Deanery)*** (1873; cons 30 June 1884)
Fr Tony Doyle
Services Sun, M (Sat 6.30pm), 9, 11. Hds, M 9.30, 7.30pm. Wkds, M 9.30.
Conf: Sat 11.30-12, 5.30-6pm.
Ecumenical Contact Parish Priest **Justice and Peace Contact** Parish Priest
Homerton University Hospital NHS Trust Chaplain
Fr William Rose OSCam **Tel: 020 8510 5555**. Sun M 11.
Camillians (OSCam) 102 Hassett Rd E9 5SJ Tel 020 8986 5181 Fr Brian Griffiths; Fr William Rose.
Daughters of Wisdom (La Sagesse) 149 Cassland Rd E9 5BS Tel 020 8985 6229
Sr Patricia Reilly; Sr Anne Beglan
Sisters of the Sacred Hearts of Jesus and Mary, 100 Hassett Rd E9 5SJ
Tel 020 8985 3047

HORNSEY, N8 SEE STROUD GREEN

HOUNSLOW + SS MICHAEL AND MARTIN ♿☏

94 Bath Road, Hounslow, Middx TW3 3EH Tel: 020 8570 1693 Fax: 020 8570 8059
E-mail: hounslow@rcdow.org.uk Website: www. rcdow.org.uk/hounslow/
(Hounslow Deanery) (1884; 1929; cons 12. 10. 38)
Fr Antony Convery; Fr Anthony Psaila
Catechetical Co-ordinator Natalie Smith **Youth Worker** Maria Josias
Services Sun, M (Sat 6.15pm), 9, 10.30, 12, 6pm. Hds, M (Eve 8pm), 9, 12, 6pm.
Wkds, M 9am; also pm daily as announced. Conf: Sat 11 to 12, 5 to 5.30pm.
Ecumenical Contact Parish Priest **Justice & Peace Contact** Corrine Lynch **Tel: 020 8893 8498**
Sisters of Charity of St Paul, 94a Bath Road Tel: 020 8570 5071

HOXTON + ST MONICA'S PRIORY A

19 Hoxton Square N1 6NT Tel: 020 7739 5006 Fax: 020 7613 0394
E-mail: augparishhsquare@aol.com and **hoxton@rcdow.org.uk**
Off Old Street at Shoreditch Town Hall ***(Hackney Deanery)*** (1863; 1864)
Augustinians (OSA) Fr Paul Graham **(Parish Priest)**;
Fr Mark Minihane; Fr Robert Marsh **(Prior)**
Parish Sisters, Sister Agnes, Sister Assumpta
Services Sun, M (Sat 6.30pm), 9, 11, 7pm. Hds, M (Eve 7pm), 10.30 & 12.
Wks M 9.30am. Conf Sat 5.15-6pm. Exp during Conf
Ecumenical Contact Parish Priest **Justice and Peace Contact** Parish Priest
Ursulines of Jesus, 150 Kingsland Road E2 8EB Tel: 020 7739 8036
Little Sisters of Jesus, 148 Fellows Court, Weymouth Terrace E2 8LW
Tel: 020 7729 3605 Sr Catharine; Sr Loide Claire; Sr Patricia
Ashwell House, Shepherdess Walk N1 7NA Tel: 020 7490 5021
Hall of residence for women university students.
Pastoral care entrusted to Prelature of Opus Dei.

ISLE OF DOGS (SEE MILLWALL)

ISLEWORTH + OUR LADY OF SORROWS AND ST BRIDGET OF SWEDEN

112 Twickenham Road, Isleworth, Middx TW7 6DL
Tel/Fax: 020 8560 1431 and 020 8568 7371 E-mail: isleworth@rcdow.org.uk
Corner of South Street (traffic lights); opp Gumley Hse ***(Hounslow Deanery)*** (1675; 1910; cons 6.10.10)
Administrator Fr Stewart Hasker
Pastoral Assistant Alex Heath **Tel: 020 8568 5292**
Services Sun, M (Sat 6pm), 8, 10, 12. Hds, M (Eve 7pm), 9, 7pm.
Wkds, M as announced. Conf: as announced.
Ecumenical Contact Mrs Monica Harrington **Tel: 020 8568 0838**
Justice and Peace Contact Clare Hickey **Tel: 020 8893 8564**
Faithful Companions of Jesus
Gumley House Convent, Twickenham Road, Isleworth TW7 6DN
Tel: 020 8560 1428 E-mail: community@gumleyhousefcj.freeserve.co.uk
Sr Gloria Calabrese; Sr Bernadette Coughlin; Sr Kate Frost; Sr Elizabeth Philips; Sr Anne Marie Ryan; Sr Bernadette O'Malley; Sr Brenda Wallace; Anouska Biggin (Postulant)

ISLINGTON + ST JOHN THE EVANGELIST

39 Duncan Terrace N1 8AL Tel: 020 7226 3277
Fax: 020 7704 8988
E-mail: islington@rcdow.org.uk Website: www.stjohnsislington.org.uk
Two minutes walk from Angel stn (LT) via Islington High St, right into Duncan St, left into Duncan Terrace
(Islington Deanery) (1839; 1843; cons 26 June 1873)
Fr Shaun Lennard; also in residence Fr Larry McGonnell MHM
Services Sun, M (Sat 6pm), 9, 10.30 (Sung, CW), 12, (sung), 6pm.
Hds, M 7.30, 10,12.30, 7.30pm. Wkds, M 10am,
Conf: Sat 10.30 -11; Sun 5.15-5.45pm. Exp. Sat 10.30-11am.
Ecumenical Contact Sr Fidelis Daly CP **Tel: 020 7359 8719**
Justice and Peace Contact Parish Priest
Sisters of the Cross and Passion, 40 Duncan Terrace N1 8AL
Tel: 020 7359 8719
Sr Fidelis Daly; Sr Marie Murphy; Sr Marcellina Cooney

ITALIAN CHURCH + ST PETER

4 Back Hill, Clerkenwell Road EC1R 5EN (Personal Parish for Italians)
Tel: 020 7837 1528
Fax: 020 7837 9071
E-mail: chiesaitaliana@aol.com Website: www.chiesaitaliana.org.uk
Opposite the top end of Hatton Garden. ***(Westminster Deanery)*** (1863)
Pallottine Fathers (SCA) Fr Carmelo Di Giovanni; Fr Andrea Fulco; Fr Riszard Wrobel
Services Sun, M (Sat 7pm), 9.30, 11 (Sung), 12.30, 7pm.
Hds, M 10, 12.15, 8pm. Wkds, M 12.15. Conf (Italian, English): Sat 9 to 7pm.
Ecumenical Contact Parish Priest **Justice and Peace Contact** Parish Priest

KENSAL NEW TOWN + OUR LADY OF THE HOLY SOULS

68 Hazlewood Crescent, Kensal Road W10 5DJ Tel: 020 8969 2660
E-mail: kensalnewtown@rcdow.org.uk
In Bosworth Road, off Kensal Road (near Halfpenny Bridge) ***(North Kensington Deanery)*** (1862; 1882)
Fr Sean O'Toole
Parish Sister Sr Margarita Cunningham RSM
Services Sun, M (Sat 6pm), 9, 11am (Family).
Hds, M 9.30, 7.30pm. Wkds, M Mon, Tues, Wed, Sat 9.30am, Thurs 8am, Fri 7pm.
Conf before M, and at call.
Ecumenical Contact Parish Priest
Justice and Peace Contact Parish Priest
Sisters of Mercy, 76 Fifth Avenue W10 4DP Tel: 020 8960 2505
E-mail: London5th@aol.com Sr Angela Moroney; Sr Margarita Cunningham
Missionaries of Charity, 177 Bravington Road W9 3AR Tel: 020 8960 2644

KENSAL RISE + CHURCH OF THE TRANSFIGURATION A

1 Wrentham Avenue NW10 3HT Tel: 020 8964 4040
E-mail: kensalrise@rcdow.org.uk
On corner of Wrentham Avenue, near Kensal Rise stn (BR) ***(Brent Deanery)*** (1977)
Fr Sean Thornton
Services Sun, M (Sat 6pm), 9, 11, 12.30 (Italian), 5pm.
Hds, M 10, 7pm. Wkds, M Mon, Fri 7pm; Tues, Wed, Thurs, Sat 10am
Conf: Sat 10.30-11am & 5.30pm. HH & B Fri 6pm
4th Sunday of the month, Ghanaian M 2pm
Ecumenical Contact Teresa Elkins **Tel: 020 8969 1619**
Justice and Peace Contact Oonagh O'Toole
St Jude's Social Centre, Kenmont Gardens NW10 6BU Tel: 020 8969 2231
St Mary's Cemetery, Harrow Road NW10 Tel: 020 8969 1145
Stigmatine Fathers (CSS), 5 Hanover Road NW10 3DJ Fr Natalino Mignolli
Tel: 020 8451 1408; also 2 Leigh Gardens NW10 5HP Tel: 020 8969 1414
Sisters of Jesus and Mary, 200 Chamberlayne Road NW10 3JX Tel: 020 8451 1957
Daughters of Charity (SVP), 58 Wrentham Avenue NW10 3HG Tel: 020 8964 9796

KENSINGTON 1 + OUR LADY OF VICTORIES

The Clergy House 16 Abingdon Road W8 6AF Tel: 020 7937 4778 Fax 020 7937 4221
E-mail: kensington1@rcdow.org.uk Website: www.rcdow.org.uk/kensington1/
235a High Street On south side of High Street, between Abingdon Road & Earls Court Road; not far from Kensington High Street stn ***(Kensington & Chelsea Deanery)*** (1794; 1812; 1869; 1958)
Fr Perry Sykes; Fr Frederick Jackson; Fr Javier Ruiz
Also in residence: Bishop Alan Hopes; **Tel: 020 7798 9023**
Fr Stuart Wilson **Tel: 020 7937 9165**
Services Sun, M (Sat 6.30pm), 8.30, 10 (Family), 11.30 (Sung Latin), 12.45, 6.30pm.
Hds, M 10, 12.30, 7.30pm.
Wkds, M 10, 12.30 (except Wed 10am & 7.30pm)
Conf: Sat 10.30 to 12.25, 5.30 to 6.25pm and at call
Exp, Wed 10.30 - 7.15pm, Sat 10.30 - 12.30pm
Ecumenical Contact Rachel Field **Tel: 020 7603 6489**
Justice and Peace Contact Parish Priest
Augustinian Recollects (OAR), 18 Cheniston Gardens W8 6TQ
Tel: 020 7937 7681
Fr Denis Caddle **Vicar Provincial** Fr Roberto Riezu; Fr Patrick O'Hagan
Daughters of St Paul, Pauline Books & Media, 199 Kensington High Street W8 6BS
Tel: 020 7937 9591 E-mail: london@pauline-uk.org
Website: www.pauline-uk.org
Society of the Holy Child Jesus 10 Holland Villas Road W14 8BU
Tel: 020 7603 7450

KENSINGTON 2 + (CARMELITE CHURCH) OUR LADY OF MOUNT CARMEL & ST SIMON STOCK

Carmelite Priory, 41 Kensington Church Street W8 4BB Tel: 020 7937 9866
Fax 020 7938 1470 E-mail: kensington2@rcdow.org.uk
500 yards from Kensington High St ***(Kensington & Chelsea Deanery)*** (1862; 1959)
Discalced Carmelites (OCD) Fr Matthew Blake (Prior and Parish Priest); Fr Isidore Carey; Fr Oliver McGettigan; Fr Fabian McCormick; Fr Ronan Murphy; Fr John Hughes; Fr Iain Matthew **Ecumenical Contact** Patricia Leathem **Justice & Peace** Parish Priest
Services Sun, M (Sat 6pm), 8.30, 10 (Family), 11 (Sung Latin), 12.15, 6pm (Folk)
Hds M (Eve 6pm), 8, 12.15, 6 Wkds, M 8, 12.15, 6pm.
Conf: Sat 10.30 to 11.45, 3.30 to 5.45, Wkds at call to 6.45pm (exc 12 to 3).
NP: Mon - Fri after pm M. R, Mon - Fri 5.40pm, Sat after pm M.
Sisters of the Assumption, Maria Assumpta Pastoral & Education Centre,
23 Kensington Square W8 5HN Tel: 020 7361 4700 Fax: 020 7361 4767
Provincial House and Youth Office M weekday during Heythrop term 1pm
Youth Office Caroline Burns; Sr Christine Charlwood **Provincial**;
Sr Elizabeth Dove; Sr Cathy Mary Jones; Sr Hilda Denyer; Sr Clare Veronica Wyman;
Sr Mary Ann Tyler; Sr Patricia Bains; Sr Catherine Cowley
St Catherine's Community Tel: 020 7937 9688
Adoratrices, Handmaids of the Blessed Sacrament and of Charity,
38 Kensington Square W8 5HP Tel: 020 7937 5237
Hostel for Working Women & Students Tel: 020 7937 4582
Religious of Mary Immaculate, 15-16 Southwell Gardens SW7 4RN. Tel: 020 7373 2738
Hostel and Club for working girls and students of all nationalities.
Social Centre for Spanish Tel: 020 7373 3869 **Cromwell Hospital**
Heythrop College (University of London), Kensington Square W8 5HQ
Tel: 020 7795 6600 Fax 020 7795 4200 Principal Fr John McDade SJ

KENTISH TOWN + OUR LADY HELP OF CHRISTIANS A

4 Lady Margaret Road NW5 2XT Tel: 020 7485 4023 Fax: 020 7267 3118
E-mail: kentishtown@rcdow.org.uk Website: www.rcdow.org.uk/kentishtown/
Corner of Falkland Rd; 3 mins Kentish Town Stn (LT) ***(Camden Deanery)*** (1859; new church cons 1979)
Fr Tom Forde; also in residence Fr Eddie Woo MAfr (Chinese Chaplaincy)
Services Sun, M (Sat 7pm), 8.30, 10 (Sung), 12 (Family), 1.15pm (Spanish), 6.30pm (Folk).
Hds, M 10, 7pm. Wkds, M 10am. Conf: Sat 10.30-11am; 6.15-6.45pm. Exp FF 10.30-1pm
Ecumenical Contact & Justice and Peace Contact Margaret Harvey **Tel: 020 7482 0093**
Irish Centre, 52 Camden Square, NW1 9XB Tel: 020 7916 2222
E-mail: irishchaplaincy@btconnect.com
Sisters of La Sainte Union, Croft Lodge, Highgate Road NW5 1RP Tel: 020 7485 6169
Daughters of Charity (SVP) (Spanish Province), 95 Huddleston Road N7 0AE
E-mail: sistersofcharity@hotmail.com
Social Service for Spanish Immigrants **Tel: 020 7607 3974** Sun, M 1.15pm (at parish church).
Congregation of Jesus (CJ) Mary Ward Hse, 39 St George's Ave N7 0HB Tel: 020 7700 3256

KENTON + ALL SAINTS ☑ ♿

2a Salehurst Close, Harrow, Middx HA3 0UG
Tel: 020 8204 3550 Fax: 020 8204 5815
E-mail: kenton@rcdow.org.uk Website: www.rcdow.org.uk/kenton/
Corner of Claremont Avenue; 600 yards west of Kingsbury Circus/Kingsbury stn (LT) ***(Brent Deanery)*** (1932; 1963)
Fr Dermot O'Neill. **Secretary** Elizabeth Galea **RE Co-ordinator** Pat Edwards
Services Sun, M (Sat 6.30pm), 8.30, 10, 11.30. Hds, M as announced
Wkds, M as announced, Conf: Sat 5.30 - 6pm
Ecumenical Contact Bernard Taylor **Justice and Peace Contact** Flora Fernandes

KILBURN + SACRED HEART OF JESUS ☑A

New Priory, Quex Road NW6 4PS
Tel: 020 7624 1701 Fax 020 7328 8176
E-mail: parish@omiquex.org.uk Website: www.omiquex.org.uk
(Camden Deanery) (1864; 1879; cons June 18, 1909)
Oblates of Mary Immaculate (OMI) Fr Raymond Warren;
Fr Herbert Bromley; Fr Brian de Burca
Parish Sister Maria Margaret LSU
Services Sun, M (Sat 6pm), 9, 11, 12.30, 7pm.
Hds, M (Eve 6pm), 8, 10, 1215, 7pm. Wkds, M Mon, Wed, Fri 7.30, 10, 12.15;
Tue, Thur, Sat 10, 12.15; (Sat 12noon.) Conf: Sat 10.30 to 12.30, 5 to 6pm
Jesuits (SJ) Copleston House, 221 Goldhurst Terrace NW6 3EP Tel: 020 7604 5860
Fax: 020 7604 5850 Fr Paul Hamill **Superior**; Fr John McDade **Principal, Heythrop College;**
Fr Robert Carty; Fr James Hanvey; Fr Keith McMillan; Fr Robert Murray; Fr Patrick
Riordan; Fr Kizito Kiyimba; Fr Brendan Callaghan; Fr Francis X Ryan
Bro James Hodkinson **Archivist, British Jesuits**
Sisters of the Holy Family of Bordeaux, 2 Aberdare Gardens NW6 3PX Tel: 020 7624 7573
Sisters of La Sainte Union, 14 Quex Road NW6 4PL Tel: 020 7624 9865
Daughters of Charity (SVP), 119 Victoria Road NW6 6TD Tel: 020 7624 3587
The Missionary Association of Mary Immaculate (OMI) 237 Goldhurst Terrace NW6 3EP
Tel: 020 7328 8610 Fr Paschal Dillon; Fr Eugene Ford
Little Sisters of the Assumption Tel: 020 8451 0141 Sr Margaret Blair

KILBURN WEST + IMMACULATE HEART OF MARY ♿☑S

Marian Parish Centre, 1 Stafford Road NW6 5RS *Off Kilburn Park Road*
Tel: 020 7624 2188 E-mail: kilburnwest@rcdow.org.uk
Fr Francis Ryan OM I ***(Camden Deanery)*** (1948)
Services Sun, M 9, 11.30 Hds M 9.20am, 7pm Wkds (Tues-Sat) M 9.20am.
Conf: Sat 9.45 am and before & after each M
Ecumenical Contact Parish Priest **Justice and Peace Contact** Parish Priest
Marian Parish Centre Manager Carlos Olivari **Tel: 020 7372 6278**

KINGSBURY GREEN + ST SEBASTIAN AND ST PANCRAS A

Presbytery, Hay Lane NW9 0NG
Tel: 020 8204 2834/2117 Fax 020 8204 5842
E-mail: kingsburygreen@rcdow.org.uk Website: www.rcdow.org.uk/kingsburygreen/
Off Edgware Road, Colindale ***(Brent Deanery)*** (1926; 2001)
Fr David Williamson
Pastoral Assistant Mrs Liz Wilson
Services Sun, M (Sat 6.30pm), 8, 10am, 12, 6.30pm
Hds, M 9.30, 7.30pm. Wkds, M 9.30, Wed & Thurs also 7.30pm.
Conf Sat 12 - 1pm
Ecumenical Contact Liz Wilson **Tel: 020 8204 2834**
Justice and Peace Contact Ann Wade **Tel: 020 8206 1515**
Colindale Hospital

KING'S CROSS, N1 SEE COPENHAGEN STREET

KINGSLAND + OUR LADY AND ST JOSEPH A

Presbytery 100a Balls Pond Road N1 4AG Tel: 020 7254 4378
E-mail: kingsland@rcdow.org.uk
Website: www.rcdow.org.uk/kingsland/
Off Kingsland High Street; at top end of Essex Road. ***(Hackney Deanery)*** (1854; 1964)
Fr Christopher Colven;
Also in residence Fr Patrick Heekin, Fr Albert Ovie Ofere (Nigerian Chaplaincy)
Parish Sister Sr Winifred UJ
Services Sun, M (Sat 7pm), 8, 9.30 (Family), 11 (Sung), 12.15, 6.30pm.
Hds, M (Eve 6pm), 9, 12, 6, 8pm.
Wkds, M Mon-Fri 9am and 6pm
Sat 12 noon followed by Nov & B
Conf: Sat 11 to 11.45, 6 to 6.45pm. Exp Sat 6-7pm, Sun 5-6.30pm
Ecumenical Contact Parish Priest
Justice and Peace Contact Simon Matthews
Ursulines of Jesus, 8 King Henry's Walk N1 4PB
Tel: 020 7254 8321
IBVM (Loreto Sisters) 57 Parkholme Road E8 3AQ
Tel: 020 7254 4345
Sr Sinead Duddy; Sr Germaine O'Neill; Sr Una O'Reilly; Sr Annie Bromham
St Martin of Tours House, 162 New North Road N1 7BH
Rehabilitation Centre Tel: 020 7226 7516

KINGSWAY, WC2 SEE LINCOLN'S INN FIELDS

KNEBWORTH + ST THOMAS MORE ☑A

72 London Road, Knebworth, Herts SG3 6HB Tel: 01438 813303
E-mail: knebworth@rcdow.org.uk *(Stevenage Deanery)* (1929; 1936)
Fr Seamus Fullam
Services Sun, M (Sat 6pm), 8, 10 (sung). Hds, M (Eve 7.30pm), 9.30, 7.30pm.
Wkds, M 9.30 (except Mon); Mon 7.15pm. Conf: Sat 5 to 5.45pm.
Exp Fri after M to 6pm
Ecumenical Contact Christine Goodwin **Tel: 01438 365918** **Justice & Peace** Parish Priest

LAXTON PLACE + ST ANNE ☑ A

Priest's House, Laxton Place, Longford Street NW1 3PT Tel: 020 7387 3833
E-mail: laxtonplace@rcdow.org.uk Website: www.rcdow.org.uk/laxtonplace/
In Longford St, off Albany St (just north of Great Portland St stn) *(Camden Deanery)*
(1853; 1857; 1938; 1970)
Fr Mark Coningsby
Services Sun, M (Sat 6.30pm), 9.30, 11. Hds, M 12.30, 7pm. Wkds, M 12.30 (Thu 9).
Conf: Sat, 6 to 6.20pm. HH Wed 6pm. M in Chaldean Rite, Sun 12.15.
Ecumenical Contact Parish Priest **Justice and Peace Contact** Parish Priest

LEBANESE CHURCH + OUR LADY OF LEBANON

6 Dobson Close NW6 4RS Tel: 020 7586 1801 Fax 020 7722 0436
E-mail: lebanesechurch@rcdow.org.uk Website: www.maronitechurch.org.uk
Lebanese Maronite Order (LMO)
Fr Augustine Aoun (Prior & Parish Priest); Fr Dany Akiki
Services M (Maronite Rite), (Sat 7pm), Sun 12.30, 7pm at
Our Lady of Sorrows, 17 Cirencester Street W2 5SR

LEICESTER SQUARE, WC2. SEE FRENCH CHURCH

LETCHWORTH + ST HUGH OF LINCOLN ☑ ♿

84 Pixmore Way, Letchworth, Herts SG6 3TP Tel: 01462 683504
Broadway *(Stevenage Deanery)* (1907; 1963)
Fr Seamus Murphy
Services Sun, M (Sat 7pm), 8, 9.30, 11, 12.30 (Polish). Hds, M 7.30, 9.30, 7.30pm.
Wkds, M 9.30; Conf: Sat 10 to 10.30, 6 to 6.30pm; and at call.
Ecumenical Contact Mr S Bain **Tel: 01462 675158** **Justice & Peace Contact** Mary Ryan
Garden House Hospice.
Sisters of Charity of Jesus and Mary,
Provincial House, 108 Spring Road, Letchworth, Herts SG6 3SL Tel: 01462 682153

LIMEHOUSE + OUR LADY IMMACULATE A

The Presbytery, 1 Island Row, 636 Commercial Road E14 7HS
Tel: 020 7987 3563 Fax 020 7536 9043 E-mail: limehouse@rcdow.org.uk
(A13), between Limehouse stn and Burdett Road ***(Tower Hamlets Deanery)*** (1881; 1934; cons 17 Oct 1945)
Fr Aidan Rossiter CJ (Also serves Bow Common)
Services Sun, M (Sat 6pm), 11.15am Hds & Wkds M as announced. Conf: Sat 5.15 to 5.45
Ecumenical Contact Parish Priest **Justice and Peace Contact** Parish Priest
Daughters of Charity (SVP), 63-64 Island Row E14 7HU Tel: 020 7987 3336
E-mail: islandrowdc@ontel.com
Tower Hamlets Police Chaplain

LINCOLN'S INN FIELDS + ST ANSELM AND ST CECILIA

70 Lincoln's Inn Fields WC2A 3JA
Tel: 020 7405 0376 Fax: 020 7405 6928
E-mail: lif@rcdow.org.uk
On east side of Kingsway, a few steps from Holborn stn (LT) ***(Westminster Deanery)*** (1687; 1909)
Fr David Barnes; also in residence Fr John O'Leary
Services Sun, M (Sat 6pm), 10 (Family), 12 (Solemn Sung); 6pm
Filipino 4th Sun 4pm
Hds, M (Eve 6pm) 8, 12.15, 1.05pm, 6pm. Wkds, M 12.30, 6pm.
Conf Mon-Fri 12-12.25 M, Sat 5 - 5.45pm.
Ecumenical Contact Parish Priest **Justice & Peace Contact** Parish Priest
Hospital for Sick Children, Gt Ormond Street Fr David Barnes
Hospital for Neurology & Neurosurgery; Homoeopathic Chaplain Fr Peter Harries OP

LITHUANIAN CHURCH + ST CASIMIR A

21 The Oval, Hackney Road E2 9DT Tel: 020 7739 8735
E-mail: lithuanianchurch@rcdow.org.uk Website: www. rcdow.org.uk/lithuanianchurch/
Fr Petras Tverijonas ***(Tower Hamlets Deanery)*** (1901; 1912)
Services Sun, M 9 (English), 11 (Lithuanian), 6pm (Lithuanian) Hds, M 7pm. Wkds, M 7pm.
Conf (Lithuanian, English): daily bef M; and at call.

LONDON AIRPORT (HEATHROW) + ST GEORGE'S CHAPEL

St George's Chapel, Heathrow Airport, Hounslow, Middx TW6 1BP Tel/Fax 020 8745 4261
Opposite Car Park no 2; close to Heathrow Central stn (LT) & bus stand ***(Hillingdon Deanery)***
Airport Chaplain Rev Robert Levett (Deacon)
Pastoral Assistants Shaun Loader **Tel: 020 8759 1351 Mobile 0956 524147**
Sr Margaret Byrnes **Tel: 020 8561 3023**
Services Sun, M 12.30pm, Hds, M 7.30am, 12.30, 6pm.
Wkds, M 12.30pm (daily); Tue 7pm (followed by prayer for healing). Conf: on request

OUR LADY QUEEN OF HEAVEN, QUEENSWAY: SEE UNDER QUEENSWAY

BERKHAMSTED + SACRED HEART CHURCH A

Sacred Heart Church, Park Street, Berkhamsted, Herts HP4 1HX
Tel: 01442 863845
E-mail: berkhamstead@rcdow.org.uk
Off Berkhamsted High Street (north side) ***(St Albans Deanery)*** (1909; 1967)
Fr Peter Grant (also serves Tring)
Services Sun, M (Sat 6pm), 8.30, 10.30 Hds & Wkds M as announced. Conf: Sat 10.30 - 11.30.
Ecumenical Contact F Furlong **Tel: 01442 862768**
Justice & Peace Contacts David & Lesley Brinsden
HM Prison, The Mount, Bovingdon (See Prison Service)

BETHNAL GREEN + OUR LADY OF THE ASSUMPTION ♿

[illegible] Park Square E2 9PB
[illegible]
E-[illegible]algreen@rcdow.org.uk
Just off [illegible] Green stn (LT) ***(Tower Hamlets Deanery)*** (1901; 1912)
Assumptionists (AA) Fr Andrew O'Dell (Parish Priest); Fr Edwin Denton;
Fr Mark Clifton; Fr Edward Chatov; Fr Brendon O'Malley; Fr Thomas O'Brien (Superior)
Catechist Sr Jo Langford
Services Sun, M (Sat 7pm), 9.30, 11.30 all +CW
Hds, M 8, 12.15, 6.30pm. Exp Wed 11-12 Conf Sat 6.15-6.45pm
Ecumenical Contact Caterina Sotiriou **Tel: 020 8257 2376** **Justice & Peace** Parish Priest
Congregation of Our Lady (Canonesses of St Augustine) Sr Jo Langford
44 Stafford Cripps House, Globe Road E2 0LN Tel/Fax: 020 8981 6221.
London Chest Hospital

BISHOP'S STORTFORD + ST JOSEPH AND THE ENGLISH MARTYRS A

St Joseph's, 3 Windhill, Bishop's Stortford, Herts CM23 2ND
Tel: 01279 654063 Fax: 01279 755416 ***(Lea Valley Deanery)*** (1900; 1906; cons June 19, 1906)
E-mail: bishopsstortford@rcdow.org.uk
Website: www.rcdow.org.uk/bishopsstortford/
Canon Edward Matthews
Services Sun, M (Sat 6pm) ,9, 11am, 6pm. Hds, M (Eve 7.30pm), 9.30, 7.30pm
Wkds, M Mon, Tues, Wed & Fri 9.30;
Conf: Sat 11- 12 (inc Exp) MP Mon, Tues, Wed, Fri 9.15am
Ecumenical Contact Michael Frost **Tel: 01279 654949**
Justice & Peace Contact Astrid Davies **Tel: 01279 652628**
Herts and Essex General Hospital

BARNET + MARY IMMACULATE AND ST GREGORY THE GREAT ☎ A

82 Union Street, Barnet, Herts EN5 4HZ Tel: 020 8449 3338 Fax: 020 8449 4761
E-mail: barnet@rcdow.org.uk Website: www. barnetrc-demon.co.uk
(Barnet Deanery) (1849; 1860; cons Dec 15, 1931; new church 1975)
Administrator Fr Jeremy M W Davies, Fr Cyriac Mattathil
Services Sun, M (Sat 6.30pm), 8, 9.30, 11.15, 6.30pm
Hds, M (Eve 7.30pm), 10, 7.30pm. Wkds, M 10am. MP 9.30, EP 5.30 (Mon-Fri)
Conf: Sat 9.30 - 10,am, 6 - 6.30pm. Exp 7 to10pm (Mon to Fri),
Ecumenical Contact John Ainslie **Tel: 020 8445 5724 Justice and Peace Contact** Jean Slade
Barnet Hospital Tel: 020 8216 4000.
Poor Clares, Poor Clare Monastery, Galley Lane, Arkley, Barnet, Herts EN5 4AN
Tel: 020 8449 8815 Sr Assumpta (Abbess); Sr Bernard; Sr Colette; Sr Michael;
Sr Francisca; Sr Bernadette; Sr Mary Paul; Sr Jane Clare
Sisters of St Martha, 22 Wood Street, Barnet EN5 4BW Tel: 020 8449 4346 also
124 Wood Street, Barnet EN5 4AY Tel: 020 8449 6759 Sr Janet; Sr Teresa; Sr Ana-Maria
Sisters of Christian Instruction, Summerhill, Leecroft Rd, Barnet EN5 2TH Tel: 020 8440 1853

BAYSWATER + ST MARY OF THE ANGELS ☎ A

The Parish House, Moorhouse Road W2 5DJ Tel: 020 7229 0487
Fax: 020 7229 3223 E-mail: bayswater@rcdow.org.uk Website: www.humilitas.org
In angle of Westbourne Grove & Chepstow Road, via Artesian Road ***(North Kensington Deanery)*** (1857)
Fr Alan Robinson; also in residence Fr Bogale Tafesse
Services Sun, M (Sat 6.30pm); 8, 9.30 (Family), 11 (Portuguese), 12 (Sung), 6pm;
Hds, M (Eve 6.30pm), 8, 10 Wkds, M Mon, Wed, Fri 8 & 10am; Tues, Thurs (also 10am),
Sat 10am Exp Fri 10.30-2pm, Sat 7.15-8pm + B. Night Vigil First Fri 9.30pm to 5am
Conf: Sat 10.30 to 11, 6 to 6.30, 7.15 to 8pm.
Spanish Catholic Chaplaincy 47 Palace Court W2 4LS Tel: 020 7229 8815 Vincentians, (CM)
Sun M 10.30, 6pm. Fr Ernesto Atañes **Superior**; Fr Segundo Peña; Br Benito Fraile.
Czech Centre 22 Ladbroke Square W11 3NA Tel: 020 7727 7849
Sun, Hds, M 8pm. Wkds, M 5.30pm (Tue, Fri 8pm). Conf: bef M and at call.
Comboni Missionaries (MCCJ), 16 Dawson Place W2 4TJ Tel: 020 7229 7059
Fr Danilo Castello; Fr Benito de Marchi; Fr Tesarmichael Debesai
Sisters of Sion, 34 Chepstow Villas W11 2QZ Tel: 020 7119 6266 (Community) Sr Mary Camilleri; Sr Marguerite Filippucci; Sr Michaela Fisher; Sr Ann Gibney; Sr Ibolya Glancz; Sr Anne Hobbs; Sr Tessa Hughes; Sr Clare Jardine; Sr Mary Kelly; Sr Ellen Knox
Sion Centre for Dialogue and Encounter, Conference Centre and Jewish/Christian Library Resource Tel: 020 7313 8286; 020 7727 3597
Bon Secours Sisters, 166 Westbourne Grove W11 2RW Tel: 020 7229 3179
Society of the Holy Child Jesus, 10 Holland Park Avenue W11 3QU Tel: 020 7727 7440
Servants of the Mother of God, 7 Pembridge Square W2 4E0 Tel: 020 7229 1424
Pembridge House, 29 Pembridge Square W2 4DS. Tel: 020 7229 3584
Pastoral care entrusted to the Prelature of Opus Dei

LONDON COLNEY + OUR LADY, ST MARY OF WALSINGHAM ♿ A

189 High Street, London Colney AL2 1RP Tel: 01727 822218 ***(St Albans Deanery)*** (1959)
Fr Mark Anwyll.
Services Sun, M (Sat 6pm), 9.30, 11, 5pm. Hds, M 9, 7.30pm. Wkds, M Mon-Thu 10; Fri 7.30pm; Sat 10. Conf: Sat 10.30 to 11, 6.30 to 7pm. R Sat 10.30; Exp Sat 6.30pm.
Ecumenical Contact Mary Crouch **Justice and Peace Contact** Parish Priest

MAIDEN LANE (COVENT GARDEN) + CORPUS CHRISTI ♿ A

Corpus Christi Presbytery, Maiden Lane WC2E 7NB Tel: 020 7836 4700
E-mail: maidenlane@rcdow.org.uk
Off Southampton St, north of Strand; nr Covent Garden ***(Westminster Deanery)*** (1873; cons Oct 18, 1956)
Administrator Fr Antonio Ritaccio
Services Sun, M (Sat 6pm), 9.30, 11.30 Hds, M 12.05, 1.05pm, 6.30pm (Tridentine). Wkds, M Mon-Fri 1.05pm; Sat 10; also Mon 6.30pm (Tridentine), Catholic Stage Guild M as announced. Bank Hol 10am Conf: wkds 12.30 to 1pm. Exp Thu 2pm to 9pm.
Ecumenical Contact Parish Priest **Justice and Peace Contact** Parish Priest

MANOR HOUSE + ST THOMAS MORE ♿ P

9 Henry Road N4 2LH Tel: 020 8802 9910
E-mail: manorhouse@rcdow.org.uk Website: www.thomasmoren4.org.uk
Off Portland Rise, south of Finsbury Park (near Manor House udgrd stn). ***(Hackney Deanery)*** (1969; 1975)
Fr Clive Lee
Services Sun, M (Sat 6pm Sung), 10 (Sung), 12 (Sung). Hds, M 7.15pm.
Wkds, M Mon & Fri 9.15am, Wed 715pm. Conf: Sat after evening M or on request.
Ecumenical Contact Parish Priest **Justice and Peace Contact** Parish Priest
Ursuline Sisters of St Angela Merici, 36 Adolphus Road N4 2AY Tel: 020 8800 5228

MARYLEBONE + OUR LADY OF THE ROSARY ♿ A

211 Old Marylebone Road NW1 5QT Tel: 020 7723 5101 Fax 020 7258 0307
E-mail: marylebone@rcdow.org.uk
Off Edgware Road (opposite Sussex Gardens) ***(Marylebone Deanery)*** (1855; new Church 1963)
Fr Duncan Adamson; also resident Fr Austin Garvey; Fr Antony Brunning (Hospital Chaplain)
Services Sun, M (Sat 6pm), 8.30, 10, 1130am 7pm; B 6pm. Hds, M 8, 12.30, 6pm.
Wkds M Mon-Fri M 8, 12.30, 6pm. Sat 10am, 12.30pm.
Conf: Sat 10.30 to 11, 5 - 5.30pm; at call wkds. Exp Sat 5 to 5.30pm.
St Mary's (Praed Street), Western Ophthalmic, Charter Nightingale Hospitals.
Tyburn Convent (Adorers of the Sacred Heart, OSB), 8 Hyde Park Place W2 2LJ
Tel: 020 7723 7262 Perpetual Exposition of the Blessed Sacrament. Chapel open daily 6.15am to 8.30 pm. M 7.30am; EP 4.30pm **Chaplain Tel: 020 7706 2842**

MILE END + THE GUARDIAN ANGELS

377 Mile End Road E3 4QS Tel: 020 8980 1845 E-mail: mileend@rcdow.org.uk
Nr Grove Rd/Burdett Rd jn; 2 mins Mile End stn ***(Tower Hamlets Deanery)*** (1869; 1901; cons 20.10.27)
Fr Anthony H. Sacré. Also in residence Fr Stephen Delany, Fr Brian Nash
Services Sun, M (Sat 5.30 Latin American), 9, 10.30, 6pm. Hds, M 9.30, 7.30pm.
Wkds, M as announced. Conf: Sat 11.45 to 12.30.
Ecumenical Contact Jean Maynard **Tel: 020 7790 2848**
Justice and Peace Contact Parish Priest
Neo-Catechumenate Communities Tony Cook **Tel: 020 7790 1380**
Mile End Hospital & The Bancroft Unit, Pat Shaw House

MILL END (& MAPLE CROSS) + ST JOHN THE EVANGELIST

St John's Church Presbytery, Berry Lane, Rickmansworth, Herts WD3 7HG
Tel: 01923 779890 E-mail: millend@rcdow.org.uk *(Watford Deanery)* (1969)
Administrator Fr Desmond Baker
Services Sun, M (Sat 6pm), 10, 6pm. Hds, M 10, 8pm. Wkds M as announced
Conf: Sat 10-10.30
Ecumenical Contact Ann Casey **Tel: 01923 445755 Justice and Peace Contact** Parish Priest

MILL HILL + SACRED HEART AND MARY IMMACULATE

2 Flower Lane NW7 2JB Tel: 020 8959 1021
E-mail: parishoffice@shmi.info Website: www.shmi.info
The Broadway Just off Watford Way (A4) at Mill Hill Circus. *(Barnet Deanery)*
(1889; 1922; 1995)
Vincentians (CM) Fr Philip Walshe **Superior and Parish Priest**;
Fr Jack Harris; Fr Fergus Kelly; Fr Hugh McMahon
Services Sun, M (Sat 6pm), 8.30, 10 (Family), 11.30, 6pm. Hds, M 7, 10, 12.15, 7.30pm.
Wkds, M 10 (daily), 7.30pm (Mon to Fri). Conf: Sat 10.30-11.30, 5-5.30pm.
HH Sat 10.30 Exp Wed & Thurs 10.30am to 12 noon
Ecumenical Michael Hull **Tel: 020 8959 8160 Justice & Peace** Mary Heffernan
Daughters of Charity (SVP), Provincial House, The Ridgeway NW7 1EH
Tel: 020 8906 3777
Director Fr Fergus Kelly CM **E-mail: Fergusbkelly@aol.com** Sun & Hds, M 9.
E-mail: londondc@aol.com Website: www.daughtersofcharity.org.uk
also **The Priory, The Ridgeway NW7 1RE**
Tel: 020 8959 2441
Franciscan Sisters of Mill Hill, St Mary's Abbey Lodge, The Ridgeway NW7 4HX
Tel: 020 8959 1364 Fax: 020 8959 4660
also **Generalate, St Francis Cottage, The Ridgeway NW7 4ER**
Tel: 020 8959 4854 Fax: 020 8906 9370

St Joseph's College, Lawrence Street NW7 4JX
E-mail: mhmgc@millhillmission.plus.com Website: www.millhillmissionaries.org
College Tel: 020 8959 8254;
Gen Council Tel: 020 8959 3222
College Fax: 020 8906 0289; General Council Fax 020 8959 8493
Mill Hill Missionaries (MHM)
General Council Fr Anthony Chantry (**Superior General**);
Fr Brendon Mulhall (**Vicar General**); Fr Jakob Kirchler; Fr Michael Corcoran
Br Jos Boerkamp; Fr Wim van der Salm PhL (**Secretary General**); Mr R Cotter (**Finance**);
Fr Hans Boerakker (**Archives**); Fr Mark Connolly (**Rector**);
Fr Tom O'Brien (**Vice Rector**)
APF Organisers Fr Francis McCarthy; Fr John Pharro; Fr John Rooney;
Fr Frank Thompson; Fr Daniel O'Connell; Fr Kevin Hughes
Other Priests Fr John Ball; Fr George Saraber; Fr Gerard Dunne; Fr John McCluskey;
Fr Brian Oswald

The Missionary Institute London (affiliated to Universities of Middlesex and Leuven),
Holcombe House, The Ridgeway NW7 4HY
Director of Studies Tel: 020 89061895 Fr Richard Parsons BD, MTh, MPhil, STL D Prof, AKC
E-mail: mil@mdx.ac.uk Website: the-mil.org.uk
Secretary, Registrar, Treasurer Tel: 020 8906 1893 President Tel: 020 8906 1894
President Fr Danilo Castello MCCJ, STL, DD **Secretary/Registrar** Fr Denis Starkey MAfr

MILLWALL + ST EDMUND ♿ ☎

297 Westferry Road E14 3RS Tel: 020 7987 4114
E-mail: millwall@rcdow.org.uk Website: www.st-edmund-millwall.org.uk
West Ferry Rd ***(Tower Hamlets Deanery)*** (1846; 1874; 2000)
Fr Peter Harris; **Pastoral Worker** Sr Sylvia Swift
Tel: 020 7537 9709 (Office); 020 7515 8944 (Home)
Services Sun M (Sat 6pm), 9.30, 11 (CW). Hds M 9.15, 8pm.
Wkds, M Mon, Wed, Fri 9.15; Tue 12.30pm Canary Wharf Prayer Room (Not August)
Conf: Sat 5.15 to 5.45pm
Ecumenical Contact Parish Priest **Justice and Peace Contact** Parish Priest

MOORFIELDS + ST MARY MOORFIELDS ☎

4/5 Eldon Street EC2M 7LS Tel: 020 7247 8390 Fax 020 7247 2537
E-mail: moorfields@rcdow.org.uk Website: www.rcdow.org.uk/moorfields/
100 yards west of Liverpool St station; just before the Red Lion. ***(Westminster Deanery)*** (1710; 1903)
Fr Peter Newby
Services Sun, M 10am Hds, M (Eve 7pm) 8.05, 12, 12.30, 1.05pm, 5.30pm. Wkds, M
Mon-Fri 8.05, 1.05pm. Conf 12.30-12.55, 1.30-1.50 Exp Mon - Fri 8.30 - 6pm
St Bartholomew's Hospital Chaplain Fr Philip Miller **Tel: 020 7531 6956** M. Sun 4pm.

MUCH HADHAM + HOLY CROSS ☎

The Priest's House, Malting Lane, Much Hadham, Herts SG10 6AW
Tel: 01279 842354 Fax: 01279 843844 *(Lea Valley Deanery)* (1939)
E-mail: muchhadham@rcdow.org.uk Website: www.rcdow.org.uk/muchhadham/
Fr Bob Styles SJ (also serves Sawbridgeworth)
Services (in Shared Church of St Andrew and Holy Cross, Church Lane, Much Hadham)
Sun, M 11. Hds, M 9.30, 12.30pm. Wkds M Tues, Thurs 9.30am.
Conf. after wkd M or by appointment.
Ecumenical Contact Hope Gilbert **Justice and Peace Contact** Jeremy Black
Daughters of the Cross, St Elizabeth's Centre, South End, Much Hadham SG10 6EW
School, College & Residential Home for adults with epilepsy, autism & other medical conditions
Sr Patricia Ainsworth; Sr Pauline McKeown; Sr Gillian Price; Sr Annette Clemence;
Sr Jane Hehir; Sr Teresa Farrelly; Sr Mary Gaffney; Sr Teresa Hehir; Sr Mary McLoughlin
Tel: 01279 843451 Chaplain Fr Paul Arnold **Tel: 01279 842145**
Services Sun, M 11; Hds M 5.30pm; Wkds M Mon, Wed, Fri 7.30am, Tue, Thur 5.30pm

MUSWELL HILL + OUR LADY OF MUSWELL ☎ A

1 Colney Hatch Lane N10 1PN Tel: 020 8883 5607 Fax: 020 8444 3464
E-mail: muswellhill@rcdow.org.uk
(Haringey Deanery) (1917; 1938; cons 23 Sept 1959)
Fr Charles Cahill; Fr Jan Swagemakers MHM
Catechetical Co-ordinator Anne Malone **Pastoral Co-ordinator** Sr Philomena Morris SSL
Services Sun, M (Sat 6.30pm), 8.30, 10, 11.45
Hds, M 10, 12.30 7.30pm. Wkds, M 10am Conf: Sat 10.30 to 11.30.
Exp Sat: (during conf) and Sun 5 - 6pm (Convent)
Ecumenical Contact Dan Bree **Justice and Peace Contact** Patricia Mulchrone
St Luke's, Woodside Hospital
Sisters of Marie Auxiliatrice, 20 Elgin Road N22 7UE Tel: 020 8881 8547
Sisters of St Louis, Flat 6, 11 Duke's Avenue N10 2PS
Sr Philomena Morris

NEASDEN + ST PATRICK ☎ A

The Presbytery, Hardie Close NW10 0UH
Tel: 020 8451 0367 Fax 020 8830 3022
E-mail: neasden@rcdow.org.uk
Just off North Circular Road (A406), west side, adjacent to IKEA. ***(Brent Deanery)*** (1981)
Fr Michael O'Doherty; also in residence Fr Mehall Lowry
Services Sun, M (Sat 6.30pm), 9.30, 11.30. Hds, M 9.30, 7.30pm.
Wkds, M 9.30 Conf: 5.45 to 6.15
Ecumenical Contact Parish Priest **Justice and Peace Contact** Parish Priest
St Patrick's Social Club Tel: 020 8459 0688.

NEW BARNET + MARY IMMACULATE AND ST PETER

63 Somerset Road, New Barnet, Herts EN5 1RF Tel: 020 8449 1961
Fax: 020 8441 1331 E-mail: newbarnet@rcdow.org.uk ***(Barnet Deanery)*** (1912; 1938)
Holy Ghost Fathers (CSSp) Fr Derek McCartney **Parish Priest**; Fr John Moriarty;
Fr William Damah. **Catechetical Co-ordinator** Jane Goring
Services Sun, M (Sat 6pm), 8, 9.30, 11. Hds, 9.30am, 7.30pm. Wkds, M 9.30; Conf: at call
Ecumenical Contact Parish Priest **Justice and Peace Contact** Parish Priest
African Missions (SMA) 33 Lyonsdown Road EN5 1JG Tel: 020 8440 4715
Fax 020 8441 8497 Fr Martin Walsh; Fr Anthony Cussen (Superior); Fr Rob Morland;
Fr Eddie Deeney

NEW SOUTHGATE + OUR LADY OF LOURDES A

373 Bowes Road N11 1AA Tel: 020 8368 1638 Fax: 020 8361 3172
E-mail: newsouthgate@rcdow.org.uk
200 yards right from Arnos Grove stn (LT) ***(Enfield Deanery)*** (1923; 1935; 1990)
Mgr Canon Thomas Egan; Fr Edward Burton. **In Residence** Fr John Bigo. **Pastoral Assistant** Mrs Aileen Adams
Services Sun, M (Sat 6.30pm), 8.30, 9.45 (Choir), 11.15 (Family), 12.30, 6.30pm.
Hds, M 8, 10, 7.30pm. Wkds, M Mon, Wed, Thurs 8 & 10am, Tue, Fri, Sat 10am (only)
Exp Fri 10.30-11am; 7-8pm; R Thurs 7.30pm Conf Sat 10.30-11, 5.30-6pm
Ecumenical Contact Mary McMullan **Tel: 020 8368 4479 Justice & Peace Contact** Peter Deegan
Sisters of Our Lady of the Missions, 2 Brookdale N11 1BL Tel: 020 8361 6848
Sr Patricia Dunne; Sr Mary Ellen O'Sullivan; Sr Anne Collett
Sisters of St Louis, 16 Chaucer Close N11 1AU Tel: 020 8361 1935

NORTHFIELDS (WEST EALING) + SS PETER AND PAUL A

38 Camborne Avenue W13 9QZ Tel: 020 8567 5421
E-mail: northfields@rcdow.org.uk Website: wwwrcdow.org.uk/northfields/
Off Northfield Ave, 1/4 mile N of Northfields stn ***(Ealing Deanery)*** (1926; 1931; cons 29 Oct 1959)
Fr Tom Quinn
Services Sun, M (Sat 6.30pm), 8.30am, 10am (Family/CW), 11.30 (sung), 6.30pm (sung)
HH Sun 5-6pm. Hds, M (eve 6.30pm), 9.30am, 8pm. Wkds, M, 9.30.+ R.
HH Fri 8.15-9.15am. Conf: Sat 10 to 10.30, 6 to 6.30pm.
Ecumenical Contact Parish Priest **Justice & Peace** Steve Stevens **Tel: 020 8579 4935**
Little Company of Mary, 33 Mattock Lane W5 5BH Tel: 020 8567 1464.
Srs Sheila Crehan; Celestine McCarthy; Francis Rattigan;Josephine Bugeja; Monica Kelliher
Medical Mission Sisters (SCMM), 11 Carew Road W13 9QL Tel: 020 8567 2869 also
Flat 27, Dean Court, Bowmans Close W13 9YU Tel: 020 8579 4485
Sisters of the Sacred Heart of Mary, 54 Grange Road W5 5BX Tel: 020 8567 7228

NORTHOLT SEE HARROW SOUTH

NORTHWOOD + ST MATTHEW A

32 Hallowell Road, Northwood, Middx HA6 1DW Tel: 01923 825639
Fax: 01923 840736
E-mail: northwood@rcdow.org.uk Website: www.rcdow.org.uk/northwood/
Off Green Lane (shopping centre); nr Northwood Stn. ***(Hillingdon Deanery)*** (1924; cons 12. 10.54)
Fr Timothy Hutton
Services Sun, M (Sat 6pm), 8, 9.15, 11 (sung), 6pm. Hds, M 7.30, 10, 8pm. Wkds, M 10
Conf: Sat 10.30 to 11.15, 5 to 5.45; & by appt. Exp Sat 10.30-11.15
Ecumenical Contact Parish Priest **Justice and Peace Contact** Parish Priest
Daughters of Charity (SVP), 32 Norwich Rd, Northwood Hills HA6 1NB Tel: 01923 835330
Joint Support Unit, Northwood; Mount Vernon Hospital; Bishops Wood Hospital; Northwood & Pinner Community Hospital; Michael Sobell House.

NOTTING HILL + ST FRANCIS OF ASSISI

The Presbytery, Pottery Lane W11 4NQ ***(North Kensington Deanery)*** (1860)
Tel: 020 7727 7968 Fax: 020 7727 6390 E-mail: nottinghill@rcdow.org.uk
Community Centre Tel: 020 7792 8259
Fr Shaun Middleton **Pastoral Assistant** David Wills
Services Sun, M (Sat 6pm), 10, 11.30, 1pm (Gheez Rite), 6.30pm.
Hds, M 8, 7.30pm. Wkds, M 9.30am, Thurs 8am; Conf: Sat 10-10.30am
Ecumenical Contact Jane Beazley **Tel: 020 7229 0512** **Justice and Peace Contact** Jane Evans
Sisters of St Mary of Namur, 47 Cornwall Crescent W11 1PJ Tel: 020 7221 4160
Kalayaan, 13 Hippodrome Place W11 4SF Tel: 020 7243 2942
Sisters of the Temple 28 Penzance Street W11 4QX Tel: 020 7602 8782

OGLE STREET + ST CHARLES BORROMEO

8 Ogle Street W1W 6HS Tel: 020 7636 2883 Fax: 020 7436 4265
E-mail: oglestreet@rcdow.org.uk Website: www. oglestreet.org
Off New Cavendish Street, near Telecom Tower. ***(Marylebone Deanery)*** (1862; cons 4 Oct 1921)
Fr Alan J Fudge **Parish Assistant** Sr Pauline Forde DC
Services Sun, M (Sat 6pm), 9, 11, 6pm. Hds, M 8, 12.30, 6pm.
Wkds, M 12.30, 6pm; Sat and Bank Hol 10am.
Conf: Wkds after 12.30 M; Sat 10.30 to 11, 5.30 to 6pm; on call.
Ecumenical Contact Parish Priest **Justice & Peace** Angeline Louis **Tel: 020 7636 2883**
Neo-Catechumenate Communities Michael Anderson **Tel: 020 7584 2579**
Portland Hospital for Women & Children
Middlesex Hospital M Sun 10am Chaplains Fr Peter Harries OP; Sr Pauline Forde DC
University College Hospital; Elizabeth Garrett Anderson;
Hospital for Tropical Diseases Chaplains Fr Peter Harries OP; Mrs Angela McCann Keetley
University Chaplaincy see separate entry

OLD HALL GREEN & PUCKERIDGE + ST EDMUND OF CANTERBURY & ENGLISH MARTYRS

1 Old Hall Green *To rear of St Edmund's College (off A10 as signposted)*
(1769; 1818; new church cons 2 Dec 1911) ***(Lea Valley Deanery)***
Served from No. 2
Services Sun, M 10.45. Conf: Sat 10 to 11.
Ecumenical Contacts Richard & Marianne Ashcroft **Tel: 01920 822000**
Libury Hall Old People's Home, Great Munden
St Edmund's College, Old Hall Green, Ware, Herts SG11 1DB (1793; 1853)
Tel: 01920 821504
Chaplain Fr Michael Pinot de Moira **Tel: 01920 821334**

2 Puckeridge + St Thomas of Canterbury
77 High Street, Puckeridge, Ware, Herts SG11 1RX Tel: 01920 821113
E-mail: oldhallgreen&puckeridge@rcdow.org.uk
Off the A10. At end of Puckeridge High Street (opposite school) (1926)
Fr Ian Dickie
Rev Ronald Saunders (Deacon) **Cedar Cottage, Levens Green, Ware, Tel: 01920 438241**
Services Sun, M (Sat 6pm), 9. Hds & Wkds M announced.
Conf: Sat 4.45-5.45 & call. Exp Fri 2-7.20pm

ORATORY + IMMACULATE HEART OF MARY ☑ A

The Oratory SW7 2RP Tel: 020 7808 0900 Fax 020 7584 1095
E-mail: OratoryPP@aol.com Website: www.bromptonoratory.com
Beside V&A Museum at convergence of Cromwell Road & Brompton Road; near South Kensington stn.
(Kensington & Chelsea Deanery) (1854; 1884; cons 16 April 1884)
Fathers of the Oratory of St Philip Neri (Oratorians) Fr Ignatius Harrison (Provost);
Fr Charles Dilke (Parish Priest); Fr Hugh Barrett-Lennard; Fr John Fordham;
Fr Ronald Creighton-Jobe; Fr George Bowen; Fr Patrick Doyle; Fr Julian Large;
Fr Rupert McHardy; Fr Michael Lang
Services Sun, M (Sat 6pm), 7, 8, 9 (Tridentine), 10am (Sung English/hymns),
11 (Solemn Latin), 12.30, 4.30, 7pm; V & B 3.30.
Hds, M (Eve 6.30), 7, 8, 9 (Tridentine), 10, 12.30, 5.30, 6.30pm (Sol Latin); V&B 5.30pm (Eve)
Wkds, M Mon-Fri 7, 10, 12.30, 6pm (Latin), Sat 7, 8.30 (Latin), 10am.
HH Thu 6.30pm. Conf (French, German, Italian, Spanish):
at all times except 12.30-3 & 6 7.45pm (Sat except 12.30-3 & 6-6.45pm).
Ecumenical Contact Fr Ronald Creighton-Jobe **Justice & Peace Contact** Parish Priest
The Little Oratory. Exercises of the Brotherhood: Sun 4.30pm
Congregation of Our Lady (Canonesses of St Augustine), More House, 53 Cromwell Road SW7 2EH Tel: 020 7584 2040 Fax: 020 7581 5748 Sr Gabriel Robin; Sr Francois Georgeault;
Sr Kathleen Delany; Sr Brigid O'Donnell; Sr Kieran Moriarty
University Chaplaincy, More House (See University)
Brompton Hospital; Royal Marsden Hospital

OSTERLEY + ST VINCENT DE PAUL ⌧

2 Witham Road, Osterley, Isleworth, Middx TW7 4AJ
Tel: 020 8560 4737 Fax: 020 8569 7422
E-mail: osterley@rcdow.org.uk Website: www.rcdow.org.uk/osterley/
Between Eversley Crescent & Spring Grove Road ***(Hounslow Deanery)*** (1934; 1936; cons 1996)
Administrator Fr Mark Leenane;
also in residence Fr Roger Reader **Tel: 020 8560 4213**
Services Sun, M (Sat 6pm), 9.30 (CW), 11.30, 6pm.
Hds, M (Eve 7.30pm), 9.30, 7.30pm.
Wkds, M 9.30 (Tue 7.30pm). Conf: Sat 10.00 to 10.30, 5 to 5.30pm and at call.
Exp Sat 10.30, B 12; MP 20 mins bef Wkd am M; R after Wkd am M.
Ecumenical Contact Ann Smith **Tel: 020 8568 7262**
Justice and Peace Contact Christine Plezia-Batchelor **Tel: 020 8232 8153**
Vincentians (CM), 29 Eversley Crescent, Isleworth, Middx TW7 4LR
Tel: 020 8560 7021 Fax: 020 8568 8677
Fr Noel Travers; Fr John Concannon; Fr Austin Mbelu; Fr Chacko Panathara
The Lillie Road Centre,
More House, 28 The Grove, Isleworth, Middx TW7 4JU
Tel: 020 8568 9487/020 8568 2079
Director Fr Ken McCabe.
Dominican Sisters (Cong of Newcastle, Natal)
121 Thornbury Road, Isleworth, Middx TW7 4ND Tel: 020 8560 9438

OXHEY, HERTS SEE BUSHEY OR CARPENDES PARK

PADDINGTON + OUR LADY OF SORROWS ⌧A

17 Cirencester Street W2 5SR
Tel: 020 7286 2672
E-mail: paddington@rcdow.org.uk
Off Harrow Road, near Royal Oak stn (LT) ***(North Kensington Deanery)*** (1912 Cons 1998)
Administrator Fr Stephen Bartlett
Services Sun, M (Sat 6pm), 9.30 & 11am.
Hds, M 9.30am, 6pm
Wkds, M 9.30am Thurs Exp at 8.50am. Conf Sat 5.40pm
Maronite Rite Sun (Sat 7pm), 12.30, 7pm Wkds M 7pm
Ecumenical Contact Parish Priest
Justice and Peace Contact Parish Priest

PADDINGTON - OUR LADY OF LOURDES. SEE HARROW ROA

PALMERS GREEN + ST MONICA ♿ ☎

The Presbytery, 1 Stonard Road N13 4DJ
Tel: 020 8886 9568 Fax: 020 8886 5143
E-mail: palmersgreen@rcdow.org.uk *(Enfield Deanery)*
Fr Roger Taylor; Fr Shaun Church
Parish Sister Sr Joyce **Catechetical Co-ordinator** Sr Eileen Toomey
Services Sun, M (Sat 6pm), 8, 9, 10.30 (Family), 12, 5.30pm.
Hds, M (Eve 7pm), 9.30, 10.30, 7pm.
Wkds, M 9.30 daily; 7pm (Tue, Thurs, Fri).
Conf: Sat 10 to 11, 5.15 to 5.45pm
Ecumenical Contact Rita McDonnell **Justice and Peace Contact** Christine Collier
Daughters of Providence, Providence Convent, Oakthorpe Road N13 5UH
Tel: 020 8886 8186
House of Prayer Tel: 020 8447 8233
Sr Mary Patricia Dowling; Sr Mary Agnes Grindley; Sr Mary Theresa Creamer
Social Centre, Cannon House, Cannon Hill N14 7HE
Tel: 020 8886 7505
Grovelands Priory Psychiatric Hospital

PARSONS GREEN + HOLY CROSS ♿ ☎

22 Cortayne Road SW6 3QA
Tel: 020 7736 1068 Fax 020 7371 8144
E-mail: parsonsgreen@rcdow.org.uk Website: www.rcdow.org.uk/parsonsgreen/
Ashington Rd Off New Kings Rd, opp Munster Rd; between Parsons Green & Putney Bridge stations (LT)
(Hammersmith & Fulham Deanery) (1843-48; 1884; 1924; cons 11 Oct 1928)
Fr Reginald Dunkling
Services Sun, M (Sat 6.30pm), 8.30, 10 (Family + SS), 11.30 (sung). Hds, M 10, 7.30pm.
Wkds, M 10 (Mon-Thu). Conf: bef M and on request. Exp 9.15 to 10 (Mon-Thu). MP 9.45.
Ecumenical Contact Frank Bedford & Peter Goldon
Justice & Peace Contact J Roche

PERIVALE + ST JOHN FISHER ☎ A

42 Langdale Gardens, Perivale, Greenford, Middx UB6 8DQ Tel: 020 8997 3164
E-mail: perivale@rcdow.org.uk
On north side of Western Avenue (A40), just past the Hoover building ***(Ealing Deanery)*** (1936; 1970)
Administrator Fr Anthony Sammarco
Services Sun, M (Sat 6.30pm), 9.30 (CW), 11.30am Hds, M 10, 7.30pm.
Wkds, M Mon, Tues, Thurs at 10am; Wed & Fri at 7.30pm.
Conf: Sat 12 to 12.30, 5.45 to 6.15pm. HH, Mon 10.30, Sat 11
Ecumenical Contact Ann Smith **Tel: 020 8997 8251**

PIMLICO + HOLY APOSTLES ☑ A

47 Cumberland Street SW1V 4LY Tel: 020 7834 6965 Fax: 020 7821 8609
E-mail: pimlico@rcdow.org.uk Website: www.rcdow.org.uk/pimlico/
Winchester St Off Lupus St, nr Pimlico stn ***(Westminster Deanery)*** (1917; 1957; cons 10.5.74)
Canon Patrick Browne; also resident Fr Gary Walsh (Albanian Chaplain) **Tel: 020 7834 1428**
Parish Sister Sr Louise Callan DC
Services Sun, M (Sat 6pm), 9, 10.30 (Family), 12.30pm (Spanish). Hds, M (Eve 7pm), 10, 7pm.
Wkds M 10am Conf: Sat 10.30-11am; Exp Sat 5-6.45 pm
Ecumenical Contact Parish Priest **Justice & Peace Contact** Catherine MacGillivray
The Maltese Mission 1 Balniel Gate, Lindsay Square SW1V 3SD.
Tel/Fax 020 7834 9512 E-mail: maltesemissionuk@easynet.co.uk
Franciscans (OFM) Fr Stephen Sciberras; Fr Charles Diacono
Franciscan Sisters of the Heart of Jesus, 9-11 St George's Drive SW1V 4DJ
Tel: 020 7834 4020 (Convent) 020 7834 5356 (Hostel)
Sisters of Notre Dame, 5 Westmoreland Terrace SW1 Tel: 020 7828 5221

PINNER + ST LUKE ☑ A

28 Love Lane, Pinner, Middx HA5 3EX Tel: 020 8866 0098 Fax: 020 8866 7869
E-mail: pinner@rcdow.org.uk
In town centre, 3 mins Pinner Metropolitan Stn, off Bridge Street. ***(Harrow Deanery)*** (1914; 1957)
Canon Robert Plourde
Pastoral Assistant (Catechetics) Winnie Brady **Tel: 020 8868 4175**
Services Sun, M (Sat 6pm), 9, 11. Hds, M (Eve 7.30pm), 10am
Wkds, M Mon to Fri 10. Conf: Sat 11 to 11.30, 4.30 to 5pm.
Ecumenical Contact Angela & Patrick Achenbach
Justice and Peace Contacts Ian and Belinda Brandon **Tel: 020 8868 4863**
Dominican Sisters, 34 Love Lane, Pinner, Middx HA5 3EX Tel: 020 8866 5460
Daughters of Charity, 43 High Street, Pinner HA5 5PJ Tel: 020 8866 4442
The Grail Secular Institute 125 Waxwell Lane, Pinner, Middx HA5 3ER
Tel: 020 8866 2195 Fax 020 8866 1408 E-mail: WAXWELL@compuserve.com

POLISH CHURCH 1 + OUR LADY OF CZESTOCHOWA A

2 Devonia Road N1 8JJ Tel: 020 7226 9944 Fax 020 7359 8042
E-mail: polishchurch1@rcdow.org.uk *Near Angel station* ***(Islington Deanery)*** (1905; 1930)
Mgr Tadeusz Kukla **Vicar Delegate & Parish Priest**;
Fr Wlodzimierz Skoczen;; Fr Stanislaw Wachala
Services Sun, M (Sat 6pm), 9, 11, 12.30, 3.30, 7pm. Hds, M 9, 11am, 7pm.
Wkds, M Mon - Fri 10.30am, 7pm, Sat 7.30am Conf before Mass.
Polish Catholic Mission, 2 Devonia Road N1 8JJ Tel: 020 7226 3439 Fax 020 7226 7677
Secretary Fr Krzysztof Kawczynski
PA Mrs Grazyna Sikora-Sikorski

POLISH CHURCH 2 + ST ANDREW BOBOLA A

I Leysfield Rd W12 9JF
Tel: 020 8743 8848/020 8740 5862 *(Hammersmith & Fulham)* (1961)
Mgr Bronislaw Gostomski; Fr Grzegorz Kudlak
Services Sun, M (Sat 6pm), 9, 10.30, 12 (sung), 5pm.
Hds, M 10am, 7pm.
Wkds, M 10, 7pm. Conf: wkds 9.30 to 10, 6.30 to 7pm; Sat 5 to 6pm.

POLISH CHURCH 3 + OUR LADY MOTHER OF THE CHURCH ♿

2 Windsor Road W5 5PD
Tel: 020 8567 1746 Fax: 020 8810 0185 *(Ealing Deanery)* (1986)
E-mail: parafiaealingmic@yahoo.co.uk
Marian Fathers (MIC)
Fr Krzysztof Wojcieszak; Fr Pawel Nawalaniec **Superior**;
Fr Dariusz Kwiatkowski, Fr Tadeusz Wyszomierski; Fr Mariusz Jarzabek
Services Sun, M (Sat 7.30pm), 9, 10.15,(Family) 11.30, 1pm, 5.15 (Youth) 7pm. (Youth)
Wkds M 8 (Latin), 10, 7.30pm.
Polish Catholic Centre (POK)
1 Courtfield Gardens W13 0EY M Sun 10.15.
Sisters of the Resurrection, 84 Gordon Road W5 2AR
Tel: 020 8998 8954 M Mon-Fri 7.30am
Sisters of the Holy Name of Jesus, 57 Mount Park Road W5 2PU
Tel: 020 8997 2030 M Sat 5pm
Kolbe House (for elderly people) **18 Hanger Lane W5 3HH**
Tel: 020 8992 4978 M Sun 10

PONDERS END + CHURCH OF MARY, MOTHER OF GOD ♿ A

192 Nags Head Road, Ponders End, Enfield, Middx EN3 7AR
Tel: 020 8804 2149 Fax: 020 8804 2749 (1912; 1921; cons 8 9 1985) *(Enfield Deanery)*
E-mail: pondersend@rcdow.org.uk
Fr John B. Shewring
Mobile: 07973 539907
Catechetical Co-ordinator Cora Coman
Tel: 020 8804 2149/020 8805 4134 (Home)
Services Sun, M (Sat 6pm), 8, 9.30 (Family), 11 (Sung), 12,30 (Italian), 6pm.
Hds, M 9.30am, 12.30, 8pm.
Wkds, M Mon, Tue, Thurs, Fri 9.15; also Tues & Fri 7.30pm, Conf: Sat 4.30-5.30pm.
Ecumenical Contact Rose Tonkin **Justice and Peace Contact** Parish Priest
Italian Catholic Centre, Mgr Agostino Gonella
Suore Collegine della Sacra Famiglia, 197 Durants Road, Enfield, Middx EN3 7DE
Tel: 020 8804 2307

POPLAR + SS MARY AND JOSEPH

Clergy House, 9 Pekin Street E14 6EZ Tel: 020 7987 4523 Fax 020 7538 4810
E-mail: poplar@rcdow.org.uk Website: www. rcdow.org.uk/poplar/
Canton Street (Tower Hamlets Deanery) (1816; 1856; 1954; new church cons 12 Oct 1960)
also in residence Fr Philip Miller **Tel: 020 7531 6956**
Chaplain Royal London & St Bartholomew's Hospitals;
Pastoral Assistant Sr Christine FCJ **Tel: 020 7987 0257**
Services Sun, M (Sat 6pm), 8, 10.30. Hds, M 10, 8pm. Wkds, M as announced.
Conf 10-10.30am, 6-6.30pm
Ecumenical Contact Sr Christine Frost **Justice & Peace** Parish Priest
Faithful Companions of Jesus, Pope John House, Hale Street E14 0BS
Tel: 020 7517 9599 Sr M Victoire Ashby; Sr Helen Downe; Sr Christine Frost;
Sr Martina Ryan; Sr Alice Sheridan
Sisters of the Assumption, 47 Bazely Street E14 0ES Tel: 020 7515 8944
Sr Simon Catlin; Sr Elizabeth Eyston; Sr Victoria Hummell; Sr Sylvia Swift
Sisters of Mercy, 9 Mountague Place E14 0EX Tel: 020 7987 2275

POTTERS BAR + OUR LADY & ST VINCENT

243 Mutton Lane, Potters Bar, Herts EN6 2AT
Tel: 01707 654359 Fax: 01707 658139
E-mail: pottersbar@rcdow.org.uk Website: www.ourladyandstvincent.co.uk
(Hatfield Deanery)
Fr Timothy O'Connor
Catechetical Co-ordinator Mrs Kate Daynes **Administrator** Mrs Bernadette Saunders
Services Sun, M (Sat 6pm), 9am (CW), 11am (venue tba);
Hds, Wkds & Conf as announced.
Ecumenical Contact Mrs Lindsey Huntley **Tel: 01707 654437**
Justice & Peace Contact Gerald Clark **Tel: 01707 657404**
Potters Bar District Hospital

PRISON SERVICE

Horseferry House, Room 625, Dean Ryle Street SW1P 2AW Tel: 020 7217 8714
Principal RC Chaplain Fr Malachy Keegan
Bovingdon: The Mount, HM Prison
Chaplain Fr Peter Grant **Tel: 01442 836300**
Feltham: HM Young Offenders Institution and Remand Centre
Chaplains Fr Roger Reader, Sr Monica Killeen **Tel: 020 8844 5326**
Holloway: HM Prison Chaplain Sr Kathleen Diamond **Tel: 020 7979 4400**
Pentonville: HM Prison Chaplain Rev Charlie Bianco **Tel: 020 7023 7000**
Wormwood Scrubs: HM Prison Chaplain Ms Helen Balby **Tel: 020 8588 3618**
Bronzefield: HM Prison Chaplain Mrs Kathleen Coates **Tel: 01784 425690**

PUCKERIDGE SEE OLD HALL GREEN

QUEENSWAY + OUR LADY, QUEEN OF HEAVEN ♿ ⧄

4a Inverness Place W2 3JF Tel: 020 7229 8153
E-mail: queensway@rcdow.org.uk
Queensway, opp Bayswater stn; close Queensway stn ***(North Kensington Deanery)*** (1954; 1973; cons 21 04. 02)
Fr Terence McGuckin
Services Sun, M (Sat 5.30pm), 8, 10, 11.30, 4.30pm.
Sun 1pm Ethiopian (Gheez rite). Hds, M 9.30am, 6.30pm.
Wkds, M as announced. Conf: Sat 6.30pm & on request
Ecumenical Contact Parish Priest
Justice and Peace Contact Parish Priest
Prelature of Opus Dei, 4 Orme Court W2 4RL
Tel: 020 7229 7574 Mgr Nicholas Morrish (Regional Vicar);
Fr Stefan Hnylycia; Fr Bernard Marsh; Fr Paul Hayward; Fr Joseph Gabiola

RADLETT + ST ANTHONY OF PADUA ⧄

22 The Crosspath, Radlett, Herts WD7 8HN
Tel/Fax 01923 856165
E-mail: radlett@rcdow.org.uk Website: www.rcdow.org.uk/radlett/
(St Albans Deanery) (1905; new church 1910)
Fr Richard de Lord
Services Sun, M (Sat 6pm), 8.30, 10.30, 6pm.
Hds, M 10, 8pm. Wkds, M 10. Conf: Sat 10.30-11.
Ecumenical Contact Peter Moss **Tel: 01923 854255**
Justice & Peace Tony Barter **Tel: 01923 856846**

REDBOURN + ST JOHN FISHER ⧄ ♿

1 Peppard Close, Redbourn, St Albans, Herts AL3 7EB Tel: 01582 792270
E-mail: redbourn@rcdow.org.uk
Dunstable Road North of the village on the old A5. ***(St Albans)*** (1936; 1967; cons 22 June 2003)
Fr Neil Reynolds
Services Sun, M (Sat 6.30pm), 10.15a m, 6.30pm. Hds, M 9.15am, 7.30pm
Wkds, M as announced Conf: Sat 10-10.30, 5.45-6.15pm
Ecumenical Contact Parish Priest
Justice and Peace Contact Parish Priest

REGENTS PARK, NW1 SEE LAXTON PLACE

RICKMANSWORTH + OUR LADY HELP OF CHRISTIANS ♿ ⊡

5 Park Road, Rickmansworth, Herts WD3 1HU
Tel: 01923 773387;
Mobile (after 10.30am) 07885 670483   E-mail: rickmansworth@rcdow.org.uk
On main road beside roundabout at bottom of Scots Hill (east end of High Street) ***(Watford Deanery)*** (1886; 1910)
Fr Jim Duffy
Services Sun, M (Sat 6.30pm), 8.30, 10.30 (Sung), 6.30pm (Folk).
Hds, M (Eve 8), 9.30, 8pm. Wkds, M Mon-Fri 9.30. Conf: Sat 11.30-12.15
Ecumenical Contact Justin Quinn **Tel: 01923 772039**
Justice & Peace Vincent Turner **Tel: 239833**
Daughters of Jesus, Blakenhall, 55 Nightingale Road, Rickmansworth WD3 7BU
Tel: 01923 773948
Housetop Centre 111A High Street, Rickmansworth WD3 1AN
Tel: 01923 779446 Fax: 01923 779447

RICKMANSWORTH ST JOHN THE EVANGELIST, MILL END. SEE MILL END

ROYSTON + ST THOMAS OF CANTERBURY AND THE ENGLISH MARTYRS ⊡ A

6 Melbourn Road, Royston, Herts SG8 7DB
Tel: 01763 243117 Fax: 01763 242891
E- mail: royston@rcdow.org.uk Website: www.rcdow.org.uk/royston/
Left side of A10 just beyond central roundabout, towards Cambridge ***(Stevenage Deanery)*** (1911; 1917)
Fr Seamus McGeoghan
Services Sun, M (Sat 6.30pm), 9, 10.30am. Hds, M 9.15am, 8pm.
Wkds, M Mon-Fri 9.15am. Conf: Sat 5.45 to 6.15pm.
Ecumenical Contact Gabriella Stables **Tel: 01763 241522**
Justice & Peace Contact Parish Priest
Royston Cottage Hospital

RUISLIP + MOST SACRED HEART ♿ ⊡

73 Pembroke Road, Ruislip, Middx HA4 8NN
Tel: 01895 632739
E-mail: ruislip@rcdow.org.uk Website: www.mostsacredheartruislip.co.uk
Ruislip Manor, nr traffic lights. Nr Ruislip Manor stn; 1/3 mile Ruislip stn ***(Hillingdon Deanery)*** (1921; 1939)
Fr Michael Johnston; Fr Mark Vickers
Services Sun, M (Sat 6pm), 8.30, 10 (Family), 11.30 (Sung), 6pm.
Hds, M (Eve 8pm), 10am, 8pm. Wkds, M 10, Exp Mon-Sat 10.30 to 12.
Conf: Sat 10.30-11.30, 5.15pm-5.30pm
Ecumenical Contact Catherine Wloch
Justice & Peace Contact Robert Nunn **Tel: 01895 677902**

RUISLIP SOUTH + ST GREGORY THE GREAT A

447 Victoria Road, South Ruislip, Middx HA4 0EG Tel: 020 8845 2186
E-mail: ruislipsouth@rcdow.org.uk Website: www.rcdow.org.uk/ruislipsouth/
Corner of Angus Drive (nr South Ruislip shops/stn). ***(Hillingdon Deanery)*** (1958; 1967; cons 01.11.75)
Fr Dennis Touw
Services Sun, M (Sat 5.30pm), 10 (Sung), 6pm. Hds, M 10am, 8pm
Wkds M 10am (except Thur) Conf: Sat 10.30 - 11.30am, 6.30 - 7pm
Ecumenical Contact Parish Priest **Justice and Peace Contact** Parish Priest

ST ALBANS + SS ALBAN AND STEPHEN A

14 Beaconsfield Road, St Albans, Herts AL1 3RB Tel: 01727 853585 Fax 01727 855410
E-mail: alban_stephen@lineone.net Website: www.albanstephen.com
Close to St Albans City stn. ***(St Albans Deanery)*** (1840; 1904; cons 1977)
Missionaries of the Sacred Heart (MSC)
Fr Patrick Courtney (Parish Priest); Fr Jerry Daly; Fr Manus Ferry
Services Sun, M (Sat 6pm), 8, 10, 12, 7pm. Hds, M (Eve 7.30pm), 9, 11, 7.30pm.
Wkds, M Mon to Sat 10. Conf: Sat 10.30 - 11.30, 6.45 - 7pm.
Ecumenical Contacts Mario and Joan D'Andrea **Tel: 01727 765625**
Justice and Peace Contact Parish Priest
Mass Centre Marshalswick (St John Fisher School), Sun, M 9am. Hds (school term), M 2.40pm.
Sisters of Mercy, Maryland, Townsend Drive Tel: 01727 858745. (Sun, M 9. Hds, M 9)
Home for Elderly Ladies **Tel: 01727 865568**
IBVM (Loreto Sisters), 5 Bedford Park Road AL1 3RS Tel: 01727 858266;
also **3/4 Bedford Park Road Tel: 01727 853144**

ST ALBANS SOUTH + ST BARTHOLOMEW

47 Vesta Avenue, St Albans, Herts AL1 2PE Tel: 01727 850066 Fax: 01727 812191
E-mail: stalbanssouth@rcdow.org.uk Website: www. rcdow.org.uk/stalbanssouth/
On Watling St (A5183) just above the North Orbital Rd/M10 rdt. ***(St Albans Deanery)*** (1959; cons 1985)
Administrator Fr Tim Edgar
Parish Team Sr Margaret, Sr Mary, Mrs Barbara Bliss
Services Sun, M (Sat 6pm), 8.30, 10.30. Hds, M as advertised
Wkds, M Mon 2.45pm; Tue 7pm (novena); Wed, Sat 9; Fri 12 (in St Albans Abbey).
Thurs 9am Euch Serv. Conf: Sat 9.30. & by appt.
Ecumenical Contact Joan Walker **Tel: 01582 460999**
Justice and Peace Contact Parish Priest
Brothers of the Sacred Heart, Watling Hse, 8 King Harry Lane AL3 4AW Tel: 01727 861969
Brs Donald Tardiff **Superior**; Clement Pelletier; Denis Bessette, Roy Pinnette;
Paul Vaillan Court ;Leo Labbe;Richard Roy, Antoine Coly; Ian Lane
Sisters of Mercy, 45 Vesta Avenue, St Albans, Herts AL1 2PE

ST CHARLES SQUARE (NORTH KENSINGTON) + ST PIUS X

79 St Charles Square W10 6EB Tel: 020 8969 6844
E-mail: stcharlessquare@rcdow.org.uk
West side of Ladbroke Grove, just north of stn & motorway bridge. ***(North Kensington Deanery)*** (1937; 1955)
Fr Marcus Winter.
(Also in residence Fr Anthony Baxter (Heythrop College). **Tel: 020 8968 6446**)
Services Sun, M (Sat 6pm), 8, 10, 12
Hds, M 8.20, 12.30 Wkds, M Mon to Fri 8.20. MP Mon-Fri 8.05
Conf: Sat 5.15 to 5.45pm.
Ecumenical Contact Michael Jeans **Justice and Peace Contact** Vanessa Davies
Princess Louise Hospital; St Charles Hospital; Pembridge Unit.
Carmelite Nuns, Monastery of the Most Holy Trinity, 87 St Charles Square W10 6EA
Tel: 020 8969 8702 M, daily 8.15am except Mon & Fri at 5.30pm
Society of the Sacred Heart, 16 Lawrence Terrace W10 5SX Tel: 020 8969 4160
Little Sisters of Jesus, 13 Wheatstone House, Telford Road W10 5XT Tel: 020 8960 0440

ST JOHN'S WOOD + OUR LADY A

54 Lodge Road NW8 8LA Tel: 020 7286 3214/020 7432 1350 Fax: 020 7266 5859
E-mail: stjohnswood@rcdow.org.uk Website: www.rcdow.org.uk/stjohnswood/
Top Lisson Grove, close junct St John's Wood Rd (Lords). ***(Marylebone Deanery)*** (1833; 1836; cons 14.5.25)
Fr Colin Davies;
also in residence Fr Richard Sloan; Canon John McDonald **Parish Sister** Sr Brigid Collins
Services Sun, M (Sat 6pm), 8, 9.30 (Family), 10.45 (sung Latin), 12, 6pm (Folk).
Hds, M (Eve 6pm), 10, 7.30pm Wkds, M 10, 6pm. Conf: Sat 10.30 to 11am, 5 to 6pm
Exp & B Sat 5 to 5.45pm.
Ecumenical Contact Parish Priest **Justice and Peace Contact** Priscilla Sharp
Wellington Hospital
Hospital of St John & St Elizabeth, 60 Grove End Road NW8 9NH
Chaplain Canon John McDonald
Tel: 020 7286 5126 Church of St John of Jerusalem M Sun 11; Hds 12.15.
Order of Malta (Grand Priory of England), Brampton House,
60 Grove End Road NW8 9NH Tel: 020 7586 3179
Sisters of Mercy, 39 Alma Square NW8 9PY Tel: 020 7289 3657
also **54 Lodge Road, NW8 8LA Tel: 020 7286 6387** Sr Brigid Collins
Handmaids of the Sacred Heart of Jesus, + Our Lady, Queen of the World,
25 St Edmund's Terrace NW8 7PY Tel: 020 7722 2756
M, Sat & Sun, 9. Hds & Wkds, M 8. Exp daily until 5.30pm.
Carmelite Missionaries, 189 Gloucester Place NW1 Tel: 020 7262 4737; Hostel 020 7723 1919
Sr Ma. Isabel Hualde; Sr Margarita Marques; Sr Orfilia Ospina; Sr Jovita Protazio;
Sr Seong-Hee (Agape); Sr Rya Jenelle S Bueno
Redemptoris Mater House of Formation, St Edward's Convent, 11 Harewood Ave NW1 6LD
Tel: 020 7723 9364 Fax: 07092 356013 E-mail: rmlondon@onetel.com Fr Francesco Donega

ST MARGARETS-ON-THAMES + ST MARGARET OF SCOTLAND ♿

130 St Margarets Road, East Twickenham, Middx TW1 1RL
Tel: 020 8892 3902
Fax: 020 8607 9001
E-mail: stmargaretsonthames@rcdow.org.uk or st.margarets@btconnect.com
Website: www. stmargaretsrctwickenham.co.uk
Opp St Margarets stn (BR); close Chertsey Rd (A316) Richmond Road (A305)
(Upper Thames Deanery) (1930; 1969)
Canon John Formby.
Also in residence Fr Christopher Gawecki **(Hillingdon Hospital)**
Pastoral Assistant Anne Reynolds
Services Sun, M (Sat 6.30pm), 8.30, 10.30, 6.30pm. Hds, M 7.15, 10, 8pm. Wkds, M 10.
Conf Sat 10.30 to 11am, after 6.30pm M on request.
Exp Thurs, Fri 11am-10pm.
Ecumenical Contact Steve Fabian **020 8744 0842**
Justice & Peace Judith Burman **020 8940 4600**
St John's Hospital, Lynde House, Dalemead Home

SAWBRIDGEWORTH, HERTS MOST HOLY REDEEMER, SAYESBURY ROAD A

The Priest House, Malting Lane, Much Hadham SG10 6AW
Tel: 01279 842354 *(Lee Valley Deanery)*
Fax: 01279 843844
E-mail: sawbridgeworth@rcdow.org.uk
Website: www. rcdow.org.uk/sawbridgeworth/
Fr Bob Styles SJ (also serves Much Hadham)
Services Sun, M (Sat 6pm), 9.30am Hds, M 12.30, 8pm.
Wkd M Wed & Fri 12.30pm
Ecumenical Contact Karin Keddy **Tel: 01279 723606**
Justice & Peace Contact Eugene Keddy

SHENLEY + THE GOOD SHEPHERD A

Catholic Church, Black Lion Hill, Shenley, Herts WD7 9DH
Tel/Fax: 01923 857005
E-mail: shenley@rcdow.org.uk *(St Albans Deanery)* (1969; 1976)
Fr Edward Carroll
Services Sun, M (Sat 6.30), 9, 11.
Hds, M (Eve 6pm) 9.30, 7.30pm.
Wkds, M Mon, Wed, Thu 9.30; Tues 9am, Fri 6pm, Sat 10am.
Conf Sat 10.45-11.15
Ecumenical Contact Mrs Simone Brew **Tel: 01923 852440**

SHEPHERDS BUSH + THE HOLY GHOST AND ST STEPHEN A

44 Ashchurch Grove W12 9BU Tel: 020 8743 5196 ***(Hammersmith & Fulham Deanery)***
E-mail: shepherdsbush@rcdow.org.uk (1889; 1904; cons April 24, 1936)
Off Askew Road, near jn with Goldhawk Road. Underground: Stamford Brook.
Fr John Whooley
Sister Joanne Whooley
Services Sun, M (Sat 6pm), 9.15, 11 (Family), 12.30, 7pm. Hds, M (Eve 8pm), 9.30, 7pm.
Wkds, M Mon, Tue, Wed, Fri, Sat 9.30am, Mon Thurs & 1st Fri also at 7pm.
Conf: Sat 10.00 to 11.00, 5.15 to 5.45pm. Exp Mon-Fri 8-9am, Sat 10-11am (B 10.45)
Ecumenical Contact Parish Priest **Justice and Peace Contact** Parish Priest
Sisters of the Sacred Heart of Mary, 37 Hadyn Park Road W12 9AQ
Tel: 020 8743 0279 Sr Barbara Bailey; Sr Celine Murphy; Sr Martin Murray
Franciscan Missionaries of Mary, Provincialate, 5 Vaughan Avenue W6 0XS Tel: 020 8748 4077
Sisters of Our Lady of Charity, 14 Dorville Crescent W6 OHJ Tel: 020 8748 4793
Augustinians (OSA) 15 Dorville Crescent W6 0HH Tel: 020 8741 7586 Community
Provincial Office Tel/Fax: 020 8748 1529 E-mail: augprov.engscot@btinternet.com
Provincial Fr Paul Graham; Fr Fionan Columba Heffernan; William Faix
Ravenscourt Park Hospital

SHEPPERTON + ST JOHN FISHER

15 Wood Road, Shepperton, Middx TW17 0DH
Tel:01932 563116 Fax: 01932 567578
E-mail: shepperton@rcdow.org.uk Website: www.rcdow.org.uk/shepperton
In Shepperton Green (sign on Shepperton-Staines road) ***(Upper Thames Deanery)*** (1936; 1965)
Fr Dominic Byrne
Services Sun, M (Sat 6pm), 8.30, 10.30 (Children's: Ist Sun; Youth: 3rd Sun).
Hds, M 6.30pm. Wkds, M as announced. Conf: Sat 5.30pm.
Ecumenical Contact Ron Colnbrook **Tel: 01932 222604** **Justice & Peace** Parish Priest

SOHO SQUARE + ST PATRICK

21a Soho Square W1D 4NR Tel: 020 7437 2010
In angle of Oxford St/Charing Cross Rd (Tottenham Court Rd stn). ***(Westminster Deanery)*** (1792; 1893)
E-mail: sohosquare@rcdow.org.uk Website: www.rcdow.org.uk/sohosquare/
Fr Alexander Sherbrooke **Parish Sister** Sr Dympna Bermingham SMG
Services Sun, M (Sat 6pm), 8, 11, 2.15pm (Cantonese), 5pm, 6pm (Spanish).
Hds M 8, 12.30, 1.05pm, 6pm. Wkds, M Mon to Fri 12.45. Exp Mon-Fri 11-12.30pm,
1.30-6pm, Sat 7.30pm-9pm Conf: Mon-Fri 12 to 12.40pm; Sat 5.30 to 6pm
Ecumenical Contact Parish Priest **Justice and Peace Contact** Parish Priest
Chinese Catholic Centre, 21a Soho Square Tel: 020 7439 1878 Fr Eddie Woo
St Patrick's School of Evangelisation Tel: 020 7434 9965
SOS Prayer Line Tel: 020 7434 9211

SOMERS TOWN + ST ALOYSIUS A

20 Phoenix Road NW1 1TA Tel: 020 7387 1971
E-mail: somerstown@rcdow.org.uk
Off Eversholt St, East of Euston station ***(Camden Deanery)*** (1798; 1808; 1968; cons 24 May 1992)
Fr James McNicholas.
Parish Sister Sr Ambrose Stafford SMG
Services Sun, M (Sat 6pm), 8.30, 10.30, 12.15pm, 6pm.
Hds, M 9.30, 12.30, 6pm. Wkds, M 12.30, 6pm. Conf: Sat 11.30-12, 5-5.30pm.
Ecumenical Contact Parish Priest
Justice & Peace Parish Priest
St Pancras Hospital
Faithful Companions of Jesus, St Aloysius Convent, 32 Phoenix Road NW1 1TA
Tel: 020 7387 7174 E-mail: somerstownfcj@btinternet.com Website: fcjsisters.org
Sr Una Conran; Sr Margaret Crank; Sr Madeline Cuddy; Sr Margarita Byron;
Sr Maura Foley; Sr Cecilia Connolly; Sr M Philomena Lyons
Servants of the Mother of God, 70-71 Euston Square NW1 1DJ
Tel: 020 7387 5855
Sr Dympna Bermingham; Sr Monica Clifford; Sr Julia Howard; Sr Ambrose Stafford;
Sr Margaret Farragher
Consolata Missionary Sisters, 11 Regent Square WC1H 8HZ
Tel: 020 7837 2256

SOUTHALL + ST ANSELM

St Anselm's Rectory, The Green, Southall, Middx UB2 4BE
Tel: 020 8574 3300
Fax: 020 8813 8784
E-mail: southall@rcdow.org.uk Website: rcdow.org.uk/southall/
To the south of Southall stn (BR), next to Phoenix House. ***(Ealing Deanery)*** (1906; 1930; 1968)
Fr James Crampsey SJ; Fr Gerard Hassay SJ; Fr Kevin Fox SJ
Services Sun, M (Sat 6.30pm), 9, 11, 6.30pm. Hds, M 9.15, 12.15, 7.30pm.
Wkds M Mon-Fri 9.15.
Conf: Sat 11-12, after evng M. .Nov Sun 5.30pm. HH Sun 4.30pm.
Ecumenical Contact Jacinta Fox
Justice and Peace Contact Ann Dolan
Missionaries of Charity, 41 Villiers Road, Southall, Middx UB1 3BS
Tel: 020 8574 1892
Brothers of St Gabriel, 2 Church Avenue, Southall, Middx UB2 4DH
Tel: 020 8843 0690
Society of Jesus, 6 Osterley Park Road, Southall, Middx UB2 4BL
Tel: 020 8571 1833
Fr Michael Barnes; Fr Patrick Purnell; Fr Damian Howard

SPANISH PLACE + ST JAMES ☑

22 George Street W1U 3QY Tel: 020 7935 0943
E-mail: spanishplace@rcdow.org.uk Website: www.rcdow.org.uk/spanishplace/
Off Baker St (East); Underground Baker St or Bond St ***(Marylebone Deanery)*** (1791; 1890; cons 28.4.49)
Fr Terence Phipps. Also in residence: Fr Nicholas Kavanagh; Fr Lule Ssennyondo
Services Sun, M (Sat 6pm), 8.30, 9.30 (Tridentine), 10.30 (sung Latin), 12, 4pm, 7pm.
Hds M 7.15, 11 (Tridentine), 12.30, 6pm. Wkds, M 7.15, 12.30, 6pm (Sat 10).
Conf Mon - Fri 12 - 1pm; Sat 10.30 - 12, 5 - 5.45pm, & at call. HH Sat 4.45pm.
London Clinic; King Edward VII Hospital for Officers;
Harley Street Clinic; Princess Grace Hospital;
Heart Hospital Chaplain Fr Peter Harries OP See separate entry **Hospitals**
Society of the Holy Child Jesus, 8 Deans Mews, Cavendish Square W1G 9EE
Tel: 020 7580 4102 E-mail: PHUSSEY952@aol.com

SPITALFIELDS, E1 SEE UNDERWOOD ROAD

STAINES + OUR LADY OF THE ROSARY ♿ ☑

The Presbytery, 59 Gresham Road, Staines, Middx TW18 2BD
Tel/Fax: 01784 452381 E-mail: staines@rcdow.org.uk
Nr Staines stn (BR), opp footbridge ***(Upper Thames Deanery)*** (1890; 1932)
Fr Saviour Grech
Services Sun, M Sun (Sat 6.30pm) 9, 11 (Family)
Hds, M 9.15, 7.30pm. Wkds, M 9.15, Sat 10.30. Conf: Sat 11 - 11.30, 5.30 - 6
Ecumenical Contact Joan Willett **Tel: 01784 246375**
Justice and Peace Contact Parish Priest

STAMFORD HILL + ST IGNATIUS ♿ ☑ S

27 High Road N15 6ND Tel: 020 8800 2121 Fax: 020 8802 8102
E-mail: stamfordhill@rcdow.org.uk *Corner of (A10) & St Ann's Rd* ***(Haringey Deanery)*** (1894; 1903)
Jesuits (SJ) Fr Timothy Curtis; Fr Paul Fletcher **Superior Tel: 1800 2020 8442 5231** *typetalk*
Fr Bernard Charles; also in residence Fr Bernard Parkin; Fr John Moffatt;
Fr Michael Bossy; Fr Peter Scally; Br Francis Fitzsimmons; Br Franc Pregelj
Catechetical Co-ordinator Mrs Ann Murphy
Social Outreach Co-Ordinator Sr Winifred Lusk
Services Sun, M (Sat 7pm), 8.30, 10 (Family), 11.30 (sung), 4.30pm (Spanish) 7pm.
Hds, M 10, 7.30pm. Wkds, M 10am, 6.30pm Conf: Sat 10.30 to 11, 6 to 6.45pm.
Ecumenical Contact Parish Priest **Justice and Peace Contact** Sr Ellen Corbett
Servite Sisters, St Mary's Convent, 90 Suffolk Road N15 5RH Tel: 020 8800 2940
Ursulines of Jesus, 11 Amhurst Park N16 5DH Tel: 020 8800 4486 (Community),
020 8802 0256 (Provincialate); also **149 Bethune Road N16 5DY Tel: 020 8800 4623**

STANMORE + ST WILLIAM OF YORK

1 Du Cros Drive, Stanmore, Middx HA7 4TJ Tel: 020 8954 1299
E-mail: stanmore@rcdow.org.uk
Off Marsh Lane, quarter-mile south of The Broadway. *(Harrow Deanery)* (1938; 1960)
Fr Daniel Magnier
Services Sun, M (Sat 6pm), 8, 10 Hds, M 9, 7pm.
Wkds, M Mon-Wed & Sat 9am, Fri 7pm. Conf: Sat 10-10.30am.
Royal National Orthopaedic Hospital; Princess Alexandra & Woodland Hall Homes

STANWELL + ST DAVID

St David's, Everest Rd, Stanwell, Staines, Middx TW19 7EE Tel/Fax: 01784 255973
E-mail: stanwell@rcdow.org.uk *(Upper Thames Deanery)* (1964; 1967)
Administrator Fr Ken Rimini
Services Sun, M (Sat 6pm), 10. Hds, M (Eve 7.30pm), 9.30am.
Wds M 9.30am Mon, Wed, Thurs, Fri (School), Exp Fri 7.15-8pm Conf: Sat 5.15-5.45pm
Ecumenical and **Justice and Peace Contact** Administrator Ashford Hospital

STEPHENDALE ROAD + OUR LADY OF PERPETUAL HELP A

Parish House, 2 Tynemouth Street SW6 2QT
Tel: 020 7736 4864 Fax: 020 7384 3710 E-mail: stephendaleroad@rcdow.org.uk
Sand's End east of Wandsworth Bdge Rd, south of New King's Rd, north of Imperial Wharf
(Hammersmith & Fulham Deanery) (1922)
Fr Roger Kirinich
Administrator Mrs Margaret McMahon **Catechetical Co-ordinator** Mrs Sara Stothert
Services Sun, M (Sat 6.30pm), 9, 11. Hds, M 9, 7.30pm. Conf: Sat 6 - 6.15pm
Ecumenical Contact George Lawson **Justice and Peace Contact** Margaret McMahon

STEVENAGE BEDWELL + PIN GREEN

St Joseph's Presbytery, Bedwell Crescent, Stevenage, Herts SG1 1NJ
Tel/Fax: 01438 351243
E-mail: stevenagebedwell@rcdow.org.uk Website: www. stjosephrcstevenage.org.uk
Off roundabout linking Bedwell Crescent and Fairlands Way *(Stevenage Deanery)*
Fr Denis Watters
Parish Sister: Sr Geraldine OP Tel: 01438 351243
Services Sun, M 10, 6pm. Hds, M 9.15
Wkds, M as announced. Conf: Sat 9.30 to 10.
Ecumenical Contact Peter Towers Tel: 01438 357056
Justice & Peace Parish Priest

All Saints, The Oval, Pin Green (Shared Church) *Off Vardon Road (within Oval Community Centre)*
Services Sun, M (Sat 6pm), 12. Hds, M 11. Wkds, M as announced. Conf: Sat 5.30pm.

STEVENAGE OLD TOWN + SYMONDS GREEN A

4 Basils Road, Stevenage, Herts SG1 3PX Tel: 01438 226857
E-mail: stevenageoldtown@rcdow.org.uk
Off Church Lane, east of High St. ***(Stevenage Deanery)***
Fr Francis Leonard **Parish Sister** Sr Loretta Dooley OP
Transfiguration of Our Lord, Grove Road, Stevenage Old Town (1912; 1914).
Services Sun, M (Sat 6pm) 11am Hds, M 10.30am
Wkds, M as announced. Conf: Sat 11 to 11.30.
Ecumenical Contact Alan Bruce
Justice and Peace Contact Hannah Wright

Christ the King, Filey Close, Symonds Green (Shared Church)
Enter from Scarborough Avenue (next to Community Centre)
Services Sun, M 9. Hds, M (Eve 7.30pm). Wkds, M as announced.
Lister Hospital Chaplain Sister Marian Davey **Tel: 01438 314333 ext 5518**
Sisters of Charity of Jesus and Mary, 3 Hitchin Road, Stevenage, Herts SG1 3BJ
Tel: 01438 354247 Fax: 01438 365277 Sr Mary Catherine Callaghan

STEVENAGE SHEPHALL + ST HILDA A

9 Breakspear, Stevenage, Herts SG2 9SQ Tel/Fax: 01438 352182
E-mail: stevenageshephall@rcdow.org.uk ***(Stevenage Deanery)*** (1958)
Fr John Ablewhite
Services Sun, M (Sat 6.30pm), 9.30, 11. Hds, M 9.30, 8pm
Wkds, M Mon, Tue, Fri, Sat 9.30; Thu 8pm. Exp Fri 10-11.
Conf: Sat 11, 5.45pm.
Ecumenical Contact Parish Priest
Justice and Peace Contact Parish Priest

STOKE NEWINGTON + OUR LADY OF GOOD COUNSEL

Presbytery, Bouverie Road N16 0AJ Tel: 020 8800 5250
E-mail: stokenewington@rcdow.org.uk ***(Hackney Deanery)*** (1882; 1936; 1976)
Fr Michael Mannion; also in residence Fr Athanasio Dzadagu
Parish Sisters Sisters of Charity (of St Jeanne Antide).
Services Sun, M (Sat 6.30pm), 9, 10.30, 12, 6.30pm.
Hds, M 10, 7.30pm.
Wkds, M Mon-Thu 10, Fri 6.30pm (followed by Marian devotions).
Conf: Sat 11.30 to 12. Zimbabwean M 2pm. HH, 1st Sat 12noon
Ecumenical Contact Parish Priest
Justice and Peace Contact Parish Priest
Sisters of Charity of St Jeanne Antide, 'Bethany', 53 Bethune Road N16
Tel: 020 8802 3430 Sr M Bernadette; Sr Margaret Mary; Sr M Letizia

STONEBRIDGE + THE FIVE PRECIOUS WOUNDS A

The Presbytery, Brentfield Road NW10 8ER
Tel/Fax 020 8965 3313
E-mail: stonebridge@rcdow.org.uk
Off Harrow Road (A404), quarter mile east of junction with North Circular Road
(Brent Deanery) (1926; 1957)
Fr Michael O'Doherty (resident at Neasden); Fr Paul Brophy.
Also in residence Fr Patrick Obike
Services Sun, M (Sat 6pm), 10 (sung), 12 (Family) Hds, M 10am, 7pm
Wkds, M Mon to Fri 10. Conf: Sat 5-5.30pm
Justice and Peace Contact Parish Priest

STROUD GREEN + ST PETER-IN-CHAINS A

12 Womersley Road N8 9AE Tel: 020 8340 3394
Fax: 020 8347 9422 *(Haringey Deanery)* (1894; 1896)
E-mail: stroudgreen@rcdow.org.uk Website: www.stpeterinchains.com
Fr David Irwin
Services Sun, M (Sat 6.30pm), 9.45, (Sung) 11.15, (Family) 7pm.
Hds, M (Eve 7.30pm) 9, 12, 7.30pm.
EP & B 6pm Wkds, M 9 daily (Mon, Wed, Fri 7.30pm also). MP/Ep 15 mins before M
Conf Sat 9.30 to 10, 6 to 6.20pm. HH Sat 9.30-10.15am
Ecumenical Contact Parish Priest **Justice & Peace Contact** Sr Margaret Corbett
Sisters of Christian Instruction,
St Gildas's Convent, 26 Briston Grove N8 9EX Tel: 020 8340 7203
Sisters of Our Lady of Sion, 63 Mount View Road N4 4SR
Tel: 020 8340 0303
Sisters of Providence, 78 Oakfield Road N4 4LB Tel: 020 8340 1088

SUDBURY + ST GEORGE

970 Harrow Road, Sudbury, Wembley, Middx HA0 2QE Tel: 020 8904 2552
Fax: 020 8904 0744 E-mail: sudbury@rcdow.org.uk
Website: www.rcdow.org.uk/sudbury/
On corner of St Andrew's Avenue, east of Greenford Road / Sudbury Court Drive junction
(Brent Deanery) (1924; 1926; cons 18 April 1928)
Fr Tony Seeldrayers; Fr Chris Silva;
Secretary Mrs Margaret Simon
Services Sun, M (Sat 6.15pm), 8.30, 9.45 (Family), 11.15 (Sung), 5.30pm (Sung).
Hds, M 9.30, 8pm. Wkds, M 9.30. Conf: Sat 5.15 to 6pm.
Ecumenical Contact Henrietta Kalogroulis **Tel: 020 8422 4751**
Justice and Peace Contact Anne Nemeth **Tel: 020 8904 2991**
Wembley Hospital, Clementine Churchill Hospital

SUNBURY-ON-THAMES + ST IGNATIUS OF LOYOLA ♿ ☑

Catholic Rectory, Green Street, Sunbury-on-Thames, TW16 6QB
Tel: 01932 783507 Fax: 01932 779134 E-mail: sunburyonthames@rcdow.org.uk
Main road, south Sunbury stn/M3 interchange. ***(Upper Thames Deanery)*** (1862; 1869; cons 22.5.84)
Fr Michael Tuck **Parish Sister** Sr Liza Randall
Services Sun, M (Sat 6pm), 9.30, 11.15. Hds, M (Eve 8), 10, 8pm.
Wkds, M 10. Conf: Sat 11 & aft M
Ecumenical Contact Robert Widrig **Tel: 01932 783050**
Justice and Peace Colin Bennett **Tel: 020 8890 4160**
Sunbury Nursing Home; Ashton Lodge.

SWISS COTTAGE + ST THOMAS MORE ☑ A

Presbytery, Maresfield Gardens NW3 5SU
Tel: 020 7435 1388
E-mail: swisscottage@rcdow.org.uk
Off Fitzjohn's Ave, nr Swiss Cottage stn & gyratory system ***(Camden Deanery)*** (1938; 1968)
Fr Gerard Sheehan.
Also in residence Canon Peter Phillips **Tel: 020 7431 6192**
Services Sun, M 10, 12, 6.30pm. Hds, M 10, 7pm.
Wkds, M 10. Conf: Sat 10.30.
Ecumenical Contact Parish Priest
Justice and Peace Contact Parish Priest
Eden Hall Hospital.
Jesuits (SJ), Southwell House, 39 Fitzjohn's Avenue NW3 5JT
Tel: 020 7435 9794
Fr Christopher Pedley; Fr Joseph Duggan; Fr David Smolira; Bro Alan Harrison
Youth Project Tel: 020 7435 8534 Fax 020 7435 9133
E-mail: secretary@southwellhouse.com Website: www.southwellhouse.com
Fr Michael Smith
Netherhall House, Nutley Terrace NW3 5SA
Tel: 020 7435 8888
Hall of Residence for men University students.
Pastoral Care entrusted to the Prelature of Opus Dei.
Mgr Richard Stork; Fr Joseph Evans
Lakefield 41a Maresfield Gardens NW3 5RY Tel: 020 7433 3454
Catering and education centre. Pastoral Care entrusted to the Prelature of Opus Dei.
Congregation of Jesus (CJ), 49 Fitzjohn's Avenue NW3 6PG
Tel: 020 7794 4972 Fax: 020 7431 6118
Sr Ann Stafford **Superior**; Sr Baptist Kenny; Sr Gabriel Kenny; Sr Clare Goodman;
Sr Barbara Barry; Sr Maria Rochford; Sr Mary Ann Flood; Sr Patricia Harris;
Sr Elizabeth Aldworth; Sr Jude Bunn; Sr Gemma Simmonds

TEDDINGTON (& HAMPTON WICK) + THE SACRED HEART

262 Kingston Road, Teddington, Middx TW11 9JQ Tel: 020 8977 2986
E-mail: teddington@rcdow.org.uk Website: www.loguk.com/sacredheart
Fr John Deehan *(Upper Thames Deanery)* (1882; 1893; cons 14 June 1944)
Services Sun, M (Sat 6.30pm), 9.30 (Family), 11.15 Hds, M 9.30, 8pm. R, aft wkd M.
Ecumenical Contact Barbara MacMahon Tel: 020 8977 4965 **Justice & Peace** Parish Priest
Sons of Divine Providence (FDP), House of Our Lady of Westminster,
25 Lower Teddington Rd, Hampton Wick KT1 4HB Tel: 020 8977 5130
E-mail: philip@ckehoe.freeserve.co.uk Frs Philip Kehoe; Stephen Beale; Joseph Tirello.
St John's House, 7 Ferry Road (Group home for women with learning difficulties);
Orione House, 12 Station Road, Hampton Wick, Kingston-upon-Thames KT1 4EU
Tel: 020 8977 0754 (Home for older people)

TOLLINGTON PARK + ST MELLITUS

The Presbytery, St Mellitus Church, Tollington Park N4 3AG Tel: 020 7272 3415
Fax: 020 7263 2211 E-mail: tollingtonpark@rcdow.org.uk Website: www.stmellitus.org.uk/
Off Stroud Green Rd; north end Fonthill Rd. 5 mins Finsbury Park stn ***(Islington Deanery)*** (1925; 1959)
Fr David Ardagh-Walter
Services Sun, M (Sat 6.30pm),9.30, 11.30, 6.30pm. 2nd Sun 2pm M in Igbo, 1st & 3rd Sun 2pm M in French & Lingala. Hds, M (Eve 6.30pm), 9.30, 6.30pm.
Wkds, M Mon, Thu 9; Tue, Fri 9,6.30pm: Wed 9.30; Sat 10. Conf: Sat 10.30-11am, 6-6.20
Ecumenical Contact Parish Priest **Justice & Peace** Ms Jo Bownas Tel: 020 7263 1897

TOTTENHAM + ST FRANCIS DE SALES

729 High Road N17 8AG Tel: 020 8808 3554 Fax 020 8365 9709
E-mail: francis.de_sales@virgin.net *Main rd, opp Spurs gr* ***(Haringey Deanery)*** (1793; 1895)
Fr John Buckley; Fr Cruz Fernandes; Fr Lamont Phillips
Services Sun, M (Sat 7pm), 8.30, 10.30 (Family), 12, 7pm. Hds, M 9.30, 7.30pm.
Wkds, M 9.30; Sat 10 +R. & Exp. Conf: Sat 10.30 to 11.15, 6 to 6.45pm.
Sisters of Marie Auxiliatrice, 93 Mount Pleasant Road N17 8NG Tel: 020 8801 9883

TOTTENHAM (SOUTH) SEE STAMFORD HILL (WEST) SEE WEST GREEN

TOWER HILL + THE ENGLISH MARTYRS

30 Prescot Street E1 8BB Tel: 020 7488 4654 Fax: 020 7488 1418
E-mail: towerhill@rcdow.org.uk *Close to junction with Mansell St* ***(Tower Hamlets)*** (1865;1876)
Oblates of Mary Immaculate (OMI) Fr Malachy Sheehan
Services Sun, M (Sat 6.30), 9, 11. Hds, M (Eve 6.30pm) 9.30, 12, 1. Wkds, M Tue-Fri 1pm.
Ecumenical Contact Parish Priest **Justice and Peace Contact** Parish Priest

TRING + CORPUS CHRISTI

51 Langdon Street, Tring, Herts HP23 6BA Tel: 01442 823161 Fax: 01442 891983
E-mail: tring@rcdow.org.uk *(St Albans Deanery)* (1910; 1913; recons 2001)
Adminsitrator Fr Peter Grant **Parish Assistant** Wendy Hinds **Tel: 01442 824369**
Services Sun, M (Sat 6pm), 8.30, 10.30. Hds, M 12 & 8pm. Wkds as announced. Conf: Sat 10.15-11.
Ecumenical Contacts Wendy Hinds **(Tel above)** & Diana Bambridge **Tel: 01442 828633**

TWICKENHAM + ST JAMES A

61 Pope's Grove, Twickenham TW1 4JZ Website: www. st-james-twickenham.org.uk
Tel: 020 8892 4578 E-mail: twickenham@rcdow.org.uk
(Upper Thames Deanery) (1883; 1885; cons 23 7 1887)
Fr Ulick Loring
Services Sun M (Sat 6pm) 8, 10.30, 12.15. Hds M 9, 7.30pm. Wkds M 9. Conf: Sat 9.45-10.45
Presentation Brothers, 7 Waldegrave Gardens, Twickenham TW1 4PQ Tel: 020 8892 2870
Christian Brothers, 38 Strawberry Hill Rd, Twickenham TW1 4PU Tel: 020 8892 7472
Xaverian Bros 58 Bonsor Rd TW1 4RG Tel: 020 8287 3008 E-mail: cfxuk@lineone.net.uk
Sisters of Mercy 88 Pope's Grove, Twickenham, Middx Tel: 020 8744 2812
St Mary's College, Waldegrave Road, Strawberry Hill, Twickenham, Middx TW1 4SX
Chaplain Fr Gerard Devlin **Tel: 020 8240 4006 E-mail: devling@smuc.ac.uk**
Assistant Chaplain Ms Rebecca Walker **Tel: 020 8240 4002 E-mail: walkerr@smuc.ac.uk**
Chaplaincy Administrator Mrs Kerry Anzollitto **Tel: 020 8240 4331 Fax: 020 8255 6190**
M Sun 11all year & (Term time only 6pm), Hds M 1pm. Wds M 8.30, except Tues 12.15

TWICKENHAM (EAST) SEE ST MARGARET'S ON THAMES

UKRAINIAN CATHEDRAL + THE HOLY FAMILY IN EXILE

21 Binney St W1K 5BQ Tel: 020 7629 1534 *Duke St Off Oxford St, opp Selfridges* (1968) ***(Marylebone)***
E-mail: ukrainiancathedral@rcdow.org.uk **Apostolic Exarch** Bishop Paul Chomnycky OSBM
Cathedral Clergy Fr Moacyr Leczuk; Fr Emerson Spack **Ukrainian Exarchate: see Index**
Services Sun, M 10.30 (High). Hds, M 6pm. Wkds, M 7. Conf: bef M; at call.

UNDERWOOD ROAD + ST ANNE

St Anne's Church, Underwood Road E1 5AW Tel: 020 7247 7833 *Off Vallance Road*
E-mail: underwoodroad@rcdow.org.uk *(Tower Hamlets Deanery)* (1850/1855; cons 27.9.05)
Fr Frederico Ribeiro **Brazilian Chaplaincy**
Services Sun, M (Sat 6pm-English, 7pm-Portuguese), 10.30 (English); 12, 4, 7pm (Portuguese)
Hds, M 9.30, 7.30pm. Wkds, M Wed-Sat 9.30am, Tues 7.30pm Conf: Sat 5pm
Sisters of Mercy, McAuley House, 1 Gunthorpe Street E1 7RG Tel: 020 7247 4958
Srs Bernadette Glynn; Aine Kirwan; Anna Burke; Eileen Barry; Mairead McGinn; Lucy Fitzpatrick

UNIVERSITY CHAPLAINCY

Newman House, 111 Gower Street WC1E 6AR Tel: 020 7387 6370 (Chaplains & Admin) 020 7380 0776 and 020 7387 5455 (students) Fax 020 7388 6431
E-mail: enquiries@universitycatholic.net Web site: www.universitycatholic.net
Chaplains Fr Peter Wilson BA, H Dip Ed (Senior Chaplain)
E-mail: pjw@universitycatholic.net
Fr Robert Marsh OSA King's College, University College (Hoxton)
Tel: 020 7739 3203 E-mail: marshrk@hotmail.com
Fr Joseph Evans SOAS, Institute for Study of the Americas, Birkbeck College
Tel: 020 7472 5722 E-mail: soascathsoc@hotmail.com
Fr Iain Matthew OCD London School of Economics (Kensington 2)
Tel: 020 7937 9866 E-mail: ism@universitycatholic.net
Fr Brian Creak Queen Mary College (St Charles Square) E-mail: bcreak@mac.com
Fr Mark Barrett OSB (in residence) E-mail: markbarrett@cesmail.net
Catherine Cruz fmvd University of Westminster, Institute of Education, School of Pharmacy, London School of Hygiene & Tropical Medicine
E-mail: catherine@universitycatholic.net
Administrator Petronella Phillips-Devaney E-mail: ppd@universitycatholic.net
Receptionist Sr Brid Miley LSU E-mail: brid@universitycatholic.net
Chaplaincy Assistant: Chris Castell E-mail: chris@universitycatholic.net
M (Term only): Sun 10.30am, 7.30pm;
Hds 12:30pm, 5:30pm, 9pm. Wkds M Mon-Fri 5.30pm MP 8:30am EP: Mon-Fri 6pm
NP Mon-Fri 9pm; Sun 8.45pm

More House, 53 Cromwell Road SW7 2EH Chaplain Fr Geoff Wheaton SJ
Imperial College, Royal College of Art, Royal College of Music
Tel: 020 7584 2040 (Chaplains and Administration) E-mail: rcchaplainmore@aol.com
Fax: 020 7581 2040 Tel: 020 7589 8433 (Students)
M Sun 11am, 6pm (Term only); Mon - Fri 6pm, Sat 10am

Imperial College Medical School Chaplain: Fr Nigel Griffin

Heythrop College, Kensington Square W8 5HQ Tel: 020 7795 4215 Fax: 020 7795 4200
Chaplain Sr Bernie Devine SP E-mail: b.devine@heythrop.ac.uk

Goodenough College, Mecklenburgh Square WC1 2AB Tel: 020 7837 4147
Chaplain Fr Casimir Adjoe E-mail: casimir.adjoe@gmail.com M (Term only) Sun 9:45am

St Mary's College, Waldegrave Road, Strawberry Hill, Twickenham TW1 4SX
Chaplain Fr Gerard Devlin Tel: 020 8240 4006 Fax: 020 8255 6190
E-mail: devling@smuc.ac.uk Website: smuc.ac.uk
Assistant Chaplain Rebecca Walker Tel: 020 8240 4002 E-mail: walkerr@smuc.ac.uk
Administrator Mrs Kerry Anzollitto Tel: 020 8240 4331 E-mail: anzolitk@smuc.ac.uk
Sun M 11am (all year) 6pm (term only) Hds M 1pm, Wds 8.30am except Tues 12.15pm

UPPER HOLLOWAY + ST GABRIEL A

15 St John's Villas N19 3EE Tel: 020 7272 8195 Fax: 020 7687 2747
E-mail: upperholloway@rcdow.org.uk
Off Holloway Rd betw Upper Holloway stn (BR) & Archway stn (LT). ***(Islington Deanery)*** (1928; 1967)
Fr Kevin McDevitt; also in residence Fr Nigel Charles
Parish Sisters Sr Pauline Cogan; Sr Noreen Maye
Services Sun M (Sat 6pm), 9, 10,30, 12, 6pm. Hds M 12, 7.30pm.
Wkds, M 12, 7.30pm (Wed 12 only). Conf: Sat 11 to 11.45, 5 to 5.45pm. Exp FF 10-7.30
Ecumenical Contact Parish Priest **Justice and Peace Contact** Rachel McGonagle
Marist Sisters, 17 St John's Villas N19 3EE Tel: 020 7272 1079
Servants of the Mother of God, 15 Goddard Place, Monnery Road N19 5GS
Tel: 020 7281 0429 Sr Mary Forrest; Sr Helen Coughlan

UXBRIDGE + OUR LADY OF LOURDES AND ST MICHAEL

Presbytery, Osborn Road, Uxbridge, Middx UB8 1UE Tel: 01895 233193
E-mail: uxbridge@rcdow.org.uk
Beside Oxford Rd, at junct with Harefield Rd. ***(Hillingdon Deanery)*** (1891; 1931; cons 14 May 1936)
Fr Matthew Heslin
Services Sun, M (Sat 6.30pm) 8.30 10.30 (Family), 5pm. Hds, M 10am, 7pm.
Wkds, M 10am (except Tues). Conf: Sat 10.30-11am
Ecumenical Contact Parish Priest **Justice and Peace Contact** Parish Priest
Clare House Nursing Home. Mass Centre: Pield Heath Convent Chapel
Sisters of the Sacred Hearts of Jesus and Mary,
Pield Heath House, Pield Heath Road, Hillingdon, Middx UB8 3NW
Special School **Tel: 01895 233092 (Convent) 01895 258507 (School)**
Also **Marian House, 100 Kingston Lane, Uxbridge, Middx UB8 3PW**
Tel: 01895 253299 For retired sisters **Chaplain** Fr Tom Harrington **Tel: 01895 232719**

WALTHAM CROSS + OUR LADY OF THE IMMACULATE CONCEPTION AND ST JOSEPH

204 High Street, Waltham Cross, Herts EN8 7DP Tel: 01992 623156 Fax 01992 640196
E-mail: walthamcross@rcdow.org.uk Website: www.rcdow.org.uk/walthamcross/
(Lea Valley Deanery) (1859; 1931; cons 3 July 1971)
Fr John Cunningham
Services Sun, M (Sat 6.30pm), 8.30, 10.45, 12.15, 6.30pm. Hds, M 10, 8pm.
Wkds, M 10. Conf: Sat 10.30 to 11, 5.45 to 6.15pm. Exp Fri 9.15-9.45am
Polish M, Sun 9.30; Italian M, Sun 5pm; M in Ukrainian Rite as announced.
Ecumenical Contact Tony Wilson **Tel: 020 8804 2111** **Justice & Peace** Parish Priest
Canossian Daughters of Charity, Holy Cross Convent,
2-3 Longlands Close, Cheshunt, Herts EN8 8LW Tel: 01992 621168/626772
Sr Teresa Bonaventura; Sr Catherine Cavalli; Sr Ann Grogan; Sr Ellen Kasonga

WAPPING + ST PATRICK ☑ A

The Presbytery, Dundee Street, Green Bank E1W 2PH Tel: 020 7481 2202
E-mail: wapping@rcdow.org.uk Website: www.stpatrickswapping.org
Off Wapping Lane; close to Wapping stn (LT) ***(Tower Hamlets Deanery)*** (1871; 1892; cons 22.5.02)
Fr Digby Samuels; Fr James Mulligan
Services Sun, M (Sat 7pm), 10, 6.30pm. Hds, M 10, 8pm. Conf: Sat 6.15-7pm
Ecumenical Contact Parish Priest **Justice and Peace Contact** Parish Priest
Sisters of Our Lady of the Missions 13 Pierhead E1 9PN Tel: 020 7265 0513

WARE + SACRED HEART OF JESUS AND ST JOSEPH ☑ A

The Presbytery, King Edward's Road, Ware, Herts SG12 7EJ
Tel: 01920 462140 Fax: 01920 486251 E-mail: ware@rcdow.org.uk
Junc King Edward's Road & New Road (off High Street) ***(Lea Valley Deanery)*** (1870; 1921; 1939)
Fr Brian Ward **Services** Sun, M (Sat 6.30pm), 8.30, 10.30 (Sung). Hds, M 10, 8pm.
Wkds, M as announced. Conf: Sat 11 to 11.30, 5.30 to 6pm; and at call.
Ecumenical Contact John Heggarty **Justice and Peace Contact** Parish Priest
Carmelite Monastery, Ware Park, Herts SG12 0DT Tel: 01920 462154
Chaplain Fr Bernard Crowe The Lodge, Ware Park, Herts SG12 0DS
Tel: 01920 460396 M Sun 11am, Wkds, M 11am Western House Hospital.

WARWICK STREET + OUR LADY OF THE ASSUMPTION AND ST GREGORY ☑

24 Golden Square W1F 9JR Tel: 020 7437 1525 Fax: 020 7025 1598
E-mail: warwickstreet@rcdow.org.uk *Betw Beak St/Glasshouse St (off Regent St, close Piccadilly Circus)*
(Westminster Deanery) (1730; 1790; cons 24 July 1928)
Canon Patrick Davies; also in residence Fr Kidane Lebasi **Eritrean Chaplaincy**
Tel: 020 7025 1594; Fr Christopher Connor
Services Sun, M (Sat 6pm), 10.30am, 5pm Hds, M 8, 12.15, 12.45, 5.45pm Wkds, M Mon to Fri 12.45pm Conf Mon-Fri 12.15-12.35pm & after M; Sat 5.15 to 5.45pm Exp FF1.15-5.40
Ecumenical Contact Parish Priest **Justice & Peace Contact** Parish Priest

WATFORD + HOLY ROOD ☑ ♿

Holy Rood House, Exchange Road, Watford, Herts WD18 0PJ Tel: 01923 224085
Fax: 01923 234961 E-mail: watford@rcdow.org.uk Website: www.holyroodrc.com/
In town centre, corner of Market St ***(Watford Deanery)*** (1883; 1890; cons 5 July 1900)
Fr Paul McAleenan; Fr Philip Dyer-Perry
Services Sun, M (Sat 7pm), 8, 9.30 (Sung), 11.00 (Folk), 6.30pm. Hds, M 8, 12, 7.30pm.
Wkds, M 8.30am, 12. Conf: Sat 11.30 to 12.30, 6 to 6.45pm. Exp, Sat 6 to 6.45pm.
Ecumenical Contact Parish Priest **Justice & Peace** Parish Priest Watford General Hosp.
Sisters of St Mary of Namur, 5 Percy Road, Watford WD18 0QA Tel: 01923 242515
Adoration Sisters, 18 Percy Road, Watford WD18 0QA Tel: 01923 222505

WATFORD NORTH + ST HELEN ☎ A

Church of St Helen, The Harebreaks, Watford, Herts WD24 6NJ Tel: 01923 223175
E-mail: watfordnorth@rcdow.org.uk Website: www. rcdow.org.uk/watfordnorth/
Fr Patrick Foley *(Watford Deanery)* (1925; 1935)
Services Sun, M 9, 11, 6pm. Hds, M 10, 8pm. Wkds, M Mon to Thu 10, Fri 6pm, Sat 10.
Conf: Sat 11.30 to 12.30.
Ecumenical Contact George Griffin **Tel: 01442 266669** **Justice & Peace Contact** Parish Priest

WEALDSTONE (& HARROW WEALD) + ST JOSEPH ☎ ♿

St Joseph's Presbytery, 191 High Rd, Harrow Weald, Middx HA3 5EA
Tel: 020 8427 1955 Fax: 020 8863 0543 E-mail: stjoseph.weald@btconnect.com
On main road, half mile north of Harrow & Wealdstone stn BR ***(Harrow Deanery)*** (1898; 1901; 1931)
Salvatorians (SDS) Fr Michael Doherty (Parish Priest); Fr Noel Keane; Fr Frank Waters
Youth & Community Worker Michael Roche **Tel: 020 8863 6339**
Services Sun, M (Sat 6pm), 8.15, 9.30 (Folk/Children alt Sun), 11 (sung), 12.30, 6pm.
Hds, M 7.30, 10, 7.15pm. Wkds, M 7.30 (not Sat) & 10am
Conf: Sat 10.30 to 11, 7 to 7.30pm. B, Sun 3pm; HH Sat 7pm followed by B at 7.30pm
Ecumenical Contact Bob Livingstone **Justice and Peace Contact** Ellen Teague
Salvatorians (SDS) Salvatorian Community House, High Road, Harrow Weald HA3 5DY
Tel: 020 8427 2808 Fr Michael Doherty **Superior;** Fr Alban Anderton; Fr Bernard Finan;
Fr Thomas Hennessey; Fr Luke Cavanagh; Fr Hugh Richmond; Fr John Murray; Fr Adrian Tate
Salvatorian College Chaplain and Provincial Fr Peter Preston
129 Spencer Road, Harrow Weald, Middx HA3 7BJ Tel: 020 8426 0495 Fax 020 8426 0927
Sisters of Our Lady of the Missions, 192 High Street, Wealdstone, Middx HA3 7UA
Tel: 020 8427 1541; also **108 Spencer Road, Wealdstone, Middx HA3 7AR**
Tel: 020 8861 4174 (Provincial House)

WELWYN GARDEN CITY + ST BONAVENTURE ☎ A

81 Parkway, Welwyn Garden City, Herts AL8 6JF Tel: 01707 322579
E-mail: welwyngdncity@rcdow.org.uk Website: www.rcdow.org.uk/welwyngardencity/
(Hatfield Deanery) (1925; 1926; cons 14 Sept 1974)
Served from WGC Digswell In residence Fr Joe Boward (Retired)
Parish Secretary/Catechetical Co-ordinator Kathryn Hubbard
Services Sun, M 8, 10.30 (CW 1st, 2nd, 4th Sun, Children's M 3rd Sun,
Latin 1st Sun). Hds, M 10.30, 7pm. Wkds, as announced
Conf: Sat 10.30 to 11
Ecumenical Contact Parish Secretary **Justice and Peace Contact** Parish Secretary
Queen Elizabeth II Hospital.
Chaplain Sr Marian Davey **Tel: 01707 328111 ext 4003 Page 07623 897178**
Focolare Movement (Residential Conference Centre),
69 Parkway, Welwyn Garden City, Herts AL8 6HH Tel: 01707 323620.

WELWYN GARDEN CITY DIGSWELL + HOLY FAMILY ☏ A

194 Knightsfield, Welwyn Garden City AL8 7RQ Tel: 01707 327434
E-mail: welwyngdncitydigs@rcdow.org.uk *(Hatfield Deanery)* (1967)
Fr William McConalogue ***also serves WGC St Bonaventure***
Services Sun, M (Sat 6.30pm), 10, 7pm, Hds, M 9.30, 11 (School), 8pm
Wkds, M as announced. Conf: Sat 11.30 to 12, 5.30 to 6pm.
Ecumenical Contact Parish Priest **Justice and Peace Contact** CAFOD Group
Queen Victoria Memorial Hospital; Danesbury Hospital

WELWYN GARDEN CITY EAST + OUR LADY, QUEEN OF APOSTLES ☏ A

141 Woodhall Lane, Welwyn Garden City, Herts AL7 3TP Tel: 01707 323234
E-mail: welwyngdncityeast@rcdow.org.uk Website: www.rcdow.org.uk/welwyngardencityeast/
(Hatfield Deanery) (1961; cons 18 Dec. 1973)
Fr Peter Maher
Services Sun, M (Sat 5.30pm), 9.30, 11.30. Hds, M 9.30, 7pm.
Wkds, M Mon, Wed, 9.30; Tue, Fri 7pm (+Nov & B) Conf: Sat 10am & 5pm.
Ecumenical Contact Freda McKenzie **Justice and Peace Contact** Ann Stapleton
Family Centre Tel: 01707 881884
Hospitaller Order of St John (OH) 97 Great Ganett, Welwyn Garden City AL7 3DD
Tel: 01707 336587 E-mail: Michaelnewman@Hospitaller.org.uk Br Michael Newman

WEMBLEY 1 + ST JOSEPH ☏ A

St Joseph's Presbytery, 339 High Road, Wembley HA9 6AG Tel: 020 8902 0081
Fax: 020 8795 0392 E-mail: wembley1@rcdow.org.uk
At 'The Triangle' (junction of High Road, Harrow Road & Wembley Hill Road) ***(Brent Deanery)*** (1901; 1957)
Fr John Gray; Fr Joseph Carter
Services Sun, M (Sat 6.30pm), 9.30, 11.30am Hds, M, (Eve 7.30pm) 9.30am, 12.30pm
Wkds, M Mon-Thurs & Sat 9.30am, Fri 12 noon, Conf: Sat 10-10.45 (inc Exp)
Ecumenical Contact Anne Turner **Tel: 020 8903 2513**
Justice and Peace Rebecca Chatelier **Tel: 020 8902 1109**

WEMBLEY 2 + ENGLISH MARTYRS ♿☏

The Presbytery, Chalkhill Road, Wembley Park, Middx HA9 9EW Tel: 020 8904 2306
E-mail: wembley2@rcdow.org.uk *Blackbird Hill, corner of Chalkhill Road, below Blackbird Cross.*
Augustinian Recollects (OAR) Fr John Docherty; Fr Jesus Perez ***(Brent Deanery)*** (1930; 1970)
Services Sun, M (Sat 6pm), 9, 11 (Family/CW), 6pm.
Hds, M 9.30, 7.30pm. Wkds, M 9.30.
Conf (Spanish & Portuguese) Sat 10 to 10.30, 5.15 to 5.45 & at call. MP, Wkds 9.15.
R, after M Thu, Fri, Sat (May & Oct daily). Exp: Thurs after 9.30 M to 11am.
Ecumenical Contact Mary Lee **Tel: 020 8904 1075** **Justice and Peace** Rita Heston

WEMBLEY 3 + ST ERCONWALD (PRESTON ROAD) ♿ ☑

112 Carlton Avenue East, Wembley, Middx HA9 8NB Tel: 020 8904 6031 Fax: 020 8385 1493
E-mail: wembley3@rcdow.org.uk Website: www.erconwald.org.uk
Off Preston Road, 400 yds east ***(Brent Deanery)*** (1932; 1970)
Fr Alan Ashton **Secretary** Joanna Sorchan; **Pastoral Assistant** Iris Phelan
Services Sun, M (Sat 5.30pm), 9, 11.30am Hds M 9.30am, 8pm. Wkds, M Mon-Fri 9.30am (not Thur) Conf: Sat 4.30-5 & after M. **Ecumenical Contact** Gio Kitton **Tel: 020 8904 6305**
Sisters of La Sainte Union, 128 Elmstead Avenue, Wembley, Middx HA9 8NZ
Tel: 020 8537 9257 Sr Mary Hardiman; Sr Ita Hynes **(Justice & Peace Contact)**
London Transport Home (Kenwood) Birchwood Grange.

WEST DRAYTON AND YIEWSLEY + ST CATHERINE ♿ ☑

20 The Green, West Drayton, Middx UB7 7PJ Tel: 01895 442777
(Hillingdon Deanery) (1867; 1869; cons 29 Sept 1893)
Fr Brian Smith
Services Sun, M (Sat 7pm), 9, 11 (Sung/CW), 6pm. Hds, M 9, 11, 7.30pm.
Wkds, M Mon to Fri, 9.30 (as announced), Sat 10. Conf: Sat 10.30 and 6.30pm.
Ecumenical Contact Maureen Birmingham **Tel: 01895 449000** **Hatton Grove**

WEST GREEN + ST JOHN VIANNEY A

4 Vincent Road N15 3QH Tel: 020 8888 5518 Fax: 020 8888 5554
E-mail: westgreen@rcdow.org.uk ***(Haringey Deanery)*** (1927; 1959; cons 20 June 1964)
Fr Joe Ryan **Parish Sister** Sr Mary Agnes Ruane OLA **Tel: 020 8888 9036**
Services Sun, M (Sat 6pm), 8.30, 10 (Family), 11.30 (Sung) Hds, M (Eve 7.30), 10
Wkds, M Mon to Fri 9.15 am, FF 7.30pm, Sat 9.15 Conf: Sat 9.45-10.15
Justice and Peace Contact Daniel St Guillaume **Tel: 020 8801 3043**
Sisters of Our Lady of the Apostles, 10 Vincent Rd N15 3QH Tel: 020 8888 9036
Comboni Missionary Sisters, 26 Black Boy Lane, N15 3AR Tel: 020 8809 4069 Fax: 020 8809 2893
Sisters of St John of God, 103 Black Boy Lane, N15 3AS Tel: 020 8374 1693

WEST HENDON SEE HENDON WEST

WHEATHAMPSTEAD + ST THOMAS MORE ♿ ☑

7 Marford Road, Wheathampstead, Herts AL4 8AY Tel: 01582 832114
E-mail: wheathampstead@rcdow.org.uk ***(St Albans Deanery)*** (1936; 1938; 1978)
Fr Brian Reynolds
Services Sun, M 8.30, 10, 5pm. Hds, M 10, 8pm. Wkds, M 9.30 (not Wed). Conf: Sat 10.30
Ecumenical Contact Tony Blythe **Tel: 01582 712017**
Justice and Peace Contact Marie-Rose Low **Tel: 01582 834158**

WHETSTONE + ST MARY MAGDALEN ☎ A

6 Athenaeum Road, N20 9AE Tel: 020 8445 0838 E-mail: whetstone@rcdow.org.uk
Off High Rd (A1000), Totteridge Lane/Oakleigh Rd intersection ***(Barnet Deanery)*** (1926; 1958; cons 1979)
Fr Philip Law
Services Sun, M (Sat 5.30), 8.30, 10 (CW), 12, 7pm (Folk). Hds, M (Eve 8pm), 9.30, 8pm.
Wkds, M 9.30. Conf: Sat 11 to 12, 4.30 to 5.30pm MP bef wkd M; Exp, Sat 4.30-5.30pm
Ecumenical Contact Patrick Lyons **Tel: 020 8368 5238** **Justice & Peace** Jean Murat
Missionaries of Africa (White Fathers) (MAfr) St Edward's, 46 Totteridge Common N20 8ND
Tel: 020 8959 2553 (Rector), **Tel: 020 8959 4477** (Students)
Fr Josef Buholzer (Rector); Fr Ignatius Anipu; Fr Jan Mol; Fr Francis Bomansaan
Also **Oak Lodge, 48 Totteridge Common, N20 8NB Tel: 020 8959 1515 Fax: 020 8959 7421**
Fr Hans Schrenk **Superior**; Fr Hermann Hauser; Fr Richard Calcutt; Fr Paul Gigli;
Fr Aylward Shorter; Fr Patrick Shanahan; Fr Gerald Stones
Sisters of the Sacred Heart of Jesus (St Jacut), 4 Oakleigh Park South N20 9JU
Tel: 020 8445 3743; Provincial House, 6 Oakleigh Park South, N20 9JV Tel: 020 8445 4655

WHITECHAPEL, E1 SEE COMMERCIAL ROAD, GERMAN CHURCH AND UNDERWOOD ROAD

WHITE CITY + OUR LADY OF FATIMA ♿☎ S

The Catholic Presbytery, Commonwealth Avenue, W12 7QR Tel: 020 8743 8334
E-mail: whitecity@rcdow.org.uk Website: www.rcdow.org.uk/whitecity/
Off Blomfontein Rd, betw Western Ave/Uxbridge Rd ***(Hammersmith & Fulham)*** (1951; 1965; cons 17.5.80)
Also serves Acton East
Fr Keith Stoakes; Fr Ephrem Andom; Rev John McKenna (Deacon)
Services Sun, M (Sat 7pm), 9, 11am, 6pm. Hds, M 9.30am, 7.30pm
Wkds, M 9.15am MP 9am; Conf: Sat 9.45 to 10.15am, 6 to 6.30pm.
Ecumenical Contact Emma Nicklen **Justice and Peace Contact** Parish Priest
Marist Sisters, 22 Bloemfontein Road, W12 7BX Tel: 020 8749 4850
Religious Sisters of Charity, 13 Arminger Road, W12 7BA Tel: 020 8749 5918

WHITTON + ST EDMUND OF CANTERBURY ☎ A

Presbytery, St Edmund's Lane, 213 Nelson Road, Whitton, Middx TW2 7BB
Tel: 020 8894 9923 E-mail: whitton@rcdow.org.uk
Right at Whitton BR Stn, left at Nelson Pub. Pres: behind Church. ***(Upper Thames Deanery)*** (1934; 1935; 1963)
Fr Seamus O'Boyle; also in residence Fr Anthony O'Gorman
Catechetical Co-ordinator Mrs Marian Keohane **Tel: 020 8894 9923**
Services Sun, M (Sat 6.30pm Folk), 9.30 (Family), 11.15 (Sung), 6pm.
Hds, M 9.30, 7.30pm. Wkds, M Mon-Fri 9.15, Sat 10.30; Conf: Sat 11 to 11.30
Ecumenical Contact Christine Pharro **Tel: 020 8893 8575**
Justice and Peace Contact Parish Priest

WILLESDEN + OUR LADY OF WILLESDEN ☎ A

The Presbytery, Nicoll Road, NW10 9AX Tel: 020 8965 4935 Fax: 020 8961 0928
E-mail: willesden@rcdow.org.uk
At junction of Acton Lane near Jubilee Clock, Harlesden. ***(Brent Deanery)*** (1886; 1931)
Shrine of Our Lady of Willesden Fr Stephen Willis; Fr Nicholas Schofield; Fr Jacques Otieno
Catechetical Co-ordinator Sr Sheila Gosney
Services Sun, M (Sat 6pm), 9, 11 (Sung), 5.30pm. Hds, M (Eve 7pm), 7, 10, 7.30pm (Sung).
Wkds, M 10, 7pm. Conf: Tues 6.30, 7pm, Sat 10.30 to 11.30, 5 to 5.45pm. Shrine Prayers Tues 7.30pm
Exp daily: Tues 10.30 to 6.50pm, Sat 10.30 to 5.50pm.
Ecumenical Contact Parish Priest
Justice & Peace Contact Bernadette Ogombu

WILLESDEN GREEN + ST MARY MAGDALEN ☎ A

Clergy House, Peter Avenue, NW10 2DD
Tel: 020 8451 4677 Fax 020 8451 0288
E-mail: willesdengreen@rcdow.org.uk ***(Brent Deanery)*** (1901, 1939, cons 1958)
Harlesden Road South side of High Road, via St Andrew's Road; not far from Willesden Green stn (LT)
Fr Hugh MacKenzie; also in residence Fr Anthony Ponweera
Parish Sister Sr Lily DC **Tel: 020 7224 3616**
Services Sun, M (Sat 6.30pm), 9, 10.30, 12, 6.30pm. Hds, M (Eve 6.30pm), 9.30, 12, 7pm.
Wkds, M Mon-Fri 9.30, 6.30pm; Sat 10.
Conf: Sat 10.30 - 11, 5.30 - 6.15pm. Exp Sat 5.30-6.15
Ecumenical Contact Parish Priest **Justice and Peace Contact** Brigid Hegarty
Jesuits (SJ), Our Lady of Mercy, 182 Walm Lane, NW2 3AX Tel: 020 8452 4304
Fr Henryk Drozdziel; Fr Tadeusz Sporny; Fr Leszek Golebiewski; Br Boleslaw Krol
Divine Word Missionaries (SVD), 8 Teignmouth Road, NW2 4HN
Tel: 020 8452 8430.
Fr Martin McPake; Fr Michael Egan; Fr Kieran Fitzharris; Fr Frank Kom;
Fr Leszek Niewdana; Fr Valan Arockiaswamy
Montfort Missionaries, 27 St Gabriel's Rd, NW2 4DS Tel: 020 8450 4291 Fr Kieran Flynn
Sisters of the Holy Family of Bordeaux, 83 St Gabriel's Road, NW2 4DU
Tel: 020 8452 3844
Little Sisters of the Assumption, 52 Kenneth Crescent, NW2 4PN
Tel: 020 8452 1687 Fax: 020 8208 3625
Sr Margaret Collins; Sr Margaret Lonergan; Sr Valerie Sparrow
De Paul Trust 247 Willesden Lane, NW2 5RY Tel: 020 8830 1093
Daughters of Wisdom (La Sagesse) 9 The Oaks, 25 Brondesbury Park, NW6 7BY
Tel: 020 8830 2530 Sr Monica Tywang
German Catholic Centre, 40 Exeter Road, NW2 4SP
Tel: 020 8452 8566
Willesden General Hospital

WOOD GREEN + ST PAUL THE APOSTLE

22 Bradley Road, N22 7SZ Tel: 020 8888 2390 Fax: 020 8829 9797
E-mail: woodgreen@rcdow.org.uk
Wood Green stn (Piccadilly line), nr jn with Mayes R d ***(Haringey Deanery)*** (1882; 1904; 1970)
Canon Michael Munnelly; Fr Jim Byrne
Services Sun, M (Sat 6.30pm), 8, 10 (Family), 11.30 (Sung), 6pm.
Hds, M 9.30, 8pm. Wkds, M 9.30 (Mon to Fri); also 7.30pm Fri; Sat 10.30am
Conf: Sat 11 to 12, 5 to 6pm. HH Sat 11-12.
Ecumenical Contact Parish Priest **Justice and Peace Contact** Parish Priest
Daughters of Providence, 82 Sylvan Avenue, N22 5HY Tel: 020 8888 6923
Daughters of Divine Love, 84 Sylvan Avenue, N22 5HY Tel: 020 8888 1898

YEADING + ST RAPHAEL

St Raphael's House, Morrison Road, Yeading, Middx UB4 9JP
Tel: 020 8845 1919 Fax: 020 8845 1215
E-mail: yeading@rcdow.org.uk Website: www. rcdow.org.uk/yeading/
In Ayles Road, off Kingshill Avenue (west of Yeading Lane)
(Hillingdon Deanery) (1957; 1961; cons 4 May 1975)
Fr John Welsh; Fr Mathew Thottathimyalil
Parish Co-ordinator Alison Read **Tel: 020 8845 1919**
Services Sun, M (Sat 7pm), 9, 10.30 (Sung), 12, 7pm.
Hds, M 9.30am, 7.30pm. Wkds, M 9.30am, Wed 7 & 9.30am,
Fri 12 noon. Conf: Sat 11am and 6.30pm. Exp, Sat 10.30 Bene 11.45am.
Ecumenical Contact Alison Read **Tel: 020 8845 1919**
Justice and Peace Contact Parish Priest

OTHER JURISDICTIONS

BISHOPRIC OF THE FORCES

Bishop of the Forces (resident in Farnborough,) Bishop Thomas Burns SM,
Secretary Major (Retd) Diana Wilson, AGPDO, Middle Hill, Aldershot GU11 1PP
Chancellor Fr I Evans RAChD Tel 01252 349004 E-mail: rcforcesbishop@freeuk.com

PRINCIPAL CHAPLAINCIES

ROYAL NAVY Room 203 Victory Building, HM Naval Base, Portsmouth PO1 3LS
Tel 02392 727903 Fax: 02392 727112 E-mail: dgncshq@a.dii.mod.uk
ARMY Ministry of Defence Chaplains (Army), Trenchard Lines, Upavon, Pewsey, Wilts SN9 6BE Tel 01980 615803 E-mail: modchaplainsarmy@tiscali.co.uk
ROYAL AIR FORCE RAF Chaplaincy Services, RAF Innsworth, Gloucester GL3 1EZ
Tel 01452 712612 ext 5166 E-mail: chapl.dgcs@ptc.raf.mod.uk

APOSTOLIC EXARCHATE FOR UKRAINIAN CATHOLICS IN GREAT BRITAIN

Chancery 22 Binney Street W1K 5BQ Tel 020 7629 1073
Apostolic Exarch Bishop Paul Chomnycky OSBM
Financial Secretary Fr Stephen Oracz, STD
See Ukrainian Catholic Cathedral entry in Parish Directory section

PERSONAL PRELATURE OF THE HOLY CROSS AND OPUS DEI

Prelate (resident in Rome) Bishop Javier Echevarría.
Regional Vicar for Great Britain Mgr Nicholas Morrish MA STD
4 Orme Court W2 4RL Tel 020 7229 7574 (1) (Queensway)
OTHER CENTRES IN THE DIOCESE
(2) Pembridge House, 29 Pembridge Square W2 4DS Tel: 020 7229 3584 (Bayswater)
(3) Dawliffe Hall, 1/2 Chelsea Embankment SW3 4LG Tel: 020 7352 1545 (Chelsea 1)
(4) Lakefield, 41a Maresfield Gardens NW3 5RY Tel: 020 7433 3454 (Swiss Cottage)
(5) Netherhall House, Nutley Terrace NW3 5SA Tel: 020 7435 8888 (Swiss Cottage)
(6) Westpark, 1 Leopold Road W5 3PB Tel: 020 8992 3954 (Gunnersbury)
(7) Woodlands, 12 Gunnersbury Avenue W5 3NJ Tel: 020 8992 4025 (Gunnersbury)
(8) Ashwell House, Shepherdess Walk N1 7NA Tel: 020 7490 5021 (Hoxton)
Priest Members Byrne, Andrew (6) Morrish, Mgr Nicholas (1) Gabiola, Joseph (1)
Sheehan, Gerard (5) Hayward, Paul (1) Marsh, Bernard (1)
Stork, Mgr Richard (5) Evans, Joseph (5) Hnylycia, Stefan (1)
Opus Dei Information Office 6 Orme Court W2 4RL Tel: 020 7221 9176,
Fax: 020 7243 9400 E-mail: info@opusdei.org.uk Website: www.opusdei.org.uk

PRIESTS OF THE DIOCESE

Seniority by year of ordination ❑ indicates a priest who is retired.

1931

❑ Fuller, Canon Reginald

1939

❑ Moore, Canon Peter

1940

❑ Smyth, Canon Frederick

1943

❑ Thomas, Canon Louis

1944

❑ McGowan, Canon Charles
❑ Bilsborrow, Edward

1945

❑ Wardle, Terence

1946

❑ Whitney, Robin
❑ Phillips, Canon Peter

1947

❑ O'Neill, John D
❑ Norris, Mgr David
❑ Anglim Mgr Peter

1948

❑ McCoy, John
❑ Groarke, Michael

1949

❑ Busuttil, Anthony

1950

❑ Miles, Mgr Canon Frederick
❑ Cassidy, Patrick
❑ Aylward, Ronald

1951

❑ Garvey, Charles A
❑ Cooke, Anthony

1952

❑ Kearney, John

1953

❑Heaney, Brian
❑ Miller, John M

1954

❑ Lyons, Patrick
❑ Arrowsmith, Mgr Canon Adrian
❑ Hamill, Harold
❑ McGonagle, Cathal
❑ Galvin, John
❑ O'Brien, Bishop James

1955

❑ Gates, Robert
Sacré, Anthony
❑ McDonald, Canon John D
❑ Crowe, Bernard
❑ Moraes, Arthur

1956

Murphy-O'Conner, Cardinal Cormac
Formby, Canon John
Pinot de Moira, Michael
❑ Harrington, John
Stark, Mgr Anthony
❑ Dangerfield, Richard

1957

Noctor, James
❑ O'Reilly, Peter
❑ Young, Henry
❑ Dwyer, Peter
❑ Webb, Geoffrey
❑ O'Halloran, John

1958

McCormick, James

1959

❑ Hosford, Horatio
❑ Rees, Joseph
Brown, Mgr Ralph
Archer, Michael

1960

❑ Dain, Kenneth
Burke, Canon Gerard T
❑ Burke, Thomas
❑ Heekin, Patrick
❑Walker, Adrian
❑ Dutton, John
❑ Howe, Mgr Antony
Stanley, Cedric
Scholes, Canon Bernard
❑ Nash, Brian
❑ Turner, John

1961

❑ Dempsey, William
Coghlan, Mgr John
Fullam, Seamus
Ward, Brian

1962

Helm, John
❑ Hart, Austin
Berry, Canon Vincent
Reynolds, Brian
Matthews, Canon Edward
❑ Ffrench, Barry F
❑ Kiernan, Thomas
❑McGrath, Dermot
Seeldrayers, Anthony

1963

❑ Gilburt, Canon Peter
❑ Brown, Norman
Crewe, Hilary
Tuck, Michael

1964

❑ Day, Peter
Brunning, Antony
Wilby, William
Brand, James

1965
❒ Ennis, George
Garnett, Michael
Delany, Stephen
❒ Wahle, Francis
Sharratt, Aidan

1966
Turner, Mgr Canon Henry
❒ Egan, Patrick

1967
❒ O'Driscoll, David
Brockie, Canon Michael
Egan, Mgr Canon Thomas
McCabe, Kenneth
Boylan, Bernard
Duffy, James

1968
Murphy, Seamus
Acton, Canon Charles
Gawecki, Christopher

1969
❒ Crewe, Vincent
❒ Whatling, Colin
McCarthy, Timothy
McGeoghan, Seamus
Baker, Desmond
Felzmann, Mgr Vladimir
McDevitt, Kevin

1970

Wilson, David
❒ Sharp, Peter
McConalogue, William
❒ Drumm, Mgr Walter
Ardagh-Walter, David
Maher, Peter

1971
❒ Fitzgibbon, Richard
Ryan, Joseph
Foley, Patrick
Fudge, Alan J
Leonard, Francis
Convery, Antony
McCumiskey, Bernard

1972
Murphy, John M
Stack, Bishop George
Watters, Denis
O'Brien, Eamonn
❒ McWeeney, Sean
McGinn, Canon Paul
❒ Donlan, John

1973
Overton, Mgr James
Cowan, Anton
O'Connor, Timothy
Munnelly, Canon Michael

1974
McNicholas, James
Davies, Jeremy
Sawyer, Guy
Cross, Canon Philip
Kennelly, Canon Matthew
Browne, Canon Patrick
Carroll, Patrick
Magnier, Daniel

1975
❒ Nolan, Patrick
Rowland, Phelim
Plourde, Canon Robert
Wiley, John
Deehan, John
Carroll, Edward
Mallon, James
Connor, Christopher
Zsidi, Gabriel
Williamson, David
Quinn, Thomas
Lebasi, Kidane

1976
Barltrop, Mgr Keith
Shewring, John
❒ Meaney, Gerard
Byrne, John
❒ Barry, Robert
Samuels, Digby
Seabrook, John
Barnes, David

1977
Law, Philip
Dickie, Ian
Cronin, Canon Daniel
Buckley, John
Kennedy, Michael
Kelly, David
Cunningham, John
Davies, Canon Patrick
Azzopardi, Frans
Psaila, Anthony
Forde, Thomas

1978
Baxter, Anthony
Sammon, Patrick
Kirinich, Roger
Winter, Marcus
Connor, Michael
Price, Richard

1979
Power, Dermot
Conlon, Antony
de l'Orme, Frederick

1980

Ryan, Paschal
❒ Holmes-Walker, Robert
Liddle, Gladstone
Kennedy, Jim
Brady, Vincent
Gullan-Steel, Stuart
Creak, Brian
McGuckin, Terence

1981
Longley, Bishop Bernard
Press, Francis
Johnston, Michael
Donaghy, Michael
❒ Wrigley, Norman
O'Boyle, Seamus
❒ McLean, Colin
Scurlock, Anthony
Doe, Anthony

1982
Whooley, John
O'Neill, Dermot
❒ Stewart, Michael

1983
Anwyll, Mark
Arnold, Mgr John
Burrows, Neil
Paris, Anthony
Phipps, Terence
Stoakes, Keith
Stokes, John
Webb, Christopher

1984
Dwyer, Anthony
Smith, Brian
Hayes, Martin
Gray, John
❒ Boward, Joseph
Quinn, Gerard
McPartlan, Paul
White, John
King, Gerard

1985
Healy, Bruno
McAleenan, Paul
Leathem, Michael
Skehan, William
Sykes, Perry
Letellier, Robert
van Son, Francis

1986
Boland, John
Dunkling, Reginald
Curry, Mgr James
Cahill, Charles
Fitzpatrick, Eugene
McLoughlin, Patrick
Mannion, Michael
Carter, Joseph

1987
Davies, Colin
Loring, Ulick

1988
❒ Carpenter, Barry
❒ Rigby, Cormac
Fernandes, Norbert
Carroll, Sean
Conneely, John
❒ Stevens, Michael
Hutton, Timothy
Elliott, John
Sherbrooke, Alexander
Poole, Robert
❒ Allan, Thomas
❒ Harrington, Thomas
Coningsby, Mark
Hannigan, Neil

1989
Thornton, Sean
Adamson, Duncan
Stevens, Peter
Middleton, Shaun
Booth, Michael

1990
Newby, Peter
Lyons, George
O'Toole, Mark
Piccolomini, Charis
❒ Durand, Michael
Langham, Mgr Mark
Wadsworth, Andrew
Seasman, Terence
Andom, Ephrem
Grech, Saviour

1991
Morris, Allen
Grant, Peter
Garvey, James
Scott, Peter
Byrne, Dominic
Lowry, Mehall
James, Howard
Przyjalkowski, Voytek

1992
O'Doherty, Michael
O'Leary, John
Dean, Timothy
Salvans, Albert
Dermody, John

1993
Whitmore, Mgr Philip
Tastard, Terry
Wagay, Gideon
O'Connell, Andrew
Ashton, Alan

1994
Antwi-Darkwah, Francis
❒ Leonard, Mgr Graham
de Lord, Richard
Harris, Peter
Welsh, John
Campbell,David
McKenna, Dominic
Lennard, Shaun
❒ Heal, Martin

1995
❒ Marriott, Canon Richard
Cullinan, Michael
❒ Hoey, Augustine
Legge, Raymond
MacKenzie, Hugh
Lyness, Peter
Reynolds, Neil
Graham, Donald
Andrew, Richard
Evans, David
Fairhead, Jeremy
Hopes, Bishop Alan
Irwin, David
Markey, Michael
Reader, Roger
Touw, Dennis
Tuckwell, Christopher
Woodruff, Mark

1996
Burgess, Robin
Coker, Stephen
Colven, Christopher
Edgar, Timothy
Hamilton-Gray, Christopher
Hasker, Stewart
❒ Palmer, David
Willis, Stephen
Wilson, Stuart
❒ Klyberg, Mgr John

1997
Silva, Christopher
Bartlett, Stephen
Griffin, Nigel,
Jackson, Frederick
Robinson, Alan
Vipers, Christopher
Wilson, Peter

1998
Arnold, Paul
Brophy, Paul
Davies, Jeremy
Gosnell, Nicholas
Kavanagh, Nicholas
Lee, Clive,
Leenane, Mark

Parsons, Richard
Rimini, Kenneth
Wang, Stephen
O'Toole, Sean

1999
❐ Bedford, Christopher
Freely, Gerald
Jordan, Kevin
Miller, Philip
Ritaccio, Antonio
Sammarco, Anthony
Heslin, Matthew
Nguyen, Simon Phillips,
Lamont

2000

Usher, Thomas
O'Boy, Michael
Pham, John Hai
Taylor, Roger
Everson, Simon
Ablewhite, John
McDermott, Paul

2001
Horan, Danny
Church, Shaun
O'Gorman, Anthony
Trood, Jeremy
Barrow, David
Burton, Edward

2002
Knights, Philip
Thomas, Thomas Kennedy
Skinner, Gerard
Sarsfield, Denis
Eastell, Kevin

2003
Vickers, Mark
Byrne, Jim
Schofield, Nicholas

2004
Braz, Cristiano
Dunne, Michael
Dyer-Perry, Philip
Pellegrini, Anthony
Ruiz, Javier

2005
Daley, Michael
Rouco Gutierrez, Hector
Witon, Slawomir

CLERGY OF THE DIOCESE

In alphabetical order, figures following each surname indicate year of birth and of ordination to priesthood, place name in brackets refers to an entry in the Parish Directory section. Unless stated otherwise, all e-mail addresses are formed:
first name+surname@rcdow.org.uk

BISHOPS

Murphy-O'Connor (1932, 1956)) STL, PhL, His Eminence Cardinal Cormac;
Archbishop's House, Ambrosden Avenue SW1P 1QJ
Hopes (1944; 1995) VG, BD, AKC, Right Rev Alan;
The Clergy House, 16 Abingdon Road W8 6AF
Tel: 020 7798 9023
Longley (1955; 1981) VG, MA, Right Rev Bernard;
64 Lichfield Road E3 5AL Tel: 020 8980 6925
Stack (1946; 1972) VG, BEd, Right Rev George;
14 Egerton Gardens NW4 4BA Tel: 020 8202 8024
O'Brien (1930; 1954) VG, Right Rev James Joseph (Retired)
The Gate House, All Saints Pastoral Centre, London Colney AL2 1AG Tel: 01727 824664

PRIESTS

Ablewhite (1943; 2000) BA, John; *9 Breakspear, Stevenage, Herts SG2 9SQ*
Tel: 01438 352182 (Stevenage Shephall)
Acton (1943; 1968) STL, Canon Charles; *Flat 4, 8 Morpeth Terrace SW1P 1EQ*
Tel: 020 7798 9021 (Seminary)
Adamson (1948; 1989) Duncan; *211 Old Marylebone Road NW1 5QT*
Tel: 020 7723 5101 (Marylebone)
Allan (1926; 1988) MA, Thomas; *Flat 22, Homeroyal House, 2 Chalmers Crescent, Edinburgh EH9 1TP Tel: 0131 668 1691* (Retired)
Andom (1960;1990) STB, STL Ephrem; *Catholic Church, Commonwealth Avenue W12 7QR*
Tel: 020 8743 8334 (White City)
Andrew (1953; 1995) MA, Richard; *45 London Road, Enfield, Middx EN2 6DS*
Tel: 020 8363 2569 (Enfield)
Anglim (1923; 1947) JCD, STL, Mgr Peter A; *Nazareth House, 162 East End Road N2 0RU*
Tel: 020 8444 6799 (Retired)
Antwi-Darkwah (1994) STB, Francis A; *337 Harrow Road W9 3RB*
Tel: 020 7286 2170 (Harrow Road)
Anwyll (1957; 1983) STL, Mark; *189 High Street, London Colney, Herts AL2 1RP*
Tel: 01727 822218 (London Colney)
Archer (1933; 1959) Michael; *Cathedral Clergy House, 42 Francis Street SW1P 1QW*
Tel: 020 7798 9055 (Cathedral)

Ardagh-Walter (1941; 1970) BA, David: *The Presbytery St Mellitus Church, Tollington Park N4 3AG Tel: 020 7272 3415* (Tollington Park)
Arnold (1953; 1983) MA, JCD, Mgr John; *Flat 1, 8 Morpeth Terrace SW1P 1EQ Tel: 020 7798 9018* (Vicar General/Chancellor)
Arnold (1953; 1998) MA, Paul; *St Elizabeth's School & Home, South End, Much Hadham, Herts SG10 6EW* (Much Hadham)
Arrowsmith (1924; 1954) Mgr Canon Adrian; *All Saints Pastoral Centre, Shenley Lane, London Colney, Herts AL2 1AF Tel: 01727 829202* (Retired)
Ashton (1945; 1993) BD, MTh, Alan; *112 Carlton Avenue East, Wembley, Middx HA9 8NB Tel: 020 8904 6031* (Wembley 3)
Aylward (1924; 1950) Ronald G; *1 Green Fielde End, Laleham, Staines, Middx TW18 1LZ Tel: 01784 450790* (Retired)
Azzopardi (1951; 1977) Frans; *28 Rossington Avenue, Borehamwood, Herts WD6 4LA Tel: 020 8953 0715* (Borehamwood North)

Baker (1940; 1969) Desmond; *The Presbytery, Berry Lane, Rickmansworth WD3 7HG Tel: 01923 779890* (Mill End)
Barltrop (1947; 1976) MA, STL, Mgr Keith; *116 West Heath Road NW3 7TX Tel: 020 8731 9796* (CASE)
Barnes (1944; 1976) BA, LicPsych, David; *70 Lincoln's Inn Fields WC2A 3JA Tel: 020 7405 0376* (Lincoln's Inn Fields)
Barrow (1963; 2001) BSc, MSc, STB, David, *115 Hertford Road N9 7EN Tel: 020 8803 6631* (Edmonton)
Barry (1945; 1976) Robert; *Nazareth House, Hammersmith Road W6 8DB* (Retired)
Bartlett (1939; 1997) STh, Stephen G H; *17 Cirencester Street W2 5SR Tel: 020 7286 2672* (Paddington)
Baxter (1944; 1978) MA, BD, MPhil, PhD, Anthony; *79 St Charles Square W10 6EB Tel: 020 8968 6446* (Heythrop College)
Bedford (1946;1999) BD, AKC, Christopher J C; *Green Roofs, Marine Drive, Brighton BN2 8LA Tel: 020 7798 9092* (Retired/Year Book/Catholic Directory)
Berry (1937; 1962) Canon Vincent; *St Mary's Rectory, Draycott Terrace SW3 2QR Tel: 020 7589 5487* (Chelsea 1)
Bilsborrow (1915; 1944) Edward; *Nazareth House, 162 East End Road N2 0RU Tel: 020 8444 1518* (Retired)
Boland (1947; 1986) John; *St Peter's Presbytery, Bishop's Rise, Hatfield, Herts AL10 9HN Tel: 01707 262121* (Hatfield South)
Booth (1954; 1989) MA, STL, Michael; *c/o Archbishop's House, Ambrosden Avenue SW1P 1QJ*
Boward (1931; 1984) Joseph; *81 Parkway, Welwyn Garden City AL8 6JF Tel: 01707 322579* (Retired)
Boylan (1942; 1967) Bernard; *110 Station Road, Hampton-on-Thames, Middx TW12 2AS Tel: 020 8979 3596* (Hampton-on-Thames)
Brady (1956; 1980) Vincent G; *54 Parkside SW19 5NF Tel: 020 8944 7189* (Nunciature)
Brand (1935; 1964) MA, STL, James; *Pont Collegio Beda, Viale di S. Paolo 18, 00146 Roma* (Spiritual Director)

Braz (1974;2004) STB, Cristiano; ***52 Uxbridge Road W7 3SU Tel: 020 8567 4056*** (Hanwell)
Brockie (1942; 1967) JCL, Canon Michael; ***7 Cheyne Row SW3 5HS Tel: 020 7352 0777*** (Chelsea 2)
Brophy (1958; 1998) MA, Paul; ***The Presbytery, Brentfield Road NW10 8ER Tel: 020 8965 3313*** (Stonebridge)
Brown (1930; 1963) Norman; ***2a Meadow Road SW8 1QH*** (Retired)
Brown (1931; 1959) ProtAp, JCD, KCHS, Mgr Ralph; ***Flat 3, 8 Morpeth Terrace SW1P 1EQ Tel: 020 7798 9020*** (Officialis)
Browne (1948; 1974) Canon Patrick; ***47 Cumberland Street SW1V 4LY Tel: 020 7834 6965*** (Director Permanent Diaconate Programme/Pimlico)
Brunning (1940; 1964) Antony; ***211 Old Marylebone Road NW1 5QT Tel: 020 7723 5101*** (Hospital Chaplain: St Mary's Paddington)
Buckley (1950; 1977) John; ***729 High Road N17 8AG Tel: 020 8808 3554*** (Tottenham)
Burgess (1949; 1996) MA, Robin; ***20 Willowmead Close W5 1PT Tel: 020 8998 4710***
Burke (1935; 1960) Canon Gerard T; ***St Lawrence Presbytery, The Green, Feltham, Middx TW134AF Tel: 020 8890 2367*** (Feltham)
Burke (1923; 1960) Thomas; ***St Francis, Churchfield, Knock, Co Mayo, Ireland*** (Retired)
Burrows (1958;1983) BD, MCIPD, Neil; ***390b Northolt Road, South Harrow HA2 8EX Tel: 020 8864 5455*** (Harrow South)
Burton (1940; 2001) AKC, Edward; ***373 Bowes Road N11 1AA Tel: 020 8368 1368*** (New Southgate)
Busuttil (1925; 1949) Anthony; ***6 Rockmead Road, Fairlight, E. Sussex TN35 4DJ Tel: 01424 814874*** (Retired)
Byrne (1955; 1991) MA, JCD, STL, Dominic; ***15 Wood Rd, Shepperton, Middx TW17 0DH Tel: 01932 563116*** (Shepperton)
Byrne (1973; 2003) Jim; ***22 Bradley Road N22 7SZ Tel: 020 8888 2390*** (Wood Green)
Byrne (1951; 1976) John; ***186 St John's Rd, Boxmoor, Herts HP1 1NR Tel: 01442 391759*** (Hemel Hempstead)

Cahill (1955; 1986) Charles; ***1 Colney Hatch Lane N10 1PN Tel: 020 8883 5607*** (Muswell Hill)
Campbell (1955; 1994) David; ***1st Battalion The Royal Scots, Dreghorn Barracks, Redford Road, Edinburgh EH13 9QW Tel: 0131 310 2875*** (Army Chaplain)
Carpenter (1943; 1988) FRSA, Barry; ***4 Merry Hill Road, Bushey, Watford, Herts WD23 1DY Tel: 020 8950 8985*** (Retired)
Carroll (1933; 1975) Edward; ***Catholic Church, Black Lion Lane, Shenley, Herts WD7 9DH Tel: 01923 857005*** (Shenley)
Carroll (1947;1974) Patrick; ***4 Church Close, Cuffley, Herts EN6 4LS Tel: 01707 873308***(Cricklewood)
Carroll (1956; 1988) Sean; ***115 Hertford Road N9 7EN Tel: 020 8803 6631*** (Edmonton)

Carter (1936; 1986) Joseph; ***339 High Road, Wembley HA9 6AG Tel: 020 8902 0081*** (Wembley 1)
Cassidy (1925; 1950) KHS, Patrick J; ***32 Nether Street N12 7NL Tel: 020 8445 7225*** (Retired)
Church (1964; 2001) STB, Shaun; ***Presbytery, Stonard Road, Green Lanes N13 4DJ Tel: 020 8886 9568*** (Palmers Green)
Coghlan (1934; 1961) Mgr John; ***c/o Archbishop's House, Ambrosden Avenue SW1P 1QJ***
Coker (1953; 1996) Stephen P; ***24 Holmes Rd, Twickenham TW1 4RE Tel: 020 8892 1444*** (Feltham)
Colven (1945; 1996) BA, Christopher G; ***Presbytery 100a Balls Pond Road N1 4AG Tel: 020 7254 4378*** (Kingsland)
Coningsby (1940; 1988) STL, Mark Raymond; ***Priest's House, Laxton Place, Longford Street NW1 3PT Tel: 020 7387 3833*** (Laxton Place)
Conlon (1949; 1979) HEL, Antony; ***The Oratory School, Woodcote, Nr Reading, Berks RG8 0PJ Tel: 01491 681074*** (School Chaplain)
Conneely (1956; 1988) JCL, John; ***165 Arlington Road NW1 7EX Tel: 020 7485 2727*** (Camden Town/Data Protection Officer/Tribunal)
Connor (1947; 1975) MA, Christopher; ***24 Golden Square W1F 9JR Tel: 0794 7561414*** (School Chaplain)
Connor (1953; 1978) BD, PSL, Michael; ***32 Field End Road, Eastcote, Pinner HA5 2QT Tel: 020 8866 6581*** (Eastcote)
Convery (1947; 1971) Antony; ***94 Bath Road, Hounslow, Middx TW3 3EH Tel: 020 8570 1693*** (Hounslow)
Cooke (1927; 1951) Anthony J; ***12 Bringewood Road, Ludlow, Salop SY8 2LZ*** (Retired)
Cowan (1941; 1973) Anton; ***17 Churchfield Path, Cheshunt, Herts EN8 9EG Tel: 01992 629878*** (Cheshunt)
Creak (1940; 1980) MA, Brian; ***Newman House, 111 Gower Street WC1E 6AR Tel: 020 8968 3373*** (University Chaplaincy)
Crewe (1933; 1963) Hilary; ***St Mary's Rectory, Draycott Terrace SW3 2QR Tel: 020 7589 5487*** (Chelsea 1)
Crewe (1930; 1969) Vincent; ***c/o Archbishop's House SW1P 1QJ*** (Retired)
Cronin (1952; 1977) LLM, KCHS, Canon Daniel; ***4 Holly Place NW3 6QU Tel: 020 7435 6678*** (Hampstead)
Cross (1936; 1974) Canon Philip; ***185 Baldwins Lane, Croxley Green, Rickmansworth WD3 3LL Tel: 01923 231969*** (Croxley Green)
Crowe (1930; 1955) Bernard; ***The Lodge, Ware Park SG12 0DS Tel: 01920 460396*** (Ware Chaplain/Retired)
Cullinan (1957; 1995) MA, PhD, STL, Michael; ***Pontificio Collegio Portughese, Via Nicolo V, 3, 00165 Roma*** (Further Studies)
Cunningham (1952; 1977) John; ***204 High Street, Waltham Cross, Herts EN8 7DP Tel: 01992 623156*** (Waltham Cross)
Curry (1960; 1986) STB, Mgr James; ***247 High Road W4 4PU Tel: 020 8994 2877*** (Chiswick)

Dain (1922; 1960) BA, Kenneth; ***13 Uplands Road N8 9NN Tel: 020 8340 0778*** (Retired)
Daley (1959; 2005) BA, BSc, STB, MA, RGN, Michael; ***247 High Road W4 4PU Tel: 020 8994 2877*** (Chiswick)
Dangerfield (1932; 1956) Richard G; ***2 New Peachey Lane, Cowley Peachey*** (Retired)
Davies (1948; 1987) Colin; ***54 Lodge Road NW8 8LA Tel: 020 7286 3214*** (St John's Wood)
Davies (1935; 1974) Jeremy; ***52 Castle Street, Luton LU1 3AG***
Davies (1960; 1998) BTh LRAM Jeremy M W; ***32 Union Street, Barnet, Herts EN5 4HZ Tel: 020 8449 3338*** (Barnet)
Davies (1938; 1977) Canon Patrick; ***24 Golden Square W1F 9JR Tel: 020 7437 1525*** (Warwick Street)
Day (1936; 1964) Peter; ***Nazareth House 162 East End Road N2 0RU*** (Retired)
Dean (1942;1992) Timothy;***42 Francis Street SW1P 1QW Tel: 020 7798 9055*** (Cathedral)
Deehan (1949; 1975) MA , STB, LSS, John; ***262 Kingston Road, Teddington, Middx TW11 9JQ Tel: 020 8977 2986*** (Teddington & Hampton Wick)
Delany (1940; 1965) Stephen; ***377 Mile End Road E3 4QS Tel: 020 8980 1845*** (Missions)
de Lord (1946; 1994) STB, Richard; ***22 The Crosspath, Radlett, Herts WD7 8HN Tel: 01923 856165*** (Radlett)
de l'Orme (1948; 1979) MEd, Frederick; ***Prior Park College, Bath*** (Chaplain)
Dempsey (1927; 1961) SRN, MA, William; ***Littlemore Rectory, Ballycommon, Co Offaly Tel: 0506 53662*** (Retired)
Dermody (1955; 1992) BA, John P; ***The Priest's House, Gravel Hill N3 3RJ Tel: 020 8346 2459*** (Finchley Church End)
Dickie (1948; 1977) Ian; ***3 Station Road, Buntingford, Herts SG9 9HT Tel: 01763 271471*** (Buntingford, Old Hall Green & Puckeridge)
Doe (1950; 1981) BA, MA, STL, Anthony; ***Monastery, St Charles Square W10 6EA Tel: 020 8964 3800*** (Chaplain)
Donaghy (1956; 1981) BD, PGCE, Michael; ***7 Barrowby Close, Luton, Beds LU2 9JL Tel: 07967 645772*** (Teaching)
Donlan (1948; 1972) John;***c/o Archbishop's House, Ambrosden Avenue SW1P 1QJ*** (Retired)
Drumm (1940; 1970) MA, Mgr Walter; ***162 East End Road N2 0RU*** (Retired)
Duffy (1938; 1967) MEd, James; ***5 Park Road, Rickmansworth, Herts WD3 1HU Tel: 01923 773387*** (Rickmansworth)
Dunkling (1962; 1986) Reginald; ***22 Cortayne Road SW6 3QA Tel: 020 7736 1068*** (Parsons Green)
Dunne (1964; 2004) BA, Michael; ***41 Brook Green W6 7BL Tel: 020 7603 3832*** (Brook Green)
Durand (1925; 1990) MA, Michael; ***Cathedral Clergy House, 42 Francis Street SW1P 1QW Tel: 020 7798 9055*** (Retired/Cathedral)
Dutton (1932; 1960) John; ***St Joseph's House, 42 Brook Green W6 7BW*** (Retired)
Dwyer (1952; 1984) Anthony; ***Allen Hall, 28 Beaufort Street SW3 5AA Tel: 020 7349 5600*** (Seminary)
Dwyer (1933; 1957) MA, Peter; ***47 The Park, St Albans AL1 4RX Tel: 01727 856483 Mobile: 07974 353184*** (Retired)
Dyer-Perry (1976; 2004) STB, Philip; ***Holy Rood House, Exchange Road, Watford, Herts WD18 0PJ Tel: 01923 224085*** (Watford)

Eastell (1942; 2002) BA, STh, MEd, PhD, Kevin; ***L'Aveau, 49700 Les Verchers Sur Layon, Maine et Loire, France Tel: 00 33 241 599750*** (Institute Director)
Edgar (1956; 1996) MA, BD, AKC, Timothy; ***47 Vesta Avenue, St Albans AL1 2PE Tel: 01727 850066 (St Albans South)***
Egan (1937; 1966) MA, MSc, Patrick; ***Domino's Chapel, 24 Frank Lloyd Wright Drive, PO Box 466, Ann Arbor, Michigan 48106-0466 USA*** (Retired)
Egan (1942; 1967) BEd, Mgr Canon Thomas; ***373 Bowes Road N11 1AA Tel: 020 8368 1638*** (New Southgate)
Elliott (1945; 1988) John; ***c/o Archbishop's House SW1P 1QJ*** (Sabbatical)
Ennis (1923; 1965) George; ***Hydrangea, St Brendan's Community Centre, Mulranny, Co Mayo, Ireland Tel: (00) 353 9836316*** (Retired)
Evans (1959; 1995) BSc, BTh, David; ***3 King Edward's Road E9 7SF Tel: 020 8985 2496*** (Hackney)
Everson (1958; 2000) BA, Simon; ***Farleigh School, Red Rice, Andover SP11 7PW Tel: 01264 710747*** (Headmaster Chaplain)

Fairhead (1960; 1995) MA, BTh, Jeremy; ***The Old Palace, St Aldate's, Oxford OX1 1RD Tel: 01865 726993*** (University Chaplaincy)
Felzmann (1939; 1969) KCHS, DD, MSc(Eng), Mgr Vladimir; ***All Saints Pastoral Centre, London Colney, St Albans, Herts AL2 1AF Tel: 01727 822010*** (All Saints Pastoral Centre)
Fernandes (1964; 1988) BD, Norbert; ***60 Rylston Road SW6 7HW Tel: 020 7385 4040*** (Fulham 1)
Ffrench (1936; 1962) Barry; ***Ballymoney, Gorey, Co Wexford, Ireland*** (Retired)
Fitzgibbon (1937; 1971) Richard; ***Nazareth House, 162 East End Road N2 0SF Tel: 020 8444 0935*** (Retired)
Fitzpatrick (1948; 1986) Eugene Jude; ***4 Thirleby Rd, Burnt Oak, Edgware, Middx HA8 0HQ Tel: 020 8959 1971*** (Burnt Oak)
Foley (1944; 1971) Patrick; ***Church of St Helen, The Harebreaks, Watford, Herts WD2 5NJ Tel: 01923 223175*** (Watford North)
Forde Thomas; (1943, 1977) ***4 Lady Margaret Road NW5 2XT Tel: 020 7485 4023*** (Kentish Town)
Formby (1931; 1956) Canon John; ***130 St Margaret's Road, East Twickenham, Middx TW1 1RL Tel: 020 8892 3902*** (St Margaret-on-Thames)
Freely (1934;1999) KCHS, Gerald; ***23 Roxborough Park, Harrow-on-the Hill HA1 3BE Tel: 020 8869 6892***
Fudge (1940; 1971) Alan J; ***8 Ogle Street W1P 7LG Tel: 020 7636 2883*** (Ogle Street)
Fullam (1932; 1961) Seamus; ***72 London Road, Knebworth, Herts SG3 6HB Tel: 01438 813303*** (Knebworth)
Fuller (1908; 1931) DD, LSS, PhD, Canon Reginald; ***Nazareth House, 162 East End Road N2 0RU*** (Retired)

Galvin (1929; 1954) John; ***Flat 5, 8 Morpeth Terrace SW1P 1EQ***
Tel: 020 7798 9022 (Retired)
Garnett (1935; 1965) MA, PhL, Michael; ***Santa Apolonia 146, Apartado 319, Cajamarca, Peru, S America Tel: 0051 76 823517 E-mail: miguelgarnett@yahoo.es*** (on loan)
Garvey (1926; 1951) MA, Charles Austin; ***211 Old Marylebone Road NW1 5QT***
Tel: 020 7723 7757 ((Retired/Marylebone/Ethnic Chaplaincy)
Garvey (1962; 1991) James P; ***160 Long Lane, Hillingdon, Middx UB10 0EH***
Tel: 01895 234577 (Hillingdon)
Gates (1920; 1955) MA, Robert; ***205 Nelson Road, Whitton, Middx TW2 7BB***
Tel: 020 8898 3768 (Retired)
Gawecki (1939; 1968) Christopher; ***130 St Margaret's Road, East Twickenham TW1 1RL***
Tel: 020 8892 3902 (St Margaret-on-Thames/Chaplain Hillingdon Hospitall)
Gilburt (1926; 1963) Canon Peter; ***56 Thornton Avenue W4 1QQ***
Tel: 020 8400 1677 (Retired)
Gosnell (1958; 1998) SRN, BTh, MA, Nicholas, ***8 Keogh Close, Mytchett, Hants GU12 5RJ***
Tel: 01252 348534 (Army Chaplain)
Graham (1952; 1995) STB, Donald; ***177 Bow Road E3 2SG Tel: 020 8980 3961*** (Bow)
Grant (1948; 1991) Peter; ***Sacred Heart Church, Park Street, Berkhampstead, Herts NP41HX***
Tel: 01442 863845 (Berkhampstead)
Gray (1944; 1984) John; ***St Joseph's Presbytery, 339 High Road, Wembley HA9 6AG***
Tel: 020 8902 0081 (Wembley 1)
Grech (1965;1990) MTh MA Saviour, ***59 Gresham Road, Staines, Middx TW18 2BD***
Tel: 01784 452381 (Staines)
Griffin (1948; 1997) BSc FRSA, Nigel; ***207 Nelson Road, Whitton, Twickenham TW2 7BB***
Tel: 020 8241 2941 (Hospital Chaplain)
Groarke (1924; 1948) STL, Michael D; ***Nazareth House, 162 East End Road N2 0RU***
Tel: 020 8883 0508 (Retired)
Gullan-Steel (1943; 1980) BD, Stuart; ***St Patrick's Rectory, 21 Main Street, Ravene, New York 12143 Tel: 518 756 3145*** *(on loan)*

Hamill (1927; 1954) Harold E; ***3 Copper Beeches, Witham Road, Osterley, Middx TW7 4AW***
Tel: 020 8568 6581 (Retired)
Hamilton-Gray (1959; 1996) BA, BSc, Dip Th, Christopher
Catholic Church, Crown Rise, Garston, Watford, Herts WD2 6NE Tel: 01923 673239 (Garston)
Hannigan (1947; 1988) Neil; ***131 Glenarm Road E5 0NB***
Tel: 020 8525 1929 (Clapton Park)
Harrington (1932; 1956) MEd John; ***103 Northfield Road, New Moston, Manchester M40 3RW*** (Retired)
Harrington (1935; 1988) Thomas; ***Marian House, 100 Kingston Lane, Uxbridge UB8 3PW*** (Retired)
Harris (1951; 1994) BEd MTh, Peter; ***297 Westferry Road E14 3RS***
Tel: 020 7987 4114 (Millwall)
Hart (1924; 1962) Austin; ***Nazareth House, 162 East End Road N2 0RU***
Tel: 020 8883 1104 (Retired)

Hasker (1961; 1996) BA Stewart P, *112 Twickenham Road, Isleworth, Middx TW7 6DL*
Tel: 020 8560 1431 (Isleworth)
Hayes (1956; 1984) BA, BD, Martin; *Allen Hall, 28 Beaufort Street SW3 5AA*
Tel: 020 7349 5782 (Amicus Clero)
Heal (1913; 1994) Guy Martin; *Charterhouse EC1M 6AN Tel: 020 7251 3943* (Retired)
Healy (1952; 1985) Bruno J; *St Joseph's Presbytery, Lamb's Passage, Bunhill Row EC1Y 8LE*
Tel: 020 7628 0326 (Bunhill Row)
Heaney (1927; 1953) Brian; *Nazareth House, 162 East End Road N2 0RU*
Tel: 020 8444 7130 (Retired/Chaplain)
Heekin (1924; 1960) Patrick; *Presbytery, 100a Balls Bond Road N1 4AG*
Tel: 020 7254 4378 (Retired/Kingsland)
Helm (1936; 1962) John; *700 Finchley Road NW11 7NE*
Tel: 020 8455 1300 (Golders Green)
Heslin (1960; 1999 BA, HDipEd, STB, Matthew; *Presbytery, Osborn Rd, Uxbridge, Middx UB8 1UE*
Tel: 01895 233193 (Uxbridge)
Hoey (1915; 1995) Ob OSB, MA, Augustine; *2a Meadow Road SW8 1QH*
Tel: 020 7582 5383 (Retired)
Holmes-Walker (1942; 1980) BSc, MRSC, Robert; *c/o Sisters of Providence,*
Limekiln Lane, Baldock, Herts SG7 6PG (Retired)
Horan (1934; 2001) Danny; *24 Sunningdale Avenue W3 7NS*
Tel: 020 8743 5732 (Acton East)
Hosford (1928; 1959) Horatio; *Flat 2, 8 Morpeth Terrace SW1P 1EQ*
Tel: 020 7798 9019 (Retired)
Howe (1933; 1960) Mgr Antony; *212 Crescent House EC1Y 0SL*
Tel: 020 7608 0911 ((Retired)
Hutton (1944; 1988) TD, FCII, Timothy CR; *32 Hallowell Rd, Northwood, Middx HA6 1DW*
Tel: 01923 825639 (Northwood)

Irwin (1944; 1995) AKC, David; *12 Womersley Rd N8 9AE Tel: 020 8340 3394* (Stroud Green)

Jackson (1943; 1997) BA, Frederick; *The Clergy House, 16 Abingdon Road W8 6AF*
Tel: 020 7937 4778 (Kensington 1)
James (1959; 1991) MA, BSc, STB, Howard; *Holy Family Cathedral, PO Box 16, St John's,*
Antigua, West Indies Tel: 001 268 461 1127 (on loan)
Johnston (1946; 1981) M Th, MA, BD ,Dip Ed Michael;
73 Pembroke Road, Ruislip, Middx HA4 8NN Tel: 01895 632739 (Ruislip)
Jordan (1968;1999) Kevin; *80 Imperial Close, North Harrow HA2 7LW*
Tel: 020 8868 7531 (Harrow North)

Kavanagh (1949; 1998) MA,BD, Nicholas; *22 George Street W1U 3QY*
Tel: 020 7935 0943 (Tribunal/Spanish Place)
Kearney (1927; 1952) John; *11/13 Grovenor Road, Westcliffe on Sea, Essex SS0 8EP* (Retired)
Kelly (1953; 1977) David; *Defence Academy of UK, HQ, Greenhill House, Shrivenham,*
Swindon, Wilts SN6 8LA Tel: 01793 785515 (Army Chaplain)

Kennedy (1943; 1980) Jim; ***157 Copenhagen Street N1 0SR***
Tel: 020 7837 4841 (Copenhagen Street)
Kennedy (1950; 1977) Michael; ***35 Cricklewood Lane NW2 1HR***
Tel: 020 8452 2475 (Cricklewood)
Kennelly (1940; 1974) Canon Matthew; ***216 Dollis Hill Lane NW2 6HE***
Tel: 020 8452 6158 (Dollis Hill)
Kiernan (1932; 1962) Thomas; ***33 Coolamber Court, Templeogue, Dublin 6***
Tel: 00 353 1 494 5204 (Retired)
King (1960; 1984) Gerard; ***26 Salisbury Square, Old Hatfield, Herts AL9 5JD***
Tel: 01707 262439 (Hatfield Marychurch)
Kirinich (1953; 1978) MA, STL, Roger; ***Parish House, 2 Tynemouth Street SW6 2QT***
Tel: 020 7736 4864 (Stephendale Road)
Klyberg (1931; 1996), Mgr Charles John; ***44 Naildown Road, Hythe Kent CT21 5TB***
Tel: 01303 239445 (Retired)
Knights (1960; 2002) MA, BA, PhD, Philip; ***114 West Heath Road NW3 7TX***
Tel: 020 8458 3316 E-mail: philipk@caseresources.org.uk (CASE)

Langham (1960; 1990) MA, STL, Mgr Mark; ***42 Francis Street SW1P 1QW***
Tel: 020 7798 9055 (Cathedral Administrator)
Law (1950; 1977) Philip; ***6 Athenaeum Road N20 9AE***
Tel: 020 8445 0838 (Whetstone)
Leathem (1960; 1985) Michael; ***c/o Archbishop's House, Ambrosden Avenue SW1P 1QJ***
(On leave)
Lebasi (1946; 1975) STL Kidane; ***24 Golden Square W1F 9JR***
Tel: 020 7025 1594 (Chaplain to Gheez Rite Community/Warwick Street)
Lee (1959; 1998) Clive; ***9 Henry Road N4 2LH Tel: 020 8802 9910*** (Manor House)
Leenane (1964; 1998) BSc (Surv), BA, Mark; ***2 Witham Road, Osterley, Isleworth TW7 4AJ***
Tel: 020 8560 4737 (Osterley)
Legge (1942; 1995) Raymond; ***The Presbytery, Rant Meadow, Hemel Hempstead, Herts HP3 8PG Tel: 01442 255471*** (Hemel Hempstead East)
Lennard (1957; 1994) Shaun; ***39 Duncan Terrace N1 8AL***
Tel 020 7226 3277 (Islington)
Leonard (1936; 1971) Francis; ***4 Basils Road, Stevenage, Herts SG1 3PX***
Tel: 01438 226857 (Stevenage Old Town)
Leonard (1921; 1994) KCVO, PC, MA, STD, Mgr Graham Douglas;
25 Woodlands Road, Witney, Oxon OX28 2DR Fax: 01993 773472 (Retired)
Letellier (1953; 1985) MA, MLitt, PhD, SSL, STD, Robert Ignatius;
7 Parker Street, Cambridge CB1 1JL (Further Studies)
Liddle (1948; 1980) BA, Gladstone; ***23 St John's Street, Hertford, Herts SG14 1RX***
Tel: 01992 582109 (Hertford)
Loring (1946; 1987) MA, BD, Ulick; ***61 Pope's Grove, Twickenham, Middx TW1 4JZ***
Tel: 020 8892 4578 (Twickenham)

Lowry (1961; 1991) Mehall; ***c/o St Patrick's, Hardie Close NW10 0UH***
(Sabbatical)
Lyness (1948; 1995) MA, Peter; ***291 Shenley Road, Borehamwood, Herts WD6 1TG***
Tel: 020 8953 1294 (Borehamwood)
Lyons (1960; 1990) BTh, George; ***c/o Archbishop's House, Ambrosden Avenue SW1P 1QJ***
Lyons (1921; 1954) BSc, Patrick; ***1st Floor Flat, 33 Lower Teddington Road, Hampton Wick, Kingston-upon-Thames, Surrey KT1 4HQ Tel: 020 8943 3232*** (Retired)

MacKenzie (1962; 1995) MSc, PhL Hugh; ***Clergy House, Peter Avenue NW10 2DD***
Tel: 020 8451 4677 (Willesden Green))

McAleenan (1951; 1985) Paul; ***Holy Rood House, Exchange Road, Watford, Herts WD1 7AJ***
Tel: 01923 224085 (Watford)
McCabe (1935; 1967) Kenneth; ***More House, 28 The Grove, Isleworth, Middx TW7 4JU***
Tel: 020 8568 9487 (Director of Lillie Road Centre)
McCarthy (1935; 1969) Timothy; ***599 Keith Road, West Vancouver, BC, Canada V7T 1L8*** (On loan)
McConalogue (1939;1970) William; ***194 Knightsfield, Welwyn Garden City AL8 7RQ***
Tel: 01707 327434 (Welwyn Garden City Digswell)
McCormick (1934; 1958) James; ***The Villa, Thornton Cottage, Thornton, Buckingham MK17 0HJ***
Tel: 01280 813866 (On loan)
McCoy (1920; 1948) John; ***41 Parkside, Welwyn, Herts AL6 9DQ Tel: 01438 718524*** (Retired)
McCumiskey (1938; 1971) MA, BSc, STL, JCL, Bernard; ***51 Nether Street N12 7NN***
Tel: 020 8446 0224 (Finchley North)
McDermott (1970; 2000) Paul; ***80 Imperial Close, North Harrow, Middx HA2 7LW***
Tel: 020 8429 5685 (Hospital Chaplain)
McDevitt (1943; 1969) Kevin; ***15 St John's Villas N19 3EE***
Tel: 020 7272 8195 (Upper Holloway)
McDonald (1930; 1955) Canon John D; ***54 Lodge Road NW8 8LA***
Tel: 020 7286 3214 (Retired/Chaplain St John & St Elizabeth/St John's Wood)
McGeoghan (1945; 1969) Seamus; ***6 Melbourne Road, Royston, Herts SG8 7DB***
Tel: 01763 243117 (Royston)
McGinn (1947; 1972) Canon Paul; ***Allen Hall, 28 Beaufort Street SW3 5AA***
Tel: 020 7349 5600 (Seminary)
McGonagle (1927; 1954) BA, Cathal; ***87 Blue Cedars, Cappry, Ballybofey, Co Donegal***
Tel: 00353 7491 89372 (Retired)
McGowan (1919; 1944); BA, Canon Charles; ***2a Meadow Road SW8 1QH*** (Retired)
McGrath (1934;1962) Dermot; ***50 McClure Meadows, Newline Road, Wexford, Ireland***
Tel: 00 353 53 21116 (Retired)
McGuckin (1950; 1980) BA, STL, MLitt, DD, Terence; ***4a Inverness Place W2 3JF***
Tel: 020 7229 8153 (Queensway)
McKenna (1950; 1994) Dominic; ***c/o Archbishop's House, Ambrosden Avenue SW1P 1QJ***
McLean (1934; 1981) Colin; ***165 Arlington NW1 7EX*** (Retired)
McLoughlin (1947; 1986) Patrick; ***5 Drumaroan Road, Ballycastle BT54 6QU***
Tel: (+44) 012657 62626 (Corrymeela)

McNicholas (1944; 1974) BD, MTh, James; ***20 Phoenix Road NW1 1TA***
Tel: 020 7387 1971 (Somers Town)
McPartlan (1955; 1984) MA, STL, DPhil, Paul; ***School of Theology, Catholic University of America, 620 Mitchigan Avenue NE, Washington DC 20064*** (On loan)
McWeeney (1936; 1972) Sean; ***13 Mill Way, Feltham, Middx TW14 0JX***
Tel: 020 8890 2863 (Retired)

Magnier (1949; 1974) Daniel; ***1 Du Cros Drive, Stanmore, Middx HA7 4TJ***
Tel: 020 8954 1299 (Stanmore)
Maher (1944; 1970) Peter; ***141 Woodhall Lane, Welwyn Garden City, Herts. AL7 3TP***
Tel: 01707 323234 (Welwyn Garden City East)
Mallon (1940; 1975) James; ***c/o Archbishop's House SW1P 1QJ*** (Sabbatical)
Mannion (1952; 1986) Michael; ***Presbytery, Bouverie Road N16 0AJ***
Tel: 020 8800 5250 (Stoke Newington)
Markey (1942;1995) Michael, ***Presbytery, London Road, Bushey, Watford WD23 1BH***
Tel: 020 8950 2077 (Bushey)
Marriott (1938; 1995) MA, Canon Richard; ***c/o Archbishop's House SW1P 1QJ*** (Retired)
Matthews (1937; 1962) LTL, Canon Edward; ***St Joseph's, 3 Windhill, Bishop's Stortford, Herts CM23 2ND Tel: 01279 654063*** (Bishop's Stortford)
Meaney (1939; 1976) Gerard; ***Nazareth House, East End Road N2 0RU***
Tel: 020 8444 3691 (Retired)
Middleton (1962; 1989) STB, MA, Shaun; ***The Presbytery, Pottery Lane W11 4NQ***
Tel: 020 7727 7968 (Notting Hill)
Miles (1925; 1950) ProtAp, MA, Mgr Canon Frederick A; ***2a Meadow Road SW8 1QH***
Tel: 020 7793 1338 (Retired)
Miller (1923; 1953) John M; ***13 Highlands, 131 Oakleigh Road North N20 9HA***
Tel: 020 8445 8896 (Retired)
Miller (1966;1999) MA,PhD,STL, Philip; ***9 Pekin Street E14 6EZ***
Tel: 020 7531 6956 (Chaplain Royal London/St Bartholomew's Hospital)
Moore (1916; 1939) Canon Peter E; ***c/o Mr A Moore,***
Pillmoss Lane, Lower Whitley, Cheshire WA4 4DW (Retired)
Moraes (1929; 1955) Arthur; ***Orione House, 12 Station Road, Hampton Wick, Kingston-upon-Thames KT1 4EV*** (Retired)
Morris (1956;1991) MA, BA, BD, Allen; ***39 Eccleston Square SW1V 1PL***
Tel: 020 7901 4850 (Department of Christian Life and Worship)
Mulligan (1946; 2005) James; ***The Presbytery, Dundee Street, Green Bank E1W 2PH***
Tel: 020 7481 2202 (Wapping)
Munnelly (1949; 1973) BD, MA, Canon Michael; ***22 Bradley Road N22 7NZ***
Tel: 020 8888 2390 (Wood Green)
Murphy (1914; 1940) John; ***Nazareth House, Hammersmith Road W6 8DB*** (Retired)
Murphy (1947; 1972) John M; ***c/o Archbishop's House, Ambrosden Avenue SW1P 1QJ***
Murphy (1937; 1968) Seamus; ***84 Pixmore Way, Letchworth, Herts SG6 3TP***
Tel: 01462 683504 (Letchworth)

Nash (1936; 1960) STL, PhL, Brian ***377 Mile End Road E3 4QS Tel: 020 8980 1845*** (Retired)
Newby (1958; 1990) MA, PhL, Peter;***4/5 Eldon St EC2M 7LS Tel: 020 7247 8390*** (Moorfields)
Nguyen (1958; 1999) STB, Simon Duc Tang; ***15 The Green, Heston Road, Heston, Middlesex TW5 0RL Tel: 020 8570 1818*** (Heston)
Noctor (1928; 1957) James; ***49 Mattison Road N4 1BG Tel: 020 8348 1378*** (Harringay)
Nolan (1929; 1975) Patrick; ***Flat 3, 165 Arlington Road NW1 7EX Tel: 020 7428 6807*** (Retired)
Norris (1922; 1947) ProtAp, MA, Mgr David J; ***Clergy House, 42 Francis Street SW1P 1QW Tel: 020 7798 9055*** (Retired/Cathedral)

O'Boy (1968;2000) BA, PhD, STB, Michael; ***Clergy House, 42 Francis Street SW1P 1QW Tel: 020 7798 9055*** (Cathedral)
O'Boyle (1957; 1981) STL,Seamus; ***Presbytery, St Edmund's Lane, 213 Nelson Road, Whitton, Middx TW2 7BB Tel: 020 8894 9923*** (Whitton)
O'Brien (1948; 1972) Dip RE Eamonn; ***St Christopher's Catholic Church, 2278 Booksin Avenue, San Jose CA 95125 4701 Tel: 408 978 8980 E-mail: eamonnobrien00@hotmail.com*** (On loan)
O'Connell (1963; 1993) Andrew, ***35 Cricklewood Lane NW2 1HR Tel: 020 8452 2475*** (Cricklewood)
O'Connor (1949; 1973) BA, Dip Rel Ed,Timothy; ***243 Mutton Lane, Potters Bar, Herts EN6 2AT Tel: 01707 654359*** (Potters Bar)
O'Doherty (1964; 1992) Michael; ***The Presbytery, Hardie Close NW10 0UH Tel: 020 8451 0367*** (Neasden)
O'Driscoll (1925; 1967) Patrick David; ***1 The Cloisters, Long Street, Sherborne DT9 3BS Tel: 01935 817979*** (Retired)
O'Gorman (1973; 2001) BA (Hons), MA, STB, Anthony; ***Presbytery, St Edmund's Lane, 213 Nelson Park Road, Whitton TW2 7BB Tel: 020 8894 9923*** (Further Studies)
O'Halloran (1924; 1957) MA, John; ***16 Hartley House, Ballards Lane N3 1NF Tel: 020 8346 1768*** (Retired)
O'Leary (1967 ; 1992) STB, PhL, John; ***70 Lincoln's Inn Fields WC2A 3JA Tel: 020 7405 0376*** (Further Studies)
O'Neill (1959; 1982) Dermot; ***The Presbytery, 2a Salehurst Close,Kenton, Middx HA3 0UG Tel 020 8204 3550*** (Kenton)
O'Neill (1921; 1947) John D; ***216 Dollis Hill Lane NW2 6HE Tel: 020 8450 4168*** (Retired)
O'Reilly (1919; 1957) Peter; ***Visitation Convent, Foxhunt Green, Waldron, Heathfield, East Sussex TN21 0RX Tel: 01435 812239*** (Retired)
O'Toole (1963; 1990) BSc, BD, MPhil, STL, Mark; ***Archbishop's House, Ambrosden Avenue SW1P 1QJ Tel: 020 7798 9033*** (Private Secretary)
O'Toole (1962;1998) STL, B Ed, Sean Patrick, ***68 Hazlewood Crescent W10 5DJ Tel: 020 8969 2660*** (Kensal New Town)

Overton (1941; 1973) MA, STL, BD, Mgr James; ***112 Clarendon Road, Ashford TW15 2QD Tel: 01784 252230*** (Ashford)

Palmer (1933; 1996) BA, David, ***29 Manor House Way, Isleworth TW7 6BJ***
Tel: 020 8847 4632 (Retired)
Paris (1956; 1983) Anthony; ***Catholic Chaplain, HQ 2 Div S Chap RC, Baden Powell House, Scotton Road, Caterick Garrison, N Yorks DL9 3JS*** (Army Chaplain)
Parsons (1946; 1998) BD, MTh, MPhil, STL, D Prof, AKC, Richard;
22 Boniface Walk, Harrow HA3 6PU Tel: 020 8428 3260/8864 8021 (Headstone Lane)
Pellegrini (1940;2004)KSG, KMCO, BA, BTh, ARCO, Anthony; ***279 High Road N2 8HG***
Tel: 020 8883 4234 (Finchley East)
Pham (1966; 2000) STB, John; ***Presbytery, Everglade Strand, Grahame Park NW9 5PX***
Tel: 020 8205 6830 (Grahame Park)
Phillips (1933;1999) Lamont; ***729 High Road N17 8AG Tel: 020 8808 3554*** (Tottenham)
Phillips (1922; 1946) MA, Canon Peter B; ***Presbytery, Maresfield Gardens NW3 5SU***
Tel: 020 7431 6192 (Retired)
Phipps (1950; 1983) MA, STL, Terence; ***22 George Street W1U 3QY***
Tel: 020 7935 0943 (Spanish Place)
Piccolomini (1955; 1990) Charis; ***c/o Archbishop's House, Ambrosden Avenue SW1P 1QJ***
Pinot de Moira (1932; 1956) Michael; ***St Edmund's College, Old Hall Green, Ware, Herts***
Tel: 01920 821334 (Old Hall Green)
Plourde (1944; 1975) Canon Robert; ***28 Love Lane, Pinner, Middx HA5 3EX***
Tel: 020 8866 0098 (Pinner)
Poole (1955; 1988) Robert; ***PO Box 7111 Ottawa, Ontario K1L 8EZ, Canada*** (On loan)
Power (1952; 1979) BA, BD, STL,STD, Dermot; ***28 Beaufort Street SW3 5AA***
Tel: 020 7349 5628 (Seminary)
Press (1955; 1981) Francis; ***4 Egerton Gardens NW4 4BA Tel: 020 8202 0560*** (Hendon)
Price (1947; 1978) Richard; ***Heythrop College, Kensington Square W8 5HQ***
Tel: 020 7795 4209 (Heythrop)
Przyjalkowski (1955; 1991) BD MTh, Voytek; ***60 Highbury Park N5 2XH***
Tel: 020 7226 0257 (Hospital Chaplain)
Psaila (1952; 1977) Anthony; ***94 Bath Road, Hounslow, Middx TW3 3EH***
Tel: 020 8570 1693 (Hounslow)

Quinn (1955; 1984) BA, STL, Gerard; ***44 Boston Park Road, Brentford, Middx TW8 9JF***
Tel: 020 8560 1671 (Brentford)
Quinn (1943 ; 1975) Thomas; ***38 Camborne Avenue W13 9QZ***
Tel: 020 8567 5421 (Northfields)

Reader (1958; 1995) BA, Roger; ***HM Young Offenders Institution, Bedfont Road, Feltham, Middx TW13 4ND Tel: 020 8844 5326*** (Prison Chaplain)
Rees (1930; 1959) Joseph; ***Nazareth House, 162 East End Road N2 0RU*** (Retired)
Reynolds (1938; 1962) Brian; ***7 Marford Road, Wheathampstead, Herts AL4 8AY***
Tel: 01582 832114 (Wheathampstead)
Reynolds (1959; 1995) BEd, Neil Francis; ***1 Peppard Close, Redbourne, St Albans AL3 7EB***
Tel: 01582 792270 (Redbourne)

Rigby (1939; 1988) MA, DPhil, Cormac; *19 Hawkswell Gardens, Oxford OX2 7EX* (Retired)
Rimini (1942; 1998) MISM, AIM, Kenneth; *St David's, Everest Rd, Stanwell, Staines TW19 7EE Tel: 01784 255973* (Stanwell)
Ritaccio (1970;1999) STB, Antonio; *Corpus Christi Presbytery, Maiden Lane WC2E 7NB Tel: 020 7836 4700* (Maiden Lane/Chaplain to Young People)
Robinson (1953; 1997) Alan Ian P; *The Parish House, Moorhouse Road W2 5DJ Tel: 020 7229 0487* (Bayswater)
Rouco Gutierrez (1972;2005) BA, BATS, Hector; *17 Kenninghall Road E5 8BS Tel 020 8985 2178* (Clapton)
Rowland (1949; 1975) Mgr Phelim; *Ministry of Defence Chaplains (Army), Trenchard Lines, Upavon Pewsey, Wilts SN9 6BE Tel: 01980 615803* (Principal RC Chaplain Army)
Ruiz (1976;2004) STB, Javier; *The Clergy House, 16 Abingdon Road W8 6AF Tel: 020 7937 4778* (Kensington 1)
Ryan (1946; 1971) Joseph; *4 Vincent Road N15 3QH Tel: 020 8888 5518* (West Green)
Ryan (1955; 1980) Paschal; *32 High Street, Cranford, Hounslow, Middx TW5 9RG Tel: 020 8759 2160* (Cranford)

Sacre (1931; 1955) Anthony; *377 Mile End Road E3 4QS Tel: 020 8980 1845* (Mile End)
Salvans (1959; 1992) MTh, Albert; *c/o Archbishop's House, Ambrosden Avenue SW1P 1QJ* (Missions)
Sammarco (1940;1999) Anthony; *42 Langdale Gardens, Perivale, Greenford UB6 8DQ Tel: 020 8997 3164* (Perivale)
Sammon (1948; 1978) Patrick; *5 Garratt Road, Edgware, Middx HA8 9AN Tel: 020 8952 0663* (Edgware)
Samuels (1948; 1976) Digby; *The Presbytery, Dundee Street, Green Bank E1 9PH Tel: 020 7481 2202* (Wapping)
Sarsfield (1962; 2002) STB, Denis; *Clergy House, 42 Francis Street SW1P 1QW Tel: 020 7798 9055* (Cathedral)
Sawyer (1946; 1974) Guy; *22 Roxborough Park, Harrow-on-the-Hill, Middx HA1 3BE Tel: 020 8422 2513* (Harrow-on-the-Hill)
Schofield (1975; 2003) MA, STB, Nicholas; *1 Nicoll Road NW10 9AX Tel: 020 8965 4935* (Willesden/Archivist)
Scholes (1936; 1960) MA, Canon Bernard; *52 Uxbridge Road W7 3SU Tel: 020 8567 4056* (Hanwell)
Scott (1965; 1991) STB, Peter Michael; *60 Rylston Road SW6 7HW Tel: 020 7385 4040* (Fulham/Seminary/Hospital Chaplains co-ordinator)
Scurlock (1951;1981) Anthony John; *Broad Haven, 2 Linden Green, Cleveleys, Lancs FY5 2QN Tel: 01253 826608*
Seabrook (1947; 1976) John; *1 Bolton Road W4 3TE Tel: 020 8994 6861* (Grove Park)
Seasman (1990) MA, BACP, Terence; *c/o Archbishop's House, Ambrosden Avenue SW1P 1QJ* (Sabbatical)
Seeldrayers, (1937; 1962) Anthony; *970 Harrow Road, Sudbury, Wembley, Middx HA0 2QE Tel: 020 8904 2552* (Sudbury)

Sharp (1938; 1970) Peter; ***25 Albert Street, Lytham, Lancs FY8 5EB***
Tel: 01253 732524 (Retired)
Sharratt (1940; 1965) BA, STL, Aidan; ***St Joseph's, Oxhey Drive, South Oxhey, Watford WD19 7SW***
Tel: 020 8428 2774 (Carpenders Park)
Sherbrooke (1957; 1988) Alexander; ***21a Soho Square W1D 4NR***
Tel: 020 7437 2010 (Soho Square)
Shewring (1941; 1976) John; ***192 Nags Head Road, Ponders End, Enfield EN3 7AR***
Tel: 020 8804 2149 (Ponders End)
Silva (1949; 1997) BSc, Christopher; ***970 Harrow Road, Sudbury, Wembley, Middx HA0 2QE***
Tel: 020 8904 2552 (Sudbury)
Skehan (1960; 1985) William; ***60 Highbury Park N5 2XH***
Tel: 020 7226 0257 (Highbury)
Skinner (1970; 2002) GRSM, LRAM, PhB, STL, FRSA, Gerard; ***45 London Rd, Enfield EN2 6DS***
Tel: 020 8363 2569 (Enfield)
Smith (1958; 1984) SLitDip, Brian; ***20 The Green, West Drayton, Middx UB7 7PJ***
Tel: 01895 442777 (West Drayton)
Smyth (1917; 1940) Canon Frederick A; ***156 Green Lane, Edgware, Middx HA8 8EJ***
Tel: 020 8958 4813 (Retired)
Stanley (1935; 1960) Cedric; ***1 Dunster Close, Park Lane, Harefield, Middx UB9 6BS***
Tel: 01895 822365 (Harefield)
Stark (1932; 1956) KCHS, Mgr Anthony G; ***31 Southdown Road SW20 8QJ***
Tel: 020 8947 2598 (Guild of Our Lady of Ransom)
Stevens (1935; 1988) Michael;***39 Barum Court, Litchdon St, Barnstable EX32 8QL*** (Retired)
Stevens (1931; 1989) Peter Francis; ***Hill Cottage, Shire Lane, Chorleywood, Rickmansworth WD3 5NH***
Tel: 01923 283616 (Chorleywood)
Stewart (1935; 1982) Michael; ***50 Bull Stag Green, Hatfield AL9 5DE***
Tel: 01707 264213 (Retired)
Stoakes (1958; 1983) Keith; ***Catholic Church, Commonwealth Avenue W12 7QR***
Tel 020 8743 8334 (White City)
Stokes (1945; 1983) John; ***HM Prison, Whitemoor, Longhill Road, March, Cambridge PE15 0PR***
Tel: 01345 660653 (Prison Chaplain)
Sykes (1959; 1985) Perry; ***16 Abingdon Road W8 6AF***
Tel: 020 7937 4778 (Kensington 1)

Tastard (1947; 1993) MA, M Phil, Terry; ***41 Brook Green W6 7BL***
Tel: 020 7603 3832 (Brook Green)
Taylor (1957: 2000) MA, STB, Roger; ***Presbytery, Stonard Road, Green Lanes N13 4DJ***
Tel: 020 8886 9568 (Palmers Green)
Thomas (1917; 1943) Canon Louis; ***22 Sherwood Hall, East End Road N2 0TA***
Tel: 020 8444 6141 (Retired)
Thomas (1971; 2002) STB; Thomas Kennedy ***c/o Archbishop's House SW1P 1QJ***
Thornton (1964; 1989) Sean; ***1 Wrentham Avenue NW10 3HT***
Tel: 020 8964 4040 (Kensal Rise)

Touw (1949; 1995) Dennis; ***447 Victoria Road, South Ruislip, Middx HA4 0EG***
Tel: 020 8845 2186 (Ruislip South)
Trood (1961; 2001) MA, ACA, STB, Jeremy; ***St Patrick's Rectory, 281 Nepean Street, Ottawa, Canada K1R 5GZ Tel: 01 613 233 1225*** (Further studies)
Tuck (1939; 1963) Michael; ***Catholic Rectory, Green Street, Sunbury-on-Thames TW16 6QB***
Tel: 01932 783507 (Sunbury-on-Thames)
Tuckwell (1945; 1995) Christopher; ***17 Kenninghall Road E5 8BS***
Tel: 020 8985 2178 (Clapton)
Turner (1941; 1966) Mgr Canon Henry; ***1 Kirkwick Avenue, Harpenden, Herts AL5 2QH***
Tel: 01582 712245 (Harpenden)
Turner (1934; 1960) John; ***St George's Retreat, Burgess Hill, Sussex RH15 0SQ***
Tel: 01444 232669 (Retired)

Usher (1942; 2000) BA, Thomas; ***c/o Archbishop's House, Ambrosden Avenue SW1P 1QJ*** (Retired)

van Son (1954; 1985) Francis; ***2 Lukin Street, Commercial Road E1 0AA***
Tel: 020 7790 5911 (Commercial Road)
Vickers (1966; 2003) BA, STB, Mark; ***73 Pembroke Road, Ruislip, Middx HA4 8NN***
Tel: 01895 632739 (Ruislip)
Vipers (1963; 1997) BA, Christopher J; ***247 High Road W4 4PU***
Tel: 020 7798 9083/020 8994 2877 (Vocations Director/Chiswick)

Wadsworth (1961; 1990) MA, GTCL, LTCL, LRAM, Andrew;
41a Peterborough Road, Harrow-on-the-Hill HA1 3DY Tel: 020 8422 3783 (Chaplain)
Wagay (1953; 1993) BA, MA,STB, Gideon; ***62 Eden Grove N7 8EN***
Tel: 020 7607 3594 (Holloway)
Wahle (1929; 1965) STL, BSc, Francis; ***17 Chiltern Court, Baker Street NW1 5TD***
Tel: 020 7487 5956 (Retired)
Walker (1931; 1960) Adrian; ***42 Bell Street Maidenhead SL6 1BR***
Tel: 01628 637796 (Retired)
Wang (1966; 1998) MA, PhL, Stephen; ***28 Beaufort Street SW3 5AA***
Tel: 020 7349 5608 (Seminary)
Ward (1937; 1961) Brian; ***The Presbytery, King Edward's Road, Ware, Herts SG12 7EJ***
Tel: 01920 462140 (Ware)
Wardle (1920; 1945) Terence L; ***7 Hutchings Lodge, High Street, Rickmansworth, Herts***
Tel: 01923 710031 (Retired)
Watters (1947; 1972) Denis; ***St Joseph's Presbytery, Bedwell Crescent, Stevenage SG1 1NJ***
Tel: 01438 351243 (Stevenage Bedwell)
Webb (1953; 1983) Christopher; ***7 Fox Close, Co Antrim BT29 4JR*** (RAF Chaplain)
Webb (1923; 1957) Geoffrey; ***93 Cowley Hill, Borehamwood*** (Retired)
Welsh (1946; 1994) John; ***St Raphael's House, Morrison Road, Yeading, Middx UB4 9JP***
Tel: 020 8845 1919 (Yeading)
Whatling (1929; 1969) Colin; ***2 Eaton Avenue, Heston TW5 0HB***
Tel: 020 8606 9544 (Retired)

White (1952; 1984) John; *167 The Broadway NW9 7EB*
Tel: 020 8202 5143 (Hendon West)
Whitmore (1959; 1993) MA, DPhil, STL, Mgr Philip; *Via di Monserrato 48/2, 00186 Roma*
Tel: 003906 687 2975 (Secretariate of State)
Whitney (1920; 1946) Robin; *Nazareth House, 162 East End Road N2 0RU* (Retired)
Whooley (1942; 1982) John; *44 Ashchurch Grove W12 9BU*
Tel: 020 8743 5196 (Shepherds Bush)
Wilby (1939; 1964) William; *St Wilfred's Convent, 29 Tite Street SW3 4JX*
Tel: 020 7351 5339 (Chaplain)
Wiley (1947; 1975) KSJ, MA, BD, John; *The Presbytery, Vale Lane W3 0DY*
Tel: 020 8992 1308 (Acton West)
Williamson (1945; 1975) STD, David; *Presbytery, Hay Lane NW9 0NG|*
Tel: 020 8204 2834 (Kingsbury Green)
Willis (1965; 1996) BA, Stephen A; *The Presbytery, Nicholl Road NW10 9RX*
Tel: 020 8965 4935 (Willesden)
Wilson (1938; 1970) David; *Les Trois Fontaines, 6 rue de l'Ecluse, Ambleteuse 62164, France*
Tel: 00 33321 999298 E-mail: davgilwil@wanadoo.fr
Wilson (1965; 1997) BA, H Dip Ed, Peter J; *Newman House, 111 Gower Street WC1E 6AR*
Tel: 020 7387 6370 (University Chaplain)
Wilson (1947; 1996) MA, BSc, Stuart M P; *16 Abingdon Road W8 6AF*
Tel: 020 7931 6059/7937 9165 (Director of Renewal Programme/Year Book Editor)
Winter (1948; 1978) Marcus; *79 St Charles Square W10 6EB*
Tel: 020 8969 6844 (St Charles Square)
Witon (1975; 2005) STB, Slawomir; *Clergy House, 42 Francis Street SW1P 1QW*
Tel: 020 7798 9055 (Cathedral)
Woodruff (1959; 1995) BA, Mark; *The Sainsbury Family Charitable Trust, Allington House Victoria Street, SW1E 5AE Tel: 020 7410 7049 E-mail: mark.woodruff@sfct.org.uk*
Wrigley (1936; 1981) BA, AKC, Norman; *6 South Road, Baldock, Herts SG7 6BX*
Tel: 01462 893127 (Retired/Baldock)

Young (1932; 1957) MA, Henry; *63 Heathfield Court, Heathfield Terrace W4 4LS* (Retired)

Zsidi (1951; 1975) Gabriel; *c/o Archbishop's House, Ambrosden Avenue SW1P 1QJ*

DEACONS

Madden, Patrick;
Conesa, Agustin (Enfield)
Salvesen, Ragnor (Chiswick)
McKenna, John (White City)

PERMANENT DEACONS

Hemming MA, MPhil, PhD, Laurence P; *Heythrop College, Kensington Square W8 5HQ*
Tel: 020 7795 6600
Levett, Robert; *St George's Chapel, Heathrow Airport, Hounslow, Middlx TW6 1BP*
Tel: 020 8745 4261
McPherson MA, D Min, Duncan; *52 Fulwell Park Avenue, Twickenham, Middx*
Tel: 020 8755 1464
Saunders, Ronald; *Cedar Cottage, Levens Green, Ware, Herts*
Tel: 01920 438241 (Old Hall Green)

WESTMINSTER STUDENTS IN TRAINING FOR THE PRIESTHOOD

Allen Hall, London
Simon Bartolo
Andrew Connick
Andrew Gallagher
Arulananthem theva Kingsley
Richard Nesbitt
Gerard O'Brien
Emile Richards
Paul Said
Graham Stokes

Venerable English College, Rome
William Johnstone
James Neal

Pontifical Beda College, Rome
William Nicol

Neo-Catechumenate
John Elliott
Paulo Bagini

Pastoral Placements
Edward Houghton
Vincent Malone

St Alban's College, Valladolid
Robert Colquhoun
Stefan Kaminski

OTHER PRIESTS IN THE DIOCESE

The entry in brackets following each surname indicates the diocese, order, congregation or society to which the priest belongs.
A place name refers to the parish entry under which further details may be found.

AA	Assumptionist
CM	Vincentian
CMF	Claretian Missionary
CP	Passionist
CSS	Stigmatine
CSSp	Holy Ghost Father
CSSR	Redemptorist
FDP	Sons of Divine Providence
IC	Rosminian (Inst. of Charity)
IMC	Consolata Father
LMO	Lebanese Maronite Order
MAfr	Missionary of Africa (White Father)
MCCJ	Comboni Missionary
MHM	Mill Hill Missionary
MIC	Marian Father
MSC	Missionaries of the Sacred Heart
MSFS	Fransalian
OAR	Augustinian Recollect
OCarm	Carmelite
ODC	Carmelite (Discalced)
OFM	Franciscan (Friar Minor)
OMI	Oblates of Mary Immaculate
OP	Dominican
OSA	Augustinian
OSB	Benedictine
OSCam	Camillian
OSM	Servite
SA	Friar of the Atonement
SCA	Pallottine
SCJ	Sacred Heart Father
SDS	Salvatorian
SJ	Jesuit
SM	Marist
SMA	Society of African Missions
SMM	Montfort Missionary
SSC	Columban Father
SS.CC	Sacred Hearts Community
SVD	Divine Word Missionary
SX	Xaverian Missionary

Addison (OSM) Paul M; ***264 Fulham Road SW10 9EL*** (Fulham Road)
Akiki (LMO) Dany; ***6 Dobson Close NW6 4RS*** (Lebanese)
Akoeso (OSB) Bernard M; ***Monastery of Christ the King, 29 Bramley Road N14 4HE*** (Cockfosters)
Anderton(SDS) Alban; ***Salvatorian Community House, High Rd, Harrow Weald HA3 5DY*** (Wealdstone)
Andraud (SM) Christian; ***5 Leicester Place WC2H 7BX*** (French Church)
Anipu (M Afr); Ignatius: ***St Edwards, 46 Totteridge Common N20 8ND***
Aoun (LMO: Maronite Rite) Augustine; ***Our Lady of Lebanon, 6 Dobson Close NW6 4RS*** (Lebanese)
Arockiaswamy (SVD) Valan; ***8 Teignmouth Road NW2 4HN*** (Willesden Green)
Atanes (CM) Ernesto; ***47 Palace Court W2 4LS*** (Bayswater)
Axelrod (CSSR) Cyril; ***165 Arlington Road NW1 7EX*** (Camden Town)

Baker (CP) Aidan; ***St Joseph's Retreat, Highgate Hill N19 5NE*** (Highgate)
Balinnya (Uganda) Gerard; ***Priests House, Gravel Hill N3 3RJ*** (Finchley Church End)
Ball (MHM) STD, John; ***St Joseph's College, Lawrence Street NW7 4JX*** (Mill Hill)

Barnes (SSCC) Kenneth; ***372 Uxbridge Road W5 3LH*** (Acton West)
Barnes (SJ) Michael; ***6 Osterley Park Road, Southall UB2 4BL*** (Southall)
Barrett-Lennard (Oratorian) Hugh; ***The Oratory, Brompton Road SW7 2RP*** (Oratory)
Beale (FDP) Stephen; ***262 Kingston Road, Teddington TW11 9JQ*** (Teddington)
Bednar (Lublin) Dwayne; ***42 Francis Street SW1P 1QW*** (Cathedral)
Blake (OCD) Matthew; ***41 Kensington Church Street W8 4BB*** (Kensington 2)
Blandford (CMF) Philip; ***Botwell House, Botwell Lane, Hayes UB3 2AB*** (Hayes)
Bloqueau (SM) Jean-Marie; ***5 Leicester Place WC2H 7BX*** (French Church)
Boerakker (MHM) BA, Hans; ***St Joseph's College, Lawrence Street NW7 4JX*** (Mill Hill)
Bomansaan (MAfr) Francis; ***46 Totteridge Common N20 8ND*** (Whetstone)
Bossy (SJ) Michael; ***27 High Road N15 6ND*** (Stamford Hill)
Bowen (Oratorian) George; ***The Oratory, Brompton Road SW7 2RP*** (Oratory)
Brinkman (SJ) Bruno; ***Highgate Nursing Home, 12 Hornsey Lane N6 5LX***
Broderick (SJ) William; ***114 Mount Street W1K 3AH*** (Farm Street)
Bromley (OMI) Herbert; ***New Priory, Quex Road NW6 4PS*** (Kilburn)
Buholzer (MAfr) Josef; ***46 Totteridge Common N20 8ND*** (Whetstone)
Burgess (AA) Christopher; ***16 Nightingale Road, Hitchin, Herts SG5 1QS*** (Hitchin)
Burns (OSB) BA, STB, Peter; ***Ealing Abbey, Charlbury Grove W5 2DY*** (Ealing)
Byrne (Opus Dei) MA, STD, Andrew; ***1 Leopold Road W5 3PB*** (Gunnersbury)

Caddle (OAR) Denis; ***18 Cheniston Gardens W8 6TQ*** (Kensington 1)
Calcutt (MAfr) Richard; ***48 Totteridge Common N20 8NB*** (Whetstone)
Callaghan (SJ) Brendan; ***Copleston House, 221 Goldhurst Terrace NW6 3EP*** (Kilburn)
Camilleri (OFM) Victor; ***47 Alder Street E1 1EE*** (German Church)
Campbell (SJ) James; ***114 Mount Street W1K 3AH*** (Farm Street)
Campbell (OSA) Michael; ***55 Fulham Palace Road W6 8AU*** (Hammersmith)
Cantwell (SDS) Desmond; ***Catholic Church, Dunny Lane, Chipperfield, King's Langley WD4 9DB*** (Chipperfield)
Carey (ODC) Isidore; ***41 Kensington Church Street W8 4BB*** (Kensington 2)
Carter (OP) Tim; ***St Dominic's Priory, Southampton Road NW5 4LB*** (Haverstock Hill)
Carty (SJ) Robert; ***Copleston House, 221 Goldhurst Terrace NW6 3EP*** (Kilburn)
Caruana (OP) Christopher; ***St Dominic's Priory, Southampton Road NW5 4LB*** (Haverstock Hill)
Casalucci (SX) Ennio; ***260 Nether Street N3 1HT*** (Finchley Church End)
Castello (MCCJ) STL, DD, Danilo, ***16 Dawson Place W2 4TJ*** (Bayswater)
Cavanagh (SDS) Luke, ***St Joseph's Presbytery, 191 High Road, Harrow Weald HA3 5EA*** (Wealdstone)
Cengel (SVD) Martin; ***8 Teignmouth Road NW2 4HN*** (Willesden Green)
Ceresoli (SX) Giovanni ***260 Nether Street N3 1HT*** (Finchley Church End)
Chann (Vietnam) Paul Huynh; ***117 Bow Common Lane E3 4AV*** (Vietnamese)
Chantry (MHM) Anthony; ***St Joseph's College, Lawrence Street NW7 4JX*** (Mill Hill)
Charles (SJ) Bernard; ***27 High Road N15 6ND*** (Stamford Hill)
Charles (Irish Chaplaincy) Nigel; ***15 St John's Villas N19 3EE*** (Upper Holloway)
Chatov (AA) Edward; ***Assumption Priory, Victoria Park Square E2 9PB*** (Bethnal Green)
Chillman (OSB) BEd, Gregory; ***Ealing Abbey, Charlbury Grove W5 2DY*** (Ealing)
Chomnycky (OSBM) Paul; ***21 Binney Street W1K 5BQ*** (Apostolic Exarch/Ukranian Cathedral)

Clarke (OCarm) Hugh; ***63 East End Road N2 0SE*** (Finchley East)
Cleere (CM) Desmond; ***Damascus House, The Ridgeway NW7 1HH*** (Mill Hill)
Clifford (OSA) Barry; ***55 Fulham Palace Road W6 8AU*** (Hammersmith)
Clifton (AA) Mark; ***Assumption Priory, Victoria Park Square E2 9PB*** (Bethnal Green)
Colella (OSM) Joseph; ***264 Fulham Road SW10 9EL*** (Fulham Road)
Collins (CSSp) Alan; ***18 Limesdale Gardens, Edgware HA8 5JA*** (Burnt Oak)
Collins (MAfr) Stephen; ***15 Corfton Road W5 2HP*** (Ealing)
Concannon (CM) John; ***29 Eversley Crescent, Isleworth TW7 4LR*** (Osterleyl)
Connelly (OP) Aelred; ***St Dominic's Priory, Southampton Road NW5 4LB*** (Haverstock Hill)
Connolly (MHM) STB,MA Mark; ***St Joseph's College, Lawrence Street NW7 4JX*** (Mill Hill 2)
Cooper (OSB) Vincent; ***Ealing Abbey, Charlbury Grove W5 2DY*** (Ealing)
Copsey (OCarm) Richard; ***63 East End Road N2 0SE*** (Finchley East)
Corcoran (MHM) Michael; ***St Joseph's College, Lawrence Street NW7 4JX*** (Mill Hill)
Courtney (MSC) Pat; ***14 Beaconsfield Road, St Albans AL1 3RB*** (St Albans)
Crampsey (SJ) James; ***St Anselm's Rectory, The Green, Southall, Middx UB2 4BE*** (Southall)
Creighton-Jobe (Oratorian) Ronald; ***The Oratory, Brompton Road SW7 2RP*** (Oratory)
Crotty (SSCC) Fintan; ***5 Berrymead Gardens W3 8AA*** (Acton)
Cullen (CP) Timothy; ***St Joseph's Retreat, Highgate Hill N19 5NE*** (Highgate)
Cunningham (IC) MBE, Christopher; ***14 Ely Place, Holborn Circus EC1N 6RY*** (Ely Place)
Curtis (SJ) Timothy; ***27 High Road N15 6ND*** (Stamford Hill)
Cussen (SMA) Anthony; ***33 Lyonsdown Road, New Barnet, Herts EN5 1JG*** (New Barnet)
Czyz (Katowice) Ludwik; ***2 Devonia Road N1 8JJ*** (Polish Church)

Dal Pont (IMC) Serafino; ***3 Salisbury Avenue N3 3AJ*** (Finchley Church End)
Dale (Salford) John, ***23 Eccleston Square SW1V 1NU*** (Pontifical Mission Societies)
Daly (MSC) Jeremiah; ***14 Beaconsfield Road, St Albans, Herts AL1 3RB*** (St Albans)
Daly (SCA) Thomas; ***358 Greenford Road, Greenford, Middx UB6 9AN*** (Greenford)
Damah (CSSp) William; ***63 Somerset Road, New Barnet EN5 1RF*** (New Barnet)
Davey (CP) DCL, Theodore; ***St Joseph's Retreat, Highgate Hill N19 5NE*** (Highgate)
Debesai (MCCJ) Tesarmichael; ***Comboni House, 16 Dawson Place W2 4TJ*** (Bayswater)
De Burca (OMI) Brian; ***New Priory, Quex Road NW6 4PS*** (Kilburn)
Deeney (SMA) Eddie; ***33 Lyonsdown Road EN5 1JG*** (New Barnet)
De Marchi (MCCJ) Benito; ***Comboni House, 16 Dawson Place W2 4TJ*** (Bayswater)
Denton (AA) Edwin; ***Assumption Priory, Victoria Park Square E2 9PB*** (Bethnal Green)
Diacono (OFM) Charles; ***1 Balniel Gate SW1V 3DS*** (Pimlico)
Digan (SSC) Parig; ***28 Redington Road NW3 7RB*** (Hampstead)
Di Giovanni (SCA) Carmelo; ***4 Back Hill, Clerkenwell Road EC1R 5EN*** (Italian Church)
Dilke (Oratorian) Charles; ***The Oratory, Brompton Road SW7 2RP*** (Oratory)
Dillon (OMI) Paschal; ***237 Goldhurst Terrace NW6 3EP*** (Kilburn)
Dionne (MSC) Nelson; ***St Columba's College, 8 King Harry Lane, St Albans AL3 4AW***
Docherty (OAR) John ***The Presbytery, Chalkhill Rd, Wembley Park HA9 9EW*** (Wembley 2)
Doherty (SDS) Michael; ***191 High Road, Harrow Weald, Middx HA3 5EA*** (Wealdstone)
Domanski (MIC) Gerald; ***2 Windsor Road W5 5PD*** (Polish 3)
Donega (Italy) STB, SLL, Francesco; ***11 Harewood Avenue NW1 6LD*** (St John's Wood)

Donovan (CP) Daniel; ***St Joseph's Retreat, Highgate Hill N19 5NE*** (Highgate)
Doyle (SVD) Anthony; ***Presbytery, Ballance Road E9 5SR*** (Homerton)
Doyle (Oratorian) Patrick; ***The Oratory SW7 2RP*** (Oratory)
Drozdziel (SJ) Henryk; ***182 Walm Lane NW2 3AX*** (Willesden Green)
Duffy (SM) Ed; ***5 Leicester Place WC2H 7BX*** (French Church)
Duffy (SJ) Hugh; ***114 Mount Street W1K 3AH*** (Farm Street)
Duggan (SJ) Joseph; ***39 Fitzjohn's Avenue NW3 5JT*** ((Swiss Cottage)
Dunne (MHM) MA, Gerard; ***St Joseph's College, Lawrence Street NW7 4JX*** (Mill Hill)

Eastwell (SJ) Ralph; ***114 Mount Street W1K 3AH*** (Farm Street)
Edgar (OP) Leo; ***St Dominic's Priory, Southampton Road NW5 4LB*** (Haverstock Hill)
Edwards (SJ) Francis; ***114 Mount Street W1K 3AH*** (Farm Street)
Edwards (SJ) John; ***114 Mount Street W1K 3AH*** (Farm Street)
Egan (SVD) Michael; ***8 Teignmouth Road NW2 4HN*** (Willesden Green)
Evans (Opus Dei) BA, STD, Joseph; ***Netherhall House, Nutley Terrace NW3 5SA*** (Swiss Cottage)

Faix (OSA) William; ***15 Dorville Crescent W6 0HH*** (Shepherds Bush)
Fernandes (Goa) Cruz; ***729 High Road N17 8AG*** (Tottenham)
Ferry (MSC) Manus; ***14 Beaconsfield Road, St Albans, Herts AL1 3RB*** (St Albans SS A&S)
Finan (SDS) Bernard; ***Community House, High Road, Harrow Weald HA3 5DY*** (Wealdstone)
Fischer (CMF) James; ***Botwell House, Botwell Lane, Hayes, Middx UB3 2AB*** (Hayes)
Fitzharris (SVD) Kieran; ***8 Teignmouth Road NW2 4HN*** (Willesden Green)
Flynn (SMM) Kieran; ***27 St Gabriel's Road NW2 4DS*** (Willesden Green)
Fletcher (SJ) Paul; ***27 High Road N15 6ND*** (Stamford Hill)
Flood (OSB) MA, PhL, Edmund; ***Ealing Abbey, Charlbury Grove W5 2DY*** (Ealing)
Ford (OMI) Eugene; ***237 Goldhurst Terrace NW6 3EP*** (Kilburn)
Forde (OCarm) Sean; ***63 East End Road N2 0SE*** (Finchley East)
Fordham (Oratorian) John; ***The Oratory, Brompton Road SW7 2RP*** (Oratory)
Fox (SJ) Kevin ***St Anselm's Rectory, The Green, Southall UB2 4BE*** (Southall)
Freeman (OSB) Laurence M; ***Monastery of Christ the King, 29 Bramley Road N14 4HE*** (Cockfosters)
Fulco (SCA) Andrea; ***4 Back Hill, Clerkenwell Road EC1R 5EN*** (Italian Church)

Gabiola (Opus Dei) PhD, JCD, Joseph; ***8 Orme Ct W2 4RL*** (Queensway)
Gardner (OP) Timothy; ***St Dominic's Priory, Southampton Road NW5 4LB*** (Haverstock Hill)
Gallager (SSC) Cathal; ***28 Redington Road NW3 7RB*** (Hampstead)
Geraghty (OP) Denis, ***St Dominic's Priory, Southampton Road NW5 4LB*** (Haverstock Hill)
Gigli (MAfr) Paul; ***48 Totteridge Common N20 8NB*** (Whetstone)
Goergen (MAfr) David; ***42 Stormont Road N6 4NP*** (Highgate)
Golebiewski (SJ) Leszek; ***182 Walm Lane NW2 3RX*** (Willesden Green)
Gonella (Alba) Mgr Agostino; ***197 Durants Road, Enfield, Middx EN3 7DE*** (Ponders End)
Gorham (OSB) STB, Timothy; ***Ealing Abbey, Charlbury Grove W5 2DY*** (Ealing)
Gostomski (Plock) Mgr Bronislaw; ***1 Leysfield Road W12 9JF*** (Polish 2)
Graham (OSA) Paul; ***19 Hoxton Square N1 6NT*** (Hoxton)
Griffiths (OSCam) Brian; ***102 Hassett Road E9 5SJ*** (Homerton)

Habash Safaa; ***28 Delancy Street NW1 7NH*** (Camden Town)
Hamill (SJ) Paul; ***221 Goldhurst Terrace NW6 3EP*** (Kilburn)
Hanly (SCA) William; ***358 Greenford Road, Greenford UB6 9AN*** (Greenford)
Harries (OP) BSc, BD, Peter; ***St Dominic's Priory, Southampton Road NW5 4LB*** (Haverstock Hill)
Harris (CM) Jack; ***2 Flower Lane NW7 2JB*** (Mill Hill)
Harrison (Oratorian) Ignatius; ***The Oratory, Brompton Road SW7 2RP*** (Oratory)
Hassay (SJ) Gerard; ***St Anselm's Rectory, The Green, Southall, Middx UB2 4BE*** (Southall)
Hauser (MAfr) Hermann; ***48 Totteridge Common N20 8LZ*** (Whetstone)
Hawe (SJ) Vincent; ***114 Mount Street W1K 3AH*** (Farm Street)
Hayward (Opus Dei) LLB, JCD, Paul; ***4 Orme Court W2 4RL*** (Queensway)
Heffernan (OSA) Columba; ***15 Dorville Crescent W6 0HH*** (Shepherds Bush)
Hennessey (SDS) Thomas; ***Community House, High Road, Harrow Weald HA3 7BJ*** (Wealdstone)
Henshaw (AA) Robert; ***16 Nightingale Road, Hitchin, Herts SG5 1QS*** (Hitchin)
Heron (OSB) Benedict M; ***Monastery of Christ the King, 29 Bramley Road N14 4HE*** (Cockfosters)
Hnylycia (Opus Dei) BSc, PGCE, Stefan; ***8 Orme Court W2 4RL*** (Queensway)
Hobbs (OSB) STL, Stanislaus; ***Ealing Abbey, Charlbury Grove W5 2DY*** (Ealing)
Holman (SJ) Michael; ***114 Mount Street W1K 3AH*** (Farm Street)
Holt (SJ) Geoffrey; ***114 Mount Street W1K 3AH*** (Farm Street)
Horsey (OSB) Kevin; ***Ealing Abbey, Charlbury Grove W5 2DY*** (Ealing)
Howard (SJ) Damian; ***6 Osterley Park Road, Southall UB2 4BL*** (Southall)
Hughes (OSB) Andrew; ***Ealing Abbey, Charlbury Grove W5 2DY*** (Ealing)
Hughes (ODC) John; ***41 Kensington Church Street W8 4BB*** (Kensington 2)
Hughes (MHM) Kevin; ***St Joseph's College, Lawrence Street NW7 4JX*** (Mill Hill 2)

Jarzabek(MIC) Mariusz; ***2 Windsor Road W5 5PD*** (Polish Church)
Jimenez Estrella (SX) Jorge; ***260 Nether Street N3 1HT*** (Finchley Church End)
Joseph (CMF) Paul; ***Botwell House, Botwell Lane, Hayes UB3 2AB*** (Hayes)

Karpinski (MIC) Aleksander; ***2 Windsor Road W5 5PD*** (Polish Church 3)
Keane (SDS) Noel; ***Salvatorians, High Road, Harrow Weald HA3 7BJ*** (Harrow Weald)
Kehoe (FDP) Philip; ***25 Lower Teddington Road, Kingston-on-Thames KT1 4HB*** (Teddington)
Kelly (CP) Christopher; ***St Joseph's Retreat, Highgate Hill N19 5NE*** (Highgate)
Kelly (CM) BA, Fergus; ***2 Flower Lane NW7 2JB*** (Mill Hill 1)
Kennedy (CMF) James; ***Botwell House, Botwell Lane, Hayes, Middx UB3 2AB*** (Hayes)
Kirchler (MHM) Jakob; ***St Joseph's College, Lawrence Street NW7 4JX*** (Mill Hill)
Kiyimba (SJ) Kizito; ***221 Goldhurst Terrace NW6 3EP*** (Kilburn)
Kom (SVD) Frank; ***8 Teignmouth Road NW2 4HN*** (Willesden Green)
Kudlak (Poland) Grzegorz; ***1 Leysfield Road W12 9JF*** (Polish Church 2)
Kukla (Poland) Tadeusz; ***2 Devonia Road N1 8JJ*** (Polish Church 1)
Kwiatkowski (MIC) Dariusz; ***2 Windsor Road W5 5PD*** (Polish 3)

Laishley (SJ) Francis; ***114 Mount Street WIK 3AH*** (Farm Street)
Lambert (AA) Michael; ***16 Nightingale Road, Hitchin, Herts SG5 1QS*** (Hitchin)
Lang (SJ) John; ***114 Mount Street W1K 3AH*** (Farm Street)

Lang (Oratorian) Michael; ***The Oratory, Brompton Road SW7 2RP*** (Oratory)
Large (Oratorian) Julian; ***The Oratory, Brompton Road SW7 2RP*** (Oratory)
Leachman (OSB) James; **Ealing Abbey, Charlbury Grove W5 2DY** (Ealing)
Leczuk (Ukrainian Exarchate) Moacyr; ***22 Binney Street W1K 5BQ*** (Ukrainian Cathedral)
Loewenstein (OP) Rudolf; ***St Dominic's Priory, Southampton Road NW5 4LB*** (Haverstock Hill)

MacCurtain (SJ) William; ***114 Mount Street W1K 3AH*** (Farm Street)
Mac Neice (OSM) Dermot; ***264 Fulham Road SW10 9EL*** (Fulham Road)
McAnaney (SM) Martin; ***5 Leicester Place WC2H 7BX*** (French Church)
McAneny (SSCC) Christopher; ***5 Berrymead Gardens W3 8AA*** (Acton)
McCarthy (MHM) MA, Francis; ***St Joseph's College, Lawrence Street NW7 4JX*** (Mill Hill)
McCartney (CSSp) Derek; **63 Somerset Road, New Barnet, Herts EN5 1RF** (New Barnet)
McClarey (SCA) Liam; ***358 Greenford Road, Greenford Middx UB6 9AN*** (Greenford)
McCluskey (MHM) John; ***St Joseph's College, Lawrence Street NW7 4JX*** (Mill Hill)
McCoog (SJ) Thomas; ***114 Mount Street W1K 3AH*** (Farm Street)
McCormick (ODC) Fabian; ***41 Kensington Church Street W8 4BB*** (Kensington 2)
McDade (SJ) John; ***221 Goldhurst Terrace NW6 3EP*** (Kilburn/Heythrop College)
McEwan (CSsR) STL, BA, PGCSE, Kevin; ***299 St Agnell's Lane, Grovehill, Hemel Hempstead HP2 6EQ*** (Hemel Hempstead North)
McFadden (CSSp) John; ***18 Limesdale Gardens, Edgware HA8 5JA*** (Burnt Oak)
McGettigan (ODC) Oliver; ***41 Kensington Church Street W8 4BB*** (Kensington 2)
McGonnell (MHM) Larry; ***39 Duncan Terrace N1 8AL*** (Islington)
McGrath (MSFS) Terry; ***The Dympna Centre, St Mary's Abbey, The Ridgeway NW7 4HX***
McHardy (Oratorian) Rupert; ***The Oratory Brompton Road SW7 2RP*** (Oratory)
McKee (MHM) Kevin; ***St Joseph's College, Lawrence Street NW7 4JX*** (Mill Hill)
McMahon (CM) Hugh; ***2 Flower Lane NW7 2JB*** (Mill Hill)
McNamara (ODC) John; ***41 Kensington Church Street W8 4BB*** (Kensington 2)
McPake (SVD) Martin; ***8 Teignmouth Road NW2 4HN*** (Willesden Green)

Magnante (IMC) Antonio; ***3 Salisbury Avenue N3 3AJ*** (Finchley Church End)
Mahoney (SJ) John; ***114 Mount Street W1K 3AH*** (Farm Street)
Manimala (SVD) Bosco; ***8 Teignmouth Road NW2 4HN*** (Willesden Green)
Marsh (Opus Dei) DIC, STD, Bernard; ***4 Orme Court W2 4RL*** (Queensway)
Marsh (OSA) Robert; ***19 Hoxton Square N1 6NT*** (Hoxton)
Martin (SSC) Richard; ***28 Redington Road NW3 7RB*** (Hampstead)
Maskalik (Byelorussian) Constantine; ***Marian House, Holden Avenue N12 8HY*** (Finchley North)
Mathew (MSFS) Saji; ***16 Wellington Road, Hampton Hill TW12 1JR*** (Hampton Hill)
Matthew (OCD) Iain; ***41 Kensington Church Street W8 4BB*** (Kensington 2)
Mbelu (CM) Austin; ***29 Eversley Crescent, Isleworth TW7 4LR*** (Osterley)
Meredith (SJ) MA, DPhil, Anthony; ***114 Mount Street W1K 3AH*** (Farm Street)
Mignolli (CSS) Natalino; ***5 Hanover Road NW10 3DJ*** (Kensal Rise)
Millane (MAfr) John; ***15 Corfton Road W5 2HP*** (Ealing)
Minihane (OSA) Mark; ***19 Hoxton Square N1 6NT*** (Hoxton)
Miranda (MSFS) Huebert Francis; ***16 Wellington Road, Hampton Hill TW12 1JR*** (Hampton Hill)

Miscampbell (OSB) Patrick; ***2 The Butts, Brentford TW8 8BQ*** (Brentford)
Moffatt (SJ) John; ***27 High Road N15 6ND*** (Stamford Hill)
Mol (MAfr) Jan; ***46 Totteridge Common N20 8ND*** (Whetstone)
Moore (OH) Robert; ***131 Mill Green Road, Welwyn Garden City AL7 3XB*** (WGC East)
Moriarty (CSSp) John; ***63 Somerset Road, New Barnet EN5 1RF*** (New Barnet)
Morland (SMA) Rob; ***33 Lyonsdown Road EN5 1JG*** (New Barnet)
Morrin (OP) Dermot; ***St Dominic's Priory, Southampton Road NW5 4LB*** (Haverstock Hill)
Morrish (Opus Dei) MA, STD, Mgr Nicholas; ***4 Orme Court W2 4RL*** (Queensway)
Morrissey (MAfr) John; ***Nazareth House, Hammersmith Road W6 8DB*** (Brook Green)
Mulcahy (CSSp) Eamonn; ***18 Limesdale Gardens, Edgware HA8 5JA*** (Burnt Oakt)
Mulhall (MHM) Brendan; ***St Joseph's College, Lawrence Street NW7 4JX*** (Mill Hill)
Mulherin (OSM) James; ***264 Fulham Road SW10 9EL*** (Fulham Road)
Mulholland (OP) BA, Seamus; ***111 Gower Street WC1E 6AR*** (University)
Murphy (OSA) John; ***55 Fulham Palace Road W6 8AU*** *(Hammersmith)*
Murphy (ODC) Ronan; ***41 Kensington Church Street W8 4BB*** (Kensington 2)
Murray (SDS) John; ***191 High Road, Harrow Weald HA3 5EA*** (Wealdstone)
Murray (SJ) Robert; ***221 Goldhurst Terrace NW6 3EP*** (Kilburn)
Murtagh (SSCC) Kieran; ***5 Berrymead Gardebs W3 8AA*** (Acton)

Nadson (Byelorussian) Alexander; ***Marian House, Holden Ave N12 8HY*** (Finchley North)
Nally (SSC) Frank; ***28 Redington Road NW3 7RB*** (Hampstead)
Nawalaniec (MIC) Pawel; ***2 Windsor Road W5 5PD*** (Polish 3)
Netto (SDB) Ivor; ***111 Gower Street WC1E 6AR*** (University Chaplain)
Nevin (SDS) Henry; ***96 The Crescent, Abbots Langley, Watford WD5 0DT*** (Abbots Langley)
Niewdana (SVD) Leszek; ***8 Teignmouth Road NW2 4HN*** (Willesden Green)
Nunn (OSB) M Mus, Alban; ***Ealing Abbey, Charlbury Grove W5 2DY*** (Ealing)

O'Brien (OSM) Christopher; ***264 Fulham Road SW10 9EL*** (Fulham Road)
O'Brien (SSC) Eamonn; ***28 Redington Road NW3 7RB*** (Hampstead)
O'Brien (AA), Tom; ***Assumption Priory, Victoria Park Square E2 9PB*** (Bethnal Green)
O'Brien (MHM) Tom; ***St Joseph's College, Lawrence Street NW7 4JX*** (Mill Hill)
O'Connell (MHM) Daniel; ***St Joseph's College, Lawrence Street NW7 4JX*** (Mill Hill)
O'Dell (AA) Andrew; ***Assumption Priory, Victoria Park Square E2 9PB*** (Bethnal Green)
O'Donovan (OCarm) Andrew; ***56 Holland Park Road W14***
O'Hagan (OAR) Patrick: ***18 Cheniston Gardens W8 6TQ*** (Kensington 1)
O'Hara (CP) Conleth; ***St Joseph's Retreat, Highgate Hill N19 5NE*** (Highgate)
O'Malley (AA) Brendan; ***Assumption Priory, Victoria Park Square E2 9PB*** (Bethnal Green)
O'Reilly (SJ) Paul; ***114 Mount Street W1K 3AH*** (Farm Street)

Ofere Albert Ovie; ***100 Kingsland Road N1 4AG*** (Kingsland)
Olliver (MHM) John; ***St Joseph's College, Lawrence Street NW7 4JX*** (Mill Hill)
Orchard (OSB) MA, DLitt, Bernard; ***Ealing Abbey, Charlbury Grove W5 2DY*** (Ealing)
Oswald (MHM), Brian; ***St Joseph's College, Lawrence Street NW7 4JX*** (Mill Hill)
Owen (CP) Charles; ***St Joseph's Retreat, Highgate Hill N19 5NE*** (Highgate)

Paganelli (SX) Natalio; ***260 Nether Street N3 1HT*** (Finchley Church End)
Panathara (CM) Chacko; ***29 Eversley Crescent, Isleworth TW7 4LR*** (Osterley)
Parish (SJ) Anthony; ***114 Mount Street W1K 3AH*** (Farm Street)
Parkin (SJ) Bernard; ***27 High Road N15 6ND*** (Stamford Hill)
Pearce (OSB) BD, MTh, LDSRCSEng, KHS, David; ***Ealing Abbey, Charlbury Grove W5 2DY*** (Ealing)
Pearsall (SJ) William ***114 Mount Street W1K 3AH*** (Farm Street)
Pedley (SJ) Christopher; ***39 Fitzjohn's Avenue NW3 5JT*** (Swiss Cottage)
Pena (CM) Segundo; ***47 Palace Court Road W2 4LS*** (Bayswater)
Pennington (OSB) Paschal; ***Monastery of Christ the King, 29 Bramley Road N14 4HE*** (Cockfosters)
Perez (OAR) Jesus; ***The Presbytery, Chalkhill Road, Wembley Park HA9 9EW*** (Wembley 2)
Pharro (MHM) John; ***St Joseph's College, Lawrence Street NW7 4JX*** (Mill Hill)
Phiri (MAfr) Felix; ***46 Woodville Gardens W5 2LO*** (Ealing)
Power (OSA) Michael Aidan; ***55 Fulham Palace Road W6 8AU*** (Hammersmith)
Preston (SJ) Dermot; ***114 Mount Street W1K 3AH*** (Farm Street)
Preston (SDS) Peter; ***Salvatorian Fathers, High Road, Harrow Weald, Middx HA3 5DY*** (Harrow Weald)
Purnell (SJ) Patrick; ***6 Osterley Park Road, Southall UB2 4BL*** (Southall)
Puthussery (OCarm) Robert; ***63 East End Road N2 0SE*** (Finchley East)

Ranahan (SCA) George; ***5 Amwell Street EC1R 1UL*** (Clerkenwell)
Raybould (SJ) Joseph; ***114 Mount Street W1K 3AH*** (Farm Street)
Regan (SSC) Frank; ***28 Redington Road NW3 7RB*** (Hampstead)
Ribeiro (Brazil) Frederico; ***St Anne's Church, Underwood Road E1 5AW*** (Underwood Road)
Rice (CP) Basil; ***St Joseph's Retreat, Highgate Hill N19 5NE*** (Highgate)
Richmond (SDS) Hugh; ***Community House, High Road, Harrow Weald HA3 5DY*** (Wealdstone)
Riezu (OAR) Robert; ***18 Cheniston Gardens W8 6TQ*** (Kensington 1)
Riordan (SJ) Patrick; ***221 Goldhurst Terrace NW6 3EP*** (Kilburn)
Rooney (MHM) MA, MSc, PhD, John; ***St Joseph's College, Lawrence Street NW7 4JX*** (Mill Hill)
Rose (OSCam) William; ***102 Hassett Road E9 5SJ*** (Homerton)
Rossiter (CJ) BSc, STB, MA, Aidan; ***1 Island Row, 636 Commercial Road E14 7HS*** (Limehouse)
Rossiter (OSB) JCL, DD, Abbot Francis; ***Ealing Abbey, Charlbury Grove W5 2DY*** (Ealing)
Rout (OFM) Paul; ***Heythrop College, Kensington Gardens W8 5HQ*** (Heythrop)
Russell (SJ) John; ***114 Mount Street W1K 3AH*** (Farm Street)
Ryall (OSM) Patrick; ***264 Fulham Road SW10 9EL*** (Fulham Road)
Ryan (OP) STL, MLitt, DPhil, Columba; ***St Dominic's Priory, Southampton Road NW5 4LB***
Ryan (OMI) Francis; ***1 Stafford Road NW6 5RS*** (Kilburn West)
Ryan (SJ) Francis X; ***221 Goldhurst Terrace NW6 3EP*** (Kilburn)
Ryan (SSC) Thomas; ***28 Redington Road NW3 7RB*** (Hampstead)

Salm (MHM) Wim Van Der; ***St Joseph's College, Lawrence Street NW7 4JX*** (Mill Hill)
Sandom (MAfr) John; ***46 Woodville Gardens W5 2LO*** (Ealing)
Saraber (MHM) George; ***St Joseph's College, Lawrence Street NW7 4JX*** (Mill Hill)
Scaglia (OSB) Constanzo M; ***29 Bramley Road N14 4HE*** (Cockfosters)
Scally (SJ) Peter; ***27 High Road N15 6ND*** (Stamford Hill)
Schiavinato (IMC) Pietro; ***3 Salisbury Avenue N3 3AJ*** (Finchley Church End)

Schlatmann (OSB) Willibrord M; ***29 Bramley Road N14 4HE*** (Cockfosters)
Schrenk (MAfr), Hans; ***48 Totteridge Common N20 8NB*** (Whetstone)
Sciberras(OFM) Stephen; ***1 Balniel Gate, Lindsay Square SW1V 3SD*** (Pimlico)
Seed (SA) STD, PhD, Michael; ***47 Francis Street SW1P 1QR*** (Ecumenical Secretary/Cathedral)
Shanahan (MAfr) Patrick; ***Oak Lodge, 48 Totteridge Common N20 8LZ*** (Whetstone)
Sheehan (Opus Dei) MA, STD, Gerard; ***Maresfield Gardens NW3 5SU*** (Swiss Cottage)
Sheehan (OMI) Malachy; ***30 Prescot Street E1 8BB*** (Tower Hill)
Shipperlee (OSB) BD, BA, Abbot Martin; ***Ealing Abbey, Charlbury Grove W5 2DY*** (Ealing)
Shorter (MAfr) Aylward; ***48 Totteridge Common N20 8NB*** (Whetstone)
Skoczen (Poland) Wlodzimierz; ***2 Devonia Road N1 8JJ*** (Polish Church 1)
Sloan (Liverpool) Richard; ***54 Lodge Road NW8 8LA*** (St John's Wood)
Smith (SJ) Michael; ***39 Fitzjohn's Avenue NW3 5JT*** (Swiss Cottage)
Smith (MAfr) Peter; ***42 Stormont Road N6 4NP*** (Highgate)
Smolira (SJ) David; ***39 Fitzjohn's Avenue NW3 5JT*** (Swiss Cottage)
Soper (OSB) STD, Abbot Laurence; ***Ealing Abbey, Charlbury Grove W5 2DY*** (Ealing)
Spack (Ukrainian Exarchate) Emerson; ***22 Binney Street W1K 5BQ*** (Ukranian Cathedral)
Sporny (SJ) Tadeusz; ***182 Walm Lane NW2 3AX*** (Willesden Green)
Stapleford (OSB) BA, Thomas; ***Ealing Abbey, Charlbury Grove W5 2DY*** (Ealing)
Steenson (CP) Malachy; ***St Joseph's, Highgate Hill N19 5NE*** (Highgate)
Stewart (SJ) David; ***114 Mount Street W1K 3AH*** (Farm Street)
Stibbles (OSA) George; ***55 Fulham Palace Road W6 8AU*** (Hammersmith)
Stone (CMF) Martin; ***Botwell House, Botwell Lane, Hayes UB3 2AB*** (Hayes)
Stones (MAfr) Gerald; ***Oak Lodge, 48 Totteridge Common N20 8LZ*** (Whetstone)
Stork (Opus Dei) MSc, STD, Mgr Richard; ***18 Netherhall Gardens NW3 5TH*** (Swiss Cottage)
Styles (SJ) Robert; ***The Priest's House, Malting Lane, Much Hadham, Herts SG10 6AW*** (Much Hadham)
Swagemakers (MHM) Jan; ***1 Colney Hatch Lane N10 1PN*** (Muswell Hill)
Sweeney (MAfr) Geoffrey; ***Nazareth House, Hammersmith Road W6 8DB*** (Brook Green)

Tait (SDS) Adrian; ***191 High Road, Harrow Weald HA3 5EA*** (Wealdstone)
Temple (OSB) Philip; ***29 Bramley Road N14 4HE*** (Cockfosters)
Thompson (MHM) Francis; ***St Joseph's College, Lawrence Street NW7 4JX*** (Mill Hill)
Tirello (FDP) Joseph; ***25 Lower Teddington Road, Hampton Wick KT1 4BH*** (Teddington)
Tokarski (SJ) Tadeusz; ***48 Links Side, Enfield EN2 7QU***
Travers (CM) Noel; ***29 Eversley Crescent, Isleworth TW7 4LR*** (Osterley)
Tutto (Nottingham) Mgr George; ***Hungarian Chaplaincy, 141 Gunnersbury Ave W3 8LE*** (Gunnersbury)
Tverijonas (Lithuanian) MA Petras; ***21 The Oval, Hackney Road E2 9DT*** (Lithuanian Church)

Vaz Pinto, (Portugal) Mgr. Jose; ***Portuguese Centre, 165 Arlington Rd NW1 7EX*** (Camden Town)
Vico, (Scalabrini Frs) Alberto ***Villa Scalabrini, Green Street, Shenley, Herts*** (Borehamwood North)

Wachala (Poland) Stanislaw; ***2 Devonia Road N1 8JJ*** (Polish Church 1)
Walsh (SMA) Martin; ***33 Lyonsdown Road, New Barnet, Herts EN5 1JG*** (New Barnet)
Walshe (CM) MA, MPhil (ecum) Philip; ***2 Flower Lane NW7 2JB*** (Mill Hill)
Ward (SCA) Kevin; ***358 Greenford Road, Greenford, Middx UB6 9AN*** (Greenford)
Warren (OMI) Raymond; ***New Priory, Quex Road NW6 4PS*** (Kilburn)
Waters (SDS) Frank; ***191 High Road, Harrow Weald HA3 5EA*** (Wealdstone)
Watine (MAfr) Damien; ***46 Woodville Gardens W5 2LO*** (Ealing)
Watkins (OSB) Dunstan; ***Ealing Abbey, Charlbury Grove W5 2DY*** (Ealing)
Wheaton (SJ) Geoff; ***More House, 53 Cromwell Road SW7 2EH*** (University)
White (OP) Allan; ***St Dominic's Priory, Southampton Road NW5 4LB*** (Haverstock Hill)
White (CP) Mark; ***St Joseph's Retreat, Highgate Hill N19 5NE*** (Highgate)
White (OP) Paul; ***St Dominic's Priory, Southampton Road NW5 4LB*** (Haverstock Hill)
Williams (SDB) Tom; ***St Dominic's Sixth Form College, Mount Park Avenue, Harrow-on-the-Hill HA1 3HX*** (Chaplain)
Wojcieszak (MIC) Krzysztof; ***2 Windsor Road W5 5PD*** (Polish 3)
Woldeghebriel (MCCJ) Teckie Hagos; ***The Priory, Barnet Lane, Elstree WD6 3QU*** (Borehamwood)
Woo (MAfr) Edward; ***4 Lady Margaret Road NW5 2XT*** (Kentish Town)
Wrobel (SCA) Riszard; ***4 Back Hill EC1R 5EN*** (Italian Church)
Wyszomierski (MIC) Tadeusz; ***2 Windsor Road W5 5PD*** (Polish 3)

Zanchi (SX) Alessandro; ***260 Nether Street N3 1HT*** (Finchley Church End)
Zielinski (MIC) Bogdan; ***2 Windsor Road W5 5PD*** (Polish Church)
Zysk (SVD) Stan; ***60 Rylston Road SW6 7HW*** (Fulham)

RELIGIOUS CONGREGATIONS & SOCIETIES OF APOSTOLIC LIFE

The names listed are those of priest-members only. A place-name in italics refers to a parish entry under which further details may be found.

African Missions, Society of (SMA):
33 Lyonsdown Rd, *New Barnet* EN5 1JG
Cussen, Anthony **Superior**
Deeney, Eddie
Morland, Rob
Walsh, Martin

Assumptionists (AA)
(1) The Priory, Victoria Park Sq E2 9PB
(Bethnal Green)
(2) 16 Nightingale Road, *Hitchin* SG5 1QS
Burgess, Christopher (2)
Chatov, Edward (1)
Clifton, Mark (1)
Denton, Edwin (1)
Henshaw, Robert (2) **Regional Superior**
Lambert, Michael (2)
O'Dell, Andrew (1)
O'Brien, Tom (1) **Superior**
O'Malley, Brendan (1)

Augustinians (OSA):
(1) 55 Fulham Palace Road W6 8AU
(Hammersmith)
(2) 19 *Hoxton* Square N1 6NT
(3) 15 Dorville Crescent W6 0HH
(Shepherds Bush)
Campbell, Michael (1) **Prior**
Clifford, Barry (1)
Faix, William (3)
Graham, Paul (2) **Provincial**
Heffernan, Columba (3)
Marsh, Robert (2)
Minihane, Mark (2)
Murphy, John (1) **Sub Prior**
Stibbles, George (1)

Augustinian Recollects (OAR):
(1) 18 Cheniston Gardens W8 6TQ
(Kensington 1)
(2) English Martyrs, Chalkhill Road, *Wembley* Park, Middx HA9 9EW
Caddle, Denis (1) **Vicar Provincial**
Docherty, John (2) **Prior**
O'Hagan, Patrick (1)
Perez, Jesus (2)
Perezde, Arrilulea (2)
Riezu, Robert (1)

Benedictines (OSB) (English Congregation)
Charlbury Grove W5 2DY *(Ealing)*
Burns, Peter
Chillman, Gregory
Cooper, Vincent
Flood, Edmund
Gorham, Timothy
Hobbs, Stanislaus
Horsey, Kevin
Hughes, Andrew
Leachman, James
Nunn, Alban
Orchard, Bernard
Pearce, David
Rossiter, Francis
Shipperlee, Martin **Abbot**
Soper, Laurence
Stapleford, Thomas
Watkins, Dunstan

Benedictines (OSB) (Olivetan)
Monastery of Christ the King, 29 Bramley Rd N14 4HE
(Cockfosters)
Akoeso, Bernard M
Freeman, Laurence M
Heron, Benedict M
Pennington, Paschal M
Scaglia, Constanzo M **Prior**
Schlatmann, Willibrord M
Temple, Philip M

Camillians (OSCam) (Order of St Camillus)
102 Hassett Road E9 5SJ
(Homerton)
Griffiths, Brian
Rose, William

Carmelites (OCarm): **63 East End Road N2 0SE** *(Finchley East)*
Clarke, Hugh
Copsey, Richard **Prior & Provincial Bursar**
Forde, Sean
Puthussery, Robert

Carmelites, Discalced (ODC):
41 *Kensington* Church Street W8 4BB
Blake, Matthew **Prior**
Carey, Isidore
Hughes, John
McCormick, Fabian
McGettigan, Oliver
Matthew, Iain
Murphy, Ronan

Charity, Institute of (IC) (Rosminians):
14 *Ely Place* EC1N 6RY
Cunningham, Christopher **Rector**

Christian Brothers 38 Strawberry Hill Rd, *Twickenham*, Middx TW1 4PU

Claretian Missionaries (CMF)
(Missionary Sons of Immaculate Heart of Mary):
Botwell House, Botwell Lane *Hayes*, Middx UB3 2AB
Blandford, Philip
Fischer, James
Joseph, Paul
Stone Martin

Columban Fathers (SSC):
28 Redington Road NW3 7RB
(Hampstead)
Digan, Parig
Gallagher, Cathal
Martin, Richard
Nally, Frank
O'Brien, Eamonn
Regan, Frank
Ryan, Thomas

Comboni Missionaries (Verona Fathers) (MCCJ):
(1) Comboni Hse, 16 Dawson Place W2 4TJ
(Bayswater)
(2) The Priory, Barnet Lane, Elstree, Herts WD6 3QU *(Borehamwood)*
Castello, Danilo (1)
Debesai Tesarmichael (1)
De Marchi, Benito (1)
Woldeghebriel, Tekie Hagos

Consolata Fathers (IMC):
3 Salisbury Avenue N3 3AJ
(Finchley Church End)
Dal Pont, Serafino
Magnante, Antonio **Superior**
Schiavinato, Pietro (1)

Divine Word Missionaries (SVD):
8 Teignmouth Road NW2 4HN
(Willesden Green)
Arockiaswamy, Valan
Doyle, Anthony **Homerton**
Egan, Michael
Fitzharris, Kieran
Kom, Frank
McPake, Martin
Niewdana, Leszek
Zysk, Stan **Fulham**

Dominicans (OP) (The Order of Preachers)
St Dominic's Priory, Southampton Rd NW5 4LB
(Haverstock Hill)
Caruana, Christopher
Connelly, Aelred
Edgar, Leo
Gardner, Timothy
Geraghty, Denis
Harries, Peter
Loewenstein, Rudolf
Morrin, Dermot **Prior and Parish Priest**
Ryan, Columba
White, Allan **Provincial**
White, Dominic

Franciscans (OFM):
The Maltese Mission, 1 Balniel Gate, Lindsay Square SW1V 3SD *(Pimlico)*
Diacono, Charles
Sciberras, Stephen

Franciscan Friars of the Atonement (SA):
St Francis Friary, 47 Francis St SW1P 1QR
(Cathedral) Seed, Michael

Fransalians (MSFS)
(Missionaries of St Francis de Sales):
16 Wellington Rd, *Hampton Hill* TW12 1JR
Mathew, Saji
McGrath, Terry **Dympna Centre Mill Hill**
Miranda Huebert Francis

Gabriel, Brothers of St:
(1) 11 Longfield Road W5 2DH *(Ealing)*
(2) 2 Church Avenue, Southall UB2 4DH
(Southall)

Holy Ghost Fathers (CSSp):
(1) 63 Somerset Rd EN5 1RF
(New Barnet)
(2) 18 Limesdale Gardens HA8 5JA
(Burnt Oak)
Collins, Alan (2)
Damah, William (1)
McCartney, Derek (1)
McFadden, John (2) **Provincial Superior**
Moriarty, John (1)
Mulcahy, Eamonn (2)

Jesuits (SJ) (Society of Jesus)
(1) Provincial Curia, 114 Mount St W1K 3AH
(2) Farm St Church, 114 Mount St W1K 3AH
(3) St Ignatius Church, 27 High Rd N15 6ND
(Stamford Hill)
(4) Southwell Hse, 39 Fitzjohn's Ave NW3 5JT
(Swiss Cottage)
(5) Polish Jesuits, 182 Walm Lane NW2 3AX
(Willesden Green)
(6) Copleston Hse, 221 Goldhurst Terr NW6 3EP
(Kilburn)
(7) 6 Osterley Park Rd *Southall* UB2 4DL
Barnes, Michael (7)
Bossy, Michael (3)
Callaghan, Brendan (6)
Campbell, James (2)
Carty, Robert (6)
Charles, Bernard (3)
Crampsey, James **Southall**
Curtis, Timothy (3)
Drozdziel, Henryk (5)
Duffy, Hugh (2) **Superior**
Duggan, Joseph (4)
Eastwell, Ralph (2)
Edwards, Francis (2)
Edwards, John (2)
Fitzsimmons, Francis (3)

Fletcher, Paul (3) **Superior**
Fox, Kevin (1) **Souhall**
Golebiewski, Leszek (5)
Hamill, Paul (6) **Superior**
Hanvey, James (6)
Harrison, Alan (4)
Hassay, Gerard **Southall**
Hawe, Vincent (2)
Hodkinson, James (6)
Holman, Michael (1) **Provincial**
Holt, Geoffrey (2)
Howard, Damian (7)
Kiyimba, Kizito (6)
Laishley, Francis (2)
Lang, John (2)
MacCurtain, William (2)
McCoog, Thomas (2)
McDade, John (6) **Principal Heythrop**
McMillan, Keith (6)
Meredith, Anthony (2)
Metcalfe, Anthony (2)
Moffatt, John (3)
Mahoney, John (2)
Murray, Robert (6)
O'Reilly, Paul 2)
Parish, Anthony (2)
Parkin, Bernard (3)
Pearsall, William (2)
Pedley, Christopher (4)
Preston, Dermot (1)
Purnell, Patrick (7)
Raybould, Joseph (2)
Riordan, Patrick (6)
Russell, John (2)
Ryan, Francis X (6)
Scally, Peter (3)
Smith, Michael (4) **Superior**
Smolira, David, (4
Sporny, Tadeusz (5)
Styles, Robert **Much Hadham**
Tokarski, Tadeusz **Enfield**
Wheaton, Geoff **More House**

John of God, Hospitaller Order of St (OH):
97 Great Ganett, WG City AL7 3DD
(Welywn Garden City)
Newman, Michael **Prior**

Lebanese Maronite Order (LMO):
6 Dobson Close NW6 4RS
(Lebanese Centre)
Aoun, Augustine;
Akiki, Dany

Malta, Order of (SMOM): **Grand Priory**
Brampton House, 60 Grove End Road NW8 9NH
(St John's Wood)
Festing, Matthew **Prior**
Crichton-Stuart, Fredrik

Marian Fathers (MIC)
2 Windsor Road W5 5PD
(Polish Church)
Jarazabek, Mariusz
Kwiatkowski, Dariusz
Nawalaniec, Pawel **Superior**
Wojcieszak, Krzysztof
Wyszomierski, Tadeusz

Marist Fathers (SM):
5 Leicester Place WC2H 7BX
(French Church)
Andraud, Christian
Bloqueau, Jean-Marie
Duffy, Ed
McAnaney, Martin

Mill Hill Missionaries (MHM)
St Joseph's College, Lawrence St NW7 4JX
Andre, Leslie **Commercial Road**
Ball, John
Boerakker, Hans
Chantry, Anthony **Superior General**
Connolly, Mark
Corcoran, Michael
Dunne, Gerard
Hughes, Kevin
Kirchler, Jakob
McCarthy, Francis
McCluskey, John
McGonnell, Larry **Islington**
Mulhall, Brendan **Vicar General**
O'Brien, Tom
O'Connell, Daniel
Oswald, Brian
Pharro, John
Rooney, John
Salm, Wim Van Der
Saraber, George
Swagemakers, Jan **Muswell Hill**
Thompson, Francis

Missionaries of Africa (MAfr) (White Fathers):
(1)15 Corfton Road W5 2HP *(Ealing)*
(2) 46 Woodville Gardens W5 2LQ *(Ealing)*
(3) St Edward's College, 46 Totteridge Common N20 8ND *(Whetstone)*
(4) Oak Lodge, 48 Totteridge Common N20 8NB *(Whetstone)*
(5) 42 Stormont Rd N6 4NP *(Highgate)*
Anipu, Ignatius (3)
Bomansaan, Francis (3)
Buholzer, Josef (3) **Rector**
Calcutt, Richard (4)
Collins, Stephen (1)
Gigli, Paul (4)
Goergen, David (5)
Hauser, Hermann (4)
Millane, John (1) **Superior**
Mol, Jan (3)
Morrissey, John **Naz. Hse, Brook Green**
Phiri, Felix (2)
Sandom, John (2)
Schrenk, Hans (4) **Superior**
Shanahan, Patrick (4)
Shorter, Aylward (4)
Smith, Adrian
Smith, Peter (5) **Provincial**
Stones, Gerald (4)
Sweeney, Geoffrey **Naz Hse, Brook Green**
Watine, Damien (2) **Superior**
Woo, Edward **Kentish Town**

Montfort Missionaries (SMM):
27 St Gabriel's Road NW2 4DS *(Willesden Green)*
Flynn, Kieran

Oblates of Mary Immaculate (OMI):
(1) New Priory, Quex Road NW6 4PS *(Kilburn)*
(2) 237 Goldstone Terr NW6 3EP *(Kilburn)*
(3) 1 Stafford Road NW6 5RS *(Kilburn West)*
(4) 30 Prescot Street E1 8BB *(Tower Hill)*
Bromley, Herbert (1)
De Burca, Brian (1)
Dillon, Paschal (2)
Ford, Eugene (2)
Ryan, Francis (3)
Sheehan, Malachy (4)
Warren, Raymond (1)

Oratorians
The Oratory, Brompton Road SW7 2RP
Barrett-Lennard, Hugh
Bowen, George
Creighton-Jobe, Ronald
Dilke, Charles
Doyle, Patrick
Fordham, John
Harrison, Ignatius **Provost**
Lang, Michael
Large, Julian
McHardy, Rupert

Pallottine Fathers (SCA)
(Society of Catholic Apostolate):
(1) 5 Amwell Street EC1R 1UL *(Clerkenwell)*
(2) 358 Greenford Rd, *Greenford* UB6 9AN
(3) 4 Back Hill EC1R 5EN *(Italian Church)*
Daly, Thomas (2)
Di Giovanni, Carmelo (3) **Superior**
Doherty, Anthony (2)
Fulco, Andrea (3)
Hanly, William (1)
Ranahan, George (2) **Provincial Delegate**
Ward, Kevin (2)
Wrobel, Riszard (3)

Passionists (CP)
(Discalced Clerks of the Cross and Passion):
St Joseph's Retreat Highgate Hill, N19 5NE *(Highgate)*
Baker, Aidan
Cullen, Timothy
Davey, Theodore
Donovan, Daniel
Kelly, Christopher
O'Hara, Conleth
Owen, Charles
Steenson, Malachy
White, Mark

Presentation Brothers 7 Waldegrave Gardens, Twickenham TW1 4PQ
(Twickenham)

Providence, Sons of Divine (FDP):
25 Lower Teddington Rd, Hampton Wick KT1 4HB
(Teddington)
Beale, Stephen
Kehoe, Philip
Tirello, Joseph

Sacred Heart, Brothers of the:
8 King Harry Lane, *St Albans* AL3 4AW

Sacred Heart, Missionaries of the (MSC)
14 Beaconsfield Rd, *St Albans* AL1 3RB
Cleary, Daniel
Courtney, Pat
Daly, Jeremiah

Sacred Hearts Community (SS.CC)(Picpus Fathers):
(1) 372 Uxbridge Road W5 3LH
(Acton West)
(2) 5 Berrymead Gdns W3 8AA *(Acton)*
Barnes, Kenneth (1)
Crotty, Fintan (2)
McAneny, Christopher (2)
Murtagh, Kieran (2)

Salvatorians (SDS) (Society of the Divine Saviour):
(1) 96 The Crescent, *Abbots Langley* WD5 0DT
(2) Salvatorian Community House, High Rd, Harrow Weald, Middx HA3 5DY
and **The Presbytery, 191 High Road, Harrow Weald, Middx HA3 5EA**
(3) Catholic Church, Dunny Lane, *Chipperfield,* Kings Langley, Herts WD4 9DB
(4) Provincial House, 129 Spencer Road, Harrow Weald, Middx HA3 7BJ
(Wealdstone)
Anderton, Alban (2)
Cantwell, Desmond (3)
Cavanagh, Luke (2)
Doherty, Michael (2) **Superior**
Finan, Bernard (2)
Hennessey, Thomas (2)
Keane, Noel (2)
Nevin, Henry (1)
Murray, John (2)
Preston, Peter(2) **Provincial Superior**
Richmond, Hugh (2)
Tait, Adrian (2)
Waters, Frank (2)

Scalabrini Fathers, Green St, Shenley
(Borehamwood North)
Vico, Alberto

Servites (OSM) (Friar Servants of Mary):
264 *Fulham Road* SW10 9EL
Addison, Paul **Prior**
Colella, Joseph
Mac Neice, Dermot **Parish Priest**
Mulherin, James
Ryall, Patrick **Prior Provincial**

Stigmatine Fathers (CSS)
5 Hanover Road NW10 3DJ *(Kensal Rise)*
Mignolli, Natalino

Vincentians (CM) (Congregation of the Mission)
(1) 2 Flower Lane NW7 2JB *(Mill Hill)*
(2) 29 Eversley Cres, Isleworth TW7 4LR *(Osterley)*
(3) Spanish Chaplaincy, 47 Palace Ct W2 4LS *(Bayswater)*
Atanes, Ernesto (3)
Concannon, John (2)
Harris, Jack (1)
Kelly, Fergus (1)
McMahon, Hugh (1)
Mbelu, Austin (2)
Panathara, Chacko (2)
Pena, Segundo (3)
Travers, Noel (2)
Walshe, Philip (1)

Xaverian Brothers
58 Bonsor Road, Twickenham TW1 4RG *(Twickenham)*

Xaverian Missionaries (SX):
260 Nether Street N3 1HT *(Finchley Church End)*
Casalucci, Ennio **Superior**
Ceresoli, Giovanni
Zanchi, Alessandro
Paganelli, Natalio
Jimenez Estrella, Jorge

RELIGIOUS CONGREGATIONS & SOCIETIES OF APOSTOLIC LIFE

Place names refer to the parish entries under which further details will be found.

Adoration Sisters: Watford
Adoratrices, Handmaids of the Blessed Sacrament and of Charity: Kensington 2
Adorers of the Sacred Heart (Contemplative Benedictines): Marylebone
Assumption, Little Sisters of the: Willesden Green.
Assumption, Sisters of the: Kensington 2, Poplar
Augustinian Sisters: Archbishop's House
Augustinian Sisters of Meaux: Highgate
Bon Secours (Paris) Sisters: Bayswater.
Canossian Daughters of Charity: Waltham Cross
Capitanio Sisters: Ealing.
Carmelite Missionaries: St Johns Wood
Carmelites: Golders Green, St Charles Square, Ware.
Cenacle, Sisters of Our Lady of the: Cockfosters
Charity, Religious Sisters of: Acton, Chiswick, Hackney, White City
Charity (of Jesus and Mary), Sisters of: Bow, Letchworth, Stevenage
Charity (of St Jeanne Antide), Sisters of: Ealing, Stoke Newington
Charity of St Paul (Selly Park), Sisters of: Hackney, Hounslow
Charity (of St Vincent de Paul), Daughters of: Cathedral, Kilburn, Limehouse, Mill Hill, Kensal Rise, Northwood, Pinner, also (Spanish Province) Kentish Town.
Christian Instruction (St Gildas), Sisters of: Barnet, Stroud Green.
Columban Sisters: Bow, Clapton Park.
Comboni Missionary Sisters: Chiswick, West Green
Congregation of Jesus: Kentish Town, Swiss Cottage
Congr. of Our Lady (Canonesses of St Augustine) Bethnal Green, Oratory
Consolata Missionary Sisters: Somers Town
Cross (Liege), Daughters of the: Chelsea, Much Hadham.
Cross, Sisters of the Holy: Ealing
Cross and Passion, Sisters of the: Fulham Road, Islington.
Daughters of Divine Love: Wood Green
Dominican Sisters (Congr. of Stone): Ealing.
Dominican Sisters (Congr. of Newcastle, Natal): Bushey, Cricklewood, Edgware, Harpenden, Haverstock Hill, Hemel Hempstead, Osterley, Stevenage.
Dominican Sisters (Oakford,): Pinner
Dorothy, Sisters of St: Hampstead
Faithful Companions of Jesus: Isleworth, Poplar, Somers Town.
Franciscan Sisters of the Heart of Jesus: Pimlico.
Franciscan Missionaries of Mary: Acton West, Shepherds Bush.
Franciscan Sisters (Mill Hill): Mill Hil.
Franciscan Sisters of Our Lady of Victories: Cathedral
Good Shepherd Sisters: Finchley East.
Handmaids of the Sacred Heart of Jesus (Rome): St John's Wood
Helpers of the Holy Souls, Society of: Camden Town
Holy Child Jesus, Society of the: Bayswater, Edmonton, Kensington1, Spanish Place.
Holy Family of Bordeaux, Sisters of the: Kilburn, Willesden Green.
Holy Family of Nazareth, Sisters of the: Enfield.

Holy Name of Jesus, Sisters of the: Polish Church 3.
IBVM (Loreto Sisters) Acton, Kingsland, St Albans
Infant Jesus Sisters: Acton East
Jesus, Daughters of: Rickmansworth
Jesus, Little Sisters of: Hoxton, St Charles Sq.
Jesus, Sisters of the Infant: Acton East
Jesus and Mary, Religious of: Kensal Rise
John of God, Sisters of St, West Green
Joseph of Peace, Sisters of St: Cricklewood, Hanwell, Wapping.
Louis, Sisters of St: Dollis Hill, Harringay, Harrow South, Harrow-on-the-Hill, Muswell Hill, New Southgate
Marcellina, Sisters of St: Hampstead.
Marie Auxiliatrice, Society of: Muswell Hill, Tottenham.
Marist Sisters: Upper Holloway, White City.
Martha, Sisters of St: Barnet.
Mary, Little Company of: Ealing, Gunnersbury, Northfields.
Mary Immaculate, Missionary Sisters of (PIME): Chiswick
Mary Immaculate, Religious of: Kensington 2.
Mary Mother of Mercy, Daughters of: Edgware
Mary of Namur, Sisters of Saint: Notting Hill, Watford.
Medical Missionaries of Mary: Ealing.
Medical Mission Sisters (Society of Catholic Medical Missionaries): Acton, Hanwell, Northfields.
Mercy, Sisters of: Acton East, Bow, Clapton Park, Commercial Road, Cricklewood, Feltham, Hillingdon, Kensal New Town, Poplar, St Albans, St John's Wood, Underwood Road.
Missionaries of Charity: Kensal New Town, Southall.
Missionary Sisters of Our Lady of Africa (White Sisters): Ealing
Nazareth, Poor Sisters of: Brook Green, Finchley East
Notre Dame, Srs of: Pimlico
Our Lady of the Apostles, Sisters of: West Green
Our Lady of the Missions, Sisters of: New Southgate, Wapping, Wealdstone
Pallottine Missionary Sisters: Clerkenwell
Paul, Daughters of St: Kensington 1.
Paul of Chartres, Sisters of St: Highbury.
Poor, Little Sisters of the: Stoke Newington.
Poor Child Jesus, Sisters of the: Finchley North.
Poor Clares: Barnet
Poor Handmaids of Jesus Christ: Hendon
Providence (St Brieuc), Daughters of: Palmers Green, Wood Green.
Providence (of The Immaculate Conception, Champion), Sisters of: Baldock, Haverstock Hill.
Providence (Ruille-sur-Loire), Sisters of: Stroud Green
Resurrection, Sisters of the: Ealing, Polish Church
Rosminian Sisters: Ely Place
Sacred Heart, Sisters Hospitallers of the: Fulham Road
Sacred Heart of Jesus (St Jacut), Sisters of the: Whetstone.
Sacred Heart, Society of the: Brook Green, Hayes, St Charles' Square,
Sacred Heart of Mary (Beziers), Sisters of the: Brentford, Northfields, Shepherds Bush.
Sacred Hearts of Jesus and Mary (Chigwell), Sisters of the: Homerton, Uxbridge.
Sainte Union des Sacres Coeurs, Congregation of the: Holloway, Kentish Town, Kilburn, Wembley 3
Santa Ana, Spanish Sisters of: Brook Grn
Servants of the Mother of God: Bayswater, Brentford, Somers Town, Hampton, Upper Holloway
Servite Sisters: Clapton, Stamford Hill.

Sion, Sisters of Our Lady of:
Bayswater, Stroud Green
Suore Collegine della Sacra Famiglia:
Ponders End
Temple, Sisters of the: Notting Hill
Ursulines of Jesus: Hoxton, Kingsland, Stamford Hill.
Ursulines of St Angela Merici: Manor House
Wisdom (La Sagesse) Daughters of:
Finchley East, Homerton, Willesden Green

AASC	Handmaids of the Blessed Sacrament & of Charity
CBS	Bon Secours Sisters de Paris
CJ	Congregation of Jesus
CM	Carmelite Missionaries
CMS	Comboni Missionary Sisters
CP	Sisters of the Cross & Passion
CSFN	Srs of Holy Family of Nazareth
CSJP	Sisters of St Joseph of Peace
CR	Sisters of the Resurrection
CSA	Congregation of Our Lady Canonesses of St Augustine
DC	Daughters of Charity (SVP)
DDL	Daughters of Divine Love
DW	Daughters of Wisdom (La Sagesse)
FC	Daughters of the Cross (Liege)
FCJ	Faithful Companions of Jesus
FMM	Franciscan Missionaries of Mary
FSP	Daughters of St Paul
HFB	Holy Family of Bordeaux
HHS	Helpers of the Holy Souls
HSC	Hospitallers of the Sacred Heart
HSHJ	Handmaids Sacred Heart Jesus
IBVM (L)	(Loreto Sisters)
JT	Sisters of Jesus in the Temple
LCM	Little Company of Mary
LSA	Little Sisters of the Assumption
LSU	La Sainte Union
MC	Consolata Missionary Sisters
MMM	Medical Missionaries of Mary
MMS	Medical Mission Sisters
MSOLA	Missionaries OL Africa (White)
NDS	Sisters of Our Lady of Sion
OP	Dominican Sisters
OSA	Augustinian Sisters
OSM	Servite Sisters
PCJ	Sisters of Poor Child Jesus
PHJC	Poor Handmaids of Jesus Christ
PIME	Missionary Srs Mary Immaculate
RC	Sisters Our Lady of the Cenacle
RCI	Christian Instruction (St Gildas)
RNDM	Srs of Our Lady of the Missions
S de C	Srs of Charity (St Jeanne Antide)
SCJM	Srs of Charity (Jesus and Mary)
SP	Srs of Charity (of St Paul)
SPC	Sisters of St Paul of Chartres
SM	Marist
SSD	Sisters of St Dorothy
SSL	Sisters of St Louis
UJ	Ursulines of Jesus
USAM	Ursulines of St Angela Merici

Consecrated Virgins and Widows, consecrated by the bishop to live an independent life within the local Church community. See Code c 604 and CCC 922 to 924.
Further details from Sr Yvonne Coudurier **Tel: 020 7603 4140**
Servants of the Word (SW) an ecumenical congregation based in Acton

Talk to us about:
> Office & Legal Supplies
> Bespoke Print
> Furniture & Interiors
> IT Supplies
> Electronic & Printed Law Forms
> Digital Dictation
> Promotional Gifts
Looking for a supplier who's ready to listen?
statplus
Tel: 0845 606 1100
www.statplus.co.uk

CATHOLIC SCHOOLS

Schools are listed under the local education authority (LEA) area in which they are situated; for primary schools, the name of the parish is also indicated. For secondary schools and colleges the deanery is only given where that is different from the LEA area in which the school or college is situated. The Parish Priest is normally Chaplain for primary schools. In secondary schools and colleges, the name of the Chaplain is given. Unless stated otherwise, all schools are voluntary aided and co-educational, and all primary schools are junior and infant. (+N) indicates that the school has a nursery. RO indicates that the school is in the trusteeship of a Religious Order: all other schools are in the trusteeship of the Diocese. **Schools with websites are listed at www.rcdow.org.uk**

CITY OF WESTMINSTER (213)

PRIMARY SCHOOLS

Our Lady of Dolours: (+N) (3381) **19 Cirencester Street W2 5SR Tel: 020 7641 4326 Fax: 020 7641 4389 Head** Mrs Mary Wilson (Paddington)

St Edward: (+N) (3432) **Lisson Grove NW1 6LH Tel: 020 7723 5911 Fax: 020 7723 5250 Head** Mrs Teresa Donnelly BEd (St John's Wood) (RO)

St Joseph: (+N) (3473) **Lanark Road W9 1DF Tel: 020 7286 3518 Fax: 020 7286 2303 E-mail: dmcd944@yahoo.co.uk Head** Mr Danny McDonald DipEd (St John's Wood)

St Mary of the Angels: (+N) (3532) **Shrewsbury Road W2 5PR Tel: 020 7229 7665 Fax: 020 7229 7665 E-mail: office@st-maryangels.westminster.sch.uk Head** Mrs Helen Connolly (Bayswater)

St Vincent: (+N) (3610) **St Vincent Street, Marylebone W1M 3HA Tel: 020 7641 6110 Fax: 020 7641 6116 Head** Miss Marina Coleman (Spanish Place)

St Vincent de Paul: (+N) (3611) **Morpeth Terrace SW1P 3EP Tel: 020 7641 5990 Fax: 020 7641 5901 Head** Mr Jack O'Neill (Cathedral)

Westminster Cathedral: (3623) **Bessborough Place, Pimlico SW1V 3SE Tel: 020 7641 5915 Fax: 020 7821 9349 Head** Mr John Hartnett (Pimlico)

Independent

St Christina Girls' School (6225) (Girls) **25 St Edmund's Terrace, NW8 7PY Tel: 020 7722 8784 Fax: 020 7586 4961 E-mail: vanda@stschristinasschool.co.uk Head** Mrs Nathalie Clyne Wilson (St John's Wood) (RO)

Westminster Cathedral Choir School: (6197) (Boys) **Ambrosden Avenue SW1P 1QH Tel: 020 7798 9081 Fax: 020 7798 9090 E-mail: headwccs@aol.com Head** Mr John Browne (Cathedral)

SECONDARY SCHOOL

St George: (4809) Lanark Road, Maida Vale W9 1RB Tel: 020 7328 0904
Fax: 020 7624 6083 E-mail: office.stgeorgesrc.westminster@lgfl.net
Head Appointment pending (Marylebone)

LONDON BOROUGH OF BARNET (302)

PRIMARY SCHOOLS

Annunciation: (Infants +N) (3500) Thirleby Road, Burnt Oak, Edgware HA8 0HQ
Tel: 020 8959 2325 Fax: 020 8906 4116 E-mail: info@annunciation-inf.barnet.sch.uk
Head Miss Teresa Lynch BA (Burnt Oak)

Annunciation: (Junior) (3514) The Meads, Burnt Oak, Middx HA8 9HQ
Tel: 020 8906 0723 Fax: 020 8906 0377 E-mail: info@annunciation-jun.barnet.sch.uk
Head Miss Moira McManus (Burnt Oak)

Blessed Dominic: (+N) (3511) Lanacre Avenue, Grahame Park NW9 5FN
Tel: 020 8205 3790 Fax: 020 8205 9341 E-mail: head.blesseddominic.barnet@lgfl.net
Head Miss Anne Marie Hendry BEd(Hons) (Grahame Park)

Our Lady of Lourdes: (+N) (3501) Bow Lane, Finchley N12 0JP Tel: 020 8346 1681
Fax: 020 8346 0579 E-mail: info@olol.barnet.sch.uk
Head Mrs Marybelle Morrissey (Finchley East)

Sacred Heart: (3510) 2 Oakleigh Park South, Whetstone N20 9JU
Tel: 020 8445 3854 Fax: 020 8445 0862 E-mail: office@sacredheart.barnet.sch.uk
Head Mrs Maureen Ruane MEd (Whetstone) (RO)

St Agnes: (+N) (3502) Thorverton Road, Cricklewood NW2 1RG
Tel: 020 8452 4565 Fax: 020 8830 6709 E-mail: info@st-agnes.barnet.sch.uk
Head Mrs Cathy Jordan BEd MA (Cricklewood)

St Catherine: (+N) (3504) Vale Drive, Barnet, Herts EN5 2ED
Tel: 020 8440 4946 Fax: 020 8441 3436 Head Mrs Eileen Quigley (Barnet)

St Joseph: (Infants +N) (3508) Watford Way, Hendon NW4 4TY
Tel: 020 8202 9852
Fax: 020 8201 5787 E-mail: info@st.joseph-inf.barnet.sch.uk
Head Mrs Mary Parsons (Hendon)

St Joseph: (Junior) (3509) Watford Way, Hendon NW4 4TY
Tel: 020 8202 5229
Fax: 020 8202 5530 E-mail: info@st-joseph-jun.barnet.sch.uk
Head Mrs Irene Ciapryna (Hendon/West Hendon)

St Theresa: (3507) 80 East End Road N3 2TD Tel: 020 8346 8826 Fax: 020 8346 0215
E-mail: officesttheresas.barnet@lgfl.net Head Mr Michael Lyons BEd (Finchley CE) (RO)

St Vincent: (3506) The Ridgeway, Mill Hill NW7 1EJ
Tel: 020 8959 3417 Fax: 020 8906 9733 E-mail: info@st-vincent.barnet.sch.uk
Head Mrs Anne O'Leary (Mill Hill) (RO)

Independent
St Martha's Convent Junior (6013) (Girls) 22 Wood Street, Barnet Herts EN5 4BW
Tel: 020 8449 4346 Head Sr Christine O'Dwyer (High Barnet) (RO)

SECONDARY SCHOOLS

Bishop Douglass Catholic High: (5408) Hamilton Rd, Finchley N2 0SQ
Tel: 020 8444 5211/3 Fax: 020 8444 0416
E-mail: schooladmin@bishopdouglass.barnet.sch.uk
Head Ms Angela Murphy Chaplain Maureen Graham

Finchley Catholic High: (Boys) (5405) Woodside Lane, Finchley N12 8TA
Tel: 020 8445 0105 Fax: 020 8446 0691 E-mail: admin@fchs.demon.co.uk
Head Mr Kevin Hoare BEd(Hons) Chaplain

St James Catholic High: (5407) Great Strand, Grahame Park, Colindale NW9 5PE
Tel: 020 8358 2800 Fax: 020 8358 2801 E-mail: admin@st-james.barnet.sch.uk
Head Appointment pending Chaplain Fr Tom O'Brien

St Michael Catholic Grammar: (Girls) (5404) Nether Street, North Finchley N12 7NJ
Tel: 020 8446 2256 Fax: 020 8343 9598 E-mail: stmichael@rmplc.co.uk
Head Miss Ursula Morrissey BA Chaplain Fr John Ball MHM (RO)

Independent
St Martha's Convent Senior: (6014) (Girls) The Mount, Camlet Way, Barnet, EN4 0NJ
Tel: 020 8449 6889 Fax: 020 8441 5632 E-mail: office@stmarthas.org.uk
Head Mr James Sheridan Chaplain Fr Derek Maguire (RO) (High Barnet)

LONDON BOROUGH OF BRENT (304)

PRIMARY SCHOOLS

Convent of Jesus & Mary: (Infants +N) (3507) 21 Park Ave, Willesden Green NW2 5AN
Tel: 020 8459 5890 Fax: 020 8451 9499 E-mail: cjmhs@cjmhs.rmplc.co.uk
Head Mrs Teresa O'Higgins (Willesden Green)

Our Lady of Grace: (Infants +N) (3510) Dollis Hill Avenue NW2 6EU
Tel: 020 8450 6757 Fax: 020 8452 1501 E-mail: admin@olginf.brent.sch.uk
Head Miss Maria Shea BEd Adv DipEd (Dollis Hill)

Our Lady of Grace: (Junior) (3500) Dollis Hill Lane NW2 6HS Tel: 020 8450 6002
Fax: 020 8208 3430 E-mail: admin@olgjr.brent.sch.uk Head Mr David O'Farrell BA(Dollis Hill)

Our Lady of Lourdes:(+N) (3508)Wesley Rd NW10 8PP Tel:020 8961 5037 Fax:020 8963 1197
E-mail: admin@lourdes.brent.sch.uk Head Mrs Mella Waterhouse (Stonebridge)

St Joseph: (Infants +N) (3509) Waverley Avenue, Wembley HA9 6TA Tel: 020 8903 6032
Fax: 020 8903 5263 E-mail: admin@josephsinf.brent.sch.uk Head Mrs Pam Gibney (Wembley)

St Joseph: (Junior) (3501) Chatsworth Avenue, Wembley, Middx HA9 6BE
Tel: 020 8902 3438 Fax: 020 8903 5482 E-mail: admin@sjjswem.brent.sch.uk
Head Mrs Pauline Moss (Wembley)

St Joseph: (+N) (5203) Goodson Road, Willesden NW10 9LS Tel: 020 8965 5651
Fax: 020 8961 9022 E-mail: admin@josephsjmi.brent.sch.uk Head Mrs Susan Riley MA

St Margaret Clitherow: (+N) (3511) Quainton St, Neasden NW10 0BG
Tel: 020 8450 3631 Fax: 020 8450 3729 E-mail: admin@clitherow.brent.sch.uk
Head Mrs Ewa McSperrin BEd (Wembley Park)

St Mary: (+N) (3602) Canterbury Road, Kilburn NW6 5ST Tel: 020 7624 3830
Fax: 7372 4932 E-mail: admin@maryrcp.brent.sch.uk Head Mr Alphonsus Reilly (Kilburn)

St Mary Magdalen: (Junior) (3505) Linacre Road NW2 5BB Tel: 020 8459 3159
Fax: 020 8459 0108 E-mail: admin@marymag.sch.uk Head Miss Mary Carney (Willesden Green)

St Robert Southwell: (+N) (3506) Slough Lane NW9 8YD Tel: 020 8204 6148
Fax: 020 8905 0287 E-mail: admin@robsouth.brent.sch.uk
Head Miss Helen Newman (Kingsbury Green)

SECONDARY SCHOOLS

St Gregory High: (5406) Donnington Road, Kenton, Harrow, Middx HA3 ONB
Tel: 020 8907 8828 Fax: 020 8909 1161 E-mail: cryan@stgregorys.harrow.sch.uk
Head Mr Martin Earley MA(Oxon) MSc(Econ) MA(Ed) Chaplain Miss Jane Porter

Federation of The Convent of Jesus and Mary and Cardinal Hinsley

Convent of Jesus & Mary:(Girls) (5404) Language College, Crownhill Rd, Willesden NW10 4EP
Tel: 020 8965 2986 Fax: 020 8838 0071 E-mail: cjmhs@cjmhs.rmplc.co.uk
Principal Mrs Geraldine Freear BSc, MEd Chaplain Mr Dominic West

Cardinal Hinsley: (Boys) (5407) Harlesden Road NW10 3RN
Tel: 020 8965 3947 Fax: 020 8965 3430
Head Mrs Geraldine Freear BSc MEd Chaplain Fr Gerard Balinnya

LONDON BOROUGH OF CAMDEN (202)

PRIMARY SCHOOLS

Our Lady's: (+N) (3655) Pratt Street NW1 0DP
Tel: 020 7485 7997 Fax: 020 7428 9426 E-mail: head@ourladys.camden.sch.uk
Head Mrs Deirdre Finan BEd (Hons) MA (Camden Town)

Rosary: (+N) (3391) 238 Haverstock Hill NW3 2AE
Tel: 020 7794 6292 Fax: 020 7794 6292 E-mail: head@rosary.camden.sch.uk
Head Miss Isobel Gaffney (Haverstock Hill)

St Aloysius: (Infants +N) (3401) 28 Phoenix Road NW1 1TA
Tel: 020 7387 3551 Fax: 020 7383 5948 E-mail: head@staloysiusinf.camden.sch.uk
Head Mrs Jackie Cox (Somers Town)

St Aloysius: (Junior) (3400) Aldenham Street NW1 1PS
Tel: 020 7387 9591 Fax: 020 7383 4082 E-mail: head@staloysiusjun.camden.sch.uk
Head Mr Michael O'Gorman (Somers Town)

St Dominic: (+N) (3429) Southampton Road NW5 4JS
Tel: 020 7485 5918 Fax: 020 7284 0961 E-mail: head@stdominic.camden.sch.uk
Head Mrs Ashley Streeter (Haverstock Hill)

St Eugene de Mazenod: (3649) Mazenod Avenue, Quex Road NW6 4LS
Tel: 020 7624 4837 Fax: 020 7328 2280 E-mail: head@steugene.camden.sch.uk
Head Miss Valerie Robertson (Kilburn)

St Joseph: (+N) (3482) Macklin Street, Drury Lane WC2B 5NA
Tel: 020 7242 7712 Fax: 020 7430 1834 E-mail: admin@stjosephs.camden.sch.uk
Head Miss Pat MacDonald (Lincoln's Inn Fields)

St Patrick: (+N) (3560) Holmes Road, Kentish Town NW5 3AH
Tel: 020 7267 1200 Fax: 020 7485 4691 E-mail: head@stpatricks.camden.sch.uk
Head Miss Christine Wells BA, MEd (Kentish Town)

Independent
St Anthony's Preparatory: (6181) (Boys) 90 Fitzjohn's Avenue NW3 6AA
Tel: 020 7435 0316 Fax: 020 7435 9223
Head Mr Philip Anderson (Hampstead) (RO)

St Mary's Preparatory: (6084) (Girls) 47 Fitzjohn's Avenue NW3 6PG
Tel: 020 7435 1868 Fax: 020 7794 7922 E-mail: enquiries@stmh.co.uk
Head Miss Angela Rawlinson (Swiss Cottage) (RO)

The Cavendish School: (6038) 31 Inverness Street NW1 7HB
Tel: 020 7485 1958 Fax: 020 7267 0098 E-mail: admissions@cavendish-school.co.uk
Head Mrs L D Hayes BA (Hons) DipEd (Camden Town) (RO)

SECONDARY SCHOOLS

La Sainte Union: (5041) (Girls) Highgate Road NW5 1RP
Tel: 020 7428 4600 Fax: 020 7267 7647 Email: general@lsu.camden.sch.uk
Head Sister Teresa Finn Chaplain Sr Mairead Mulligan (RO)

Maria Fidelis: (4652) (Girls) 34 Phoenix Road, Euston NW1 1TA
Tel: 020 7387 3856 Fax: 020 7388 9558 Email: mail@mariafidelis.camden.sch.uk
Head Ms Pauline Williams Chaplain Sr Cecelia (RO)

LONDON BOROUGH OF EALING (307)

PRIMARY SCHOOLS

Mount Carmel: (3500) (+N) Little Ealing Lane, Ealing W5 4EA
Tel: 020 8567 4646 Fax: 020 8579 5362 E-mail: mtcarmel@tiscali.co.uk
Head Mrs Josephine Wales (Northfields)

Our Lady of the Visitation: (3503) Greenford Road, Greenford UB6 9AN
Tel: 020 8575 5344 Fax: 020 8575 6734 E-mail: ourlady@visitation.ealing.sch.uk
Head Mr Bruno Grzegorzek BA DipSC (Greenford)

St Anselm: (3505) Church Avenue, Southall, Middx UB2 4BH
Tel: 020 8574 3906 Fax: 020 8571 6308 E-mail: office@st-anselm.ealing.sch.uk
Head Mrs Ita King (Southall)

St Gregory: (3506) Woodfield Road, W5 1SL Tel: 020 8997 7550 Fax: 020 8810 6506
E-mail: admin@st-gregory.ealing.sch.uk Head Mrs Pat McCarthy (Ealing)

St John Fisher: (3504) (+N) Thirlmere Avenue, Rydal Cres, Perivale, Greenford UB6 7AF
Tel: 020 8998 4426 Fax: 020 8810 9131 (Infant & Nursery Dept Tel: 020 8998 9830)
Head Mrs Gillian Scannell (Perivale)

St Joseph: (3507) (+N) York Avenue W7 3HU Tel: 020 8567 6293 Fax: 020 8840 0278
E-mail: stjospg@ealing.gov.uk Head Mr Ben Cassidy BA (Hanwell)

St Raphael: (3508) Hartfield Avenue, Northolt, Middx UB5 6NL
Tel: 020 8841 0848 Fax: 020 8842 4617 E-mail: admin@st-raphael.ealing.sch.uk
Head Mrs Ann Staunton (Yeading)

St Vincent: (3509) 1 Pierrepoint Road W3 9JR Tel: 020 8992 6625 Fax: 020 8896 0623
E-mail: st-vincents@ealing.sch.uk Head Mrs Tina Cleugh (Acton)

Independent

St Benedict Junior: (6067) (Boys) **5 Montpelier Avenue, Ealing W5 2XP**
Tel: 020 8862 2052 Fax: 020 8862 2058 E-mail: secretary@stbenedictsjunior.org.uk
Head Mr Denis McSweeney BSc MA (Ealing) (RO)

SECONDARY SCHOOL

Cardinal Wiseman School: (4603) **Greenford Road, Greenford UB6 9AW**
Tel: 020 8575 8222 Fax: 020 8575 9963 E-mail: info@cwhsit.demon.co.uk
Head Mr Paul Patrick BEd (Hons) MBA FRSA **Chaplain** Mrs Celia Finn

Independent

St Benedict: (6006) (Boys) **54 Eaton Rise W5 2ES**
Tel: 020 8862 2010 Fax: 020 8862 2199 E-mail: headmaster@stbenedicts.org.uk
Head Mr Christopher Cleugh MSc **Chaplain** Fr Thomas Stapleford (RO)

PRIMARY & SECONDARY SCHOOL

Independent

St Augustine's Priory School: (Girls) **Hillcrest Road, Ealing W5 2JL**
Tel: 020 8997 2022 Fax: 020 8810 6501
Head Mrs Frances Gumley-Mason MA (Cantab) **Chaplain** Dom Gregory Chillman OSB (RO)

LONDON BOROUGH OF ENFIELD (308)

PRIMARY SCHOOLS

Our Lady of Lourdes: (3504) **The Limes Avenue, New Southgate N11 1RD**
Tel: 020 8361 0767 Fax: 020 8361 6682 E-mail: admin@ololschool.enfield.sch.uk
Head Miss Mairead Devery (New Southgate)

St Edmund: (3501) **Hertford Road N9 7HS Tel: 020 8807 2664 Fax: 020 8807 8877**
E-mail: St-Edmunds_office/school/lbe@lbe Head Richard Greenfield BSc MEd (Edmonton)

St George: (3502) **Gordon Road, Enfield, Middx EN2 0QA Tel: 020 8363 3729**
Fax: 020 8367 2275 E-mail: st-georges.office@enfield.gov.uk Head Mrs Trish Alder (Enfield)

St Mary: (5403) (+N) **Durants Road, Ponders End, Enfield, Middx EN3 7DE**
Tel: 020 8804 2396 Fax: 020 8805 8847 E-mail: pfcoleman@stmarys.enfield.sch.uk
Head Miss Maeve Creed (Ponders End)

St Monica: (3503) **Cannon Hill, Cannon Road, Southgate N14 7HE**
Tel: 020 8886 4647 Fax: 020 8882 8424 E-mail: st-monicas.office@enfield.gov.com
Head Mr Ted Getley BA Hons (Palmers Green)

Independent

Vita et Pax School: (6056) Priory Close, Green Road, Southgate N14 4AT
Tel: 020 8449 8336 Fax: 020 8440 0483 E-mail: vitaetpax@lineone.net
Head Mrs Margaret O'Connor BEd (Hons) MSc (Cockfosters) (RO)

SECONDARY SCHOOLS

St Anne Catholic High: (4706) (Girls) Oakthorpe Rd, Palmers Green N13 5TY
Tel: 020 8886 2165 Fax: 020 8886 6552
Head Cheryl Byamukama Chaplain

St Ignatius College: (3500) (Boys) Turkey Street, Enfield, Middx EN1 4NP
Tel: 01992 717835/760520 Fax: 01992 652070 E-mail: e-munns@yahoo.co.uk
Head Mr Paul Adams Chaplain Fr John Moffatt (RO)

LONDON BOROUGH BOROUGH OF HACKNEY (204)

PRIMARY SCHOOLS

Our Lady and St Joseph (3371) (+N) Buckingham Road N1 4DG
Tel: 020 7254 7353 Fax: 020 7249 3870 E-mail: seanjflood@yahoo.co.uk
Head Sean Flood MA BEd (Hons) (Kingsland)

St Dominic: (2900) (+N) Ballance Road, Homerton E9 5SR
Tel: 020 8985 0995 Fax: 020 8985 2915 E-mail: mariehogg@learninglife.co.uk
Head Marie Hogg (Homerton)

St Monica: (3553) (+N) Hoxton Square N1 6NT
Tel: 020 7739 5824 Fax: 020 7613 4465 E-mail: admin@st.monicas.hackney.sch.uk
Head Miss Carmel Connors (Hoxton)

St Scholastica (3659) (+N) Kenninghall Road E5 8BS
Tel: 020 8985 3466 Fax: 020 8533 0014
Head Mrs Dympna Brotherton (Clapton)

SECONDARY SCHOOLS

Cardinal Pole: (4714) Kenworthy Road, Homerton E9 5RB
Tel: 020 8985 5150 Fax: 020 8533 7325
E-mail: cardinalpole@learninglife.co.uk
Head Ms Katherine Hartigan Chaplain

Our Lady's Convent High: (4641) (Girls) 6-16 Amhurst Park, N16 5AF
Tel: 020 8800 2158 Fax: 020 8809 8898
E-mail: Rhoden@learninglife.co.uk
Head Mrs Jane Gray Chaplain Sr Dominic Savio (RO)

LONDON BOROUGH OF HAMMERSMITH & FULHAM (205)

PRIMARY SCHOOLS

Holy Cross: (3354) (+N) Basuto Road, Fulham SW6 4BL
Tel: 020 7736 1447 Fax: 020 7371 9954 E-mail: admin@holy-crossrc.lbhf.school.uk
Head Mr Gerry Mulligan (Parsons Green)

The Good Shepherd: (3602) (+N) Gayford Road W12 9BY
Tel: 020 8743 5060 Fax: 020 8740 1626
E-mail: sao1@goodshepherdrc.lbhf.sch.uk
Head Ms Cathy Doogan (Shepherds Bush)

Larmenier & Sacred Heart: (3649) (+N) Great Church Lane W6 8DH Tel: 020 8748 9444
Fax: 020 8748 2387 E-mail: secretary@Larmenier.hammersmith-fulham.sch.uk
Head Sister Hannah Dwyer MA BEd (Hons) (Brook Green)

Pope John: (3645) (+N) Commonwealth Avenue W12 7QR
Tel: 020 8743 9428 Fax: 020 8749 7117 E-mail: popejohnuk@hotmail.com
Head Mrs Gillian Wickham MBAC FRSA (White City)

St Augustine: (3378) Disbrowe Road W6 8QE Tel: 020 7385 4333
Fax: 020 7386 7751 E-mail: admin@st-augustines.hammersmith-fulham.sch.uk
Head Miss Mary Kelliher (Hammersmith)

St Mary: (3529) (+N) Masbro Road W14 0CT
Tel: 020 7603 7717 Fax: 020 7602 7432 E-mail: st.mary@btconnect.com
Head Mrs Caroline Allen BEd (Brook Green)

St Thomas of Canterbury: (3648) Estcourt Road London, SW6 7HB
Tel: 020 7385 8165 Fax: 020 7385 0918 E-mail: head@stthomasrclbhf.sch.uk
Head Mrs Angela Rundle MA BA PGCE (Fulham)

SECONDARY SCHOOLS

Sacred Heart High: (3394) (Girls) 212 Hammersmith Road W6 7DG
Tel: 020 8748 7600 Fax: 020 8748 0392 E-mail: jhunt@sacredh.lbhf.sch.uk
Head Dr Christine Carpenter BA PhD FRSA Chaplain

The London Oratory: (5400) (Boys) Seagrave Road SW6 1RX
Tel: 020 7385 0102 Fax: 020 7381 7676 E-mail: admin@los.ac
Head Mr John McIntosh OBE MA FRSA Hon FCP Chaplain Fr George Bowen (RO)

LONDON BOROUGH OF HARINGEY (309)

PRIMARY SCHOOLS

Our Lady of Muswell: (3500) (+N) **Pages Lane N10 1PS Tel/Fax: 020 8444 9997 E-mail: office@ourladymuswell.haringey.sch.uk Head** Appointment pending (Muswell Hill)

St Francis de Sales: (3507) (Infants+N) **Brereton Road N17 8DA Tel: 020 8808 4432 Fax: 020 8801 7023 E-mail: m.mooney@sfds.haringey.sch.uk Head** Miss Marguerita Mooney BEd (Tottenham)

St Francis de Sales: (3501) (Junior) **Brereton Road, Tottenham N17 8DA Tel: 020 8808 2923 Fax: 020 8801 7438 E-mail: StFrancisJunior.School@Haringey.sch.uk Head** Mr Hugh McBride MA (Tottenham)

St Gildas: (3509) (Junior) **1 Oakington Way, Crouch End N8 9EP Tel: 020 8348 1902 Fax: 020 8340 7805 E-mail: StGildasJuniorSchool@haringey.gov.uk Head** Mrs Irene Rincon (Stroud Green)

St Ignatius: (3502) (+N) **St Ann's Road N15 6ND Tel: 020 8800 2771 Fax: 020 8802 7156 E-mail: StIgnatiusPrimarySchool@haringey.gov.uk Head** Mr Con Bonner (Stamford Hill)

St John Vianney: (3510) (+N) **Stanley Road, West Green N15 3HD Tel: 020 8889 8421 Fax: 020 8881 2528 E-mail: St-john-primary-school@haringey.gov.uk Head** Mrs Rosemary Kilbride (West Green)

St Martin de Porres: (3508) (+N) **Blake Road, Wood Green N11 2AF Tel: 020 8361 1445 Fax: 020 8361 5849 E-mail: St Martin.School@haringey.gov.uk Head** Miss Irene Tyrrell (Wood Green)

St Mary Priory: (3505) (Infants +N) **Hermitage Road N15 5RE Tel: 020 8800 9229 Fax: 020 8800 1375 E-mail: StMarysRCInfant.School@haringey.gov.uk Head** Appointment pending (Stamford Hill) (RO)

St Mary Priory: (3503) (Junior) **Hermitage Road, Stamford Hill N15 5RE Tel: 020 8800 9305 Fax: 020 8880 1142 E-mail: StMaryRCJunior.School@haringey.gov.uk Head** Mrs Florence Collins (Stamford Hill) (RO)

St Paul: (3504) **Bradley Rd, Wood Green N22 4SZ Tel: 020 8888 7081 Fax: 020 8889 1397 E-mail: staffroom@stpaulsrc.haringey.sch.uk Head** Mr Peter Keane (Wood Green)

St Peter-in-Chains: (3506) (Infants) **3 Elm Grove N8 9AJ Tel: 020 8340 6789 Fax: 020 8340 3653 E-mail:stpeter.school@haringey.gov.uk Head** Miss Mary Falvey BEd (Stroud Green)

The Cavendish School NW1

Girls 3-11 years

Small friendly preparatory school

Original foundation - 1875

Lively, well balanced academic education

Spacious premises; School Chapel

Secluded playgrounds

Catholic instruction

Extensive extra curricular programme

After-school care service

To receive further details or to visit the school please contact:

School secretary: Mrs F Jones,
31 Inverness Street,
London NW1 7HB
Tel: 020 7485 1958
Fax: 020 7267 0098

More House School

Mrs L Falconer BSc
22\24 Pont Street, London SW1X OAA

Patron: Cardinal Cormac Murphy-O'Connor

Independent Day School for Girls 11-18
A Catholic foundation which welcomes all faiths

2005 Advanced Level Pass Rate 100%
81% of entry at grades A and B

Class sizes up to 20 pupils

For further details and information on current vacancies telephone Admissions Secretary on 020 7235 2855
or e-mail: office@morehouse.org.uk
website: www. morehouse.org.uk

Registered Charity No. 312737 for educational purposes

WILBY & BURNETT

Total Design & Management

- *Project Management*
- *Architecture*
- *Building Surveying*
- *Quantity Surveying*

***Wilby & Burnett** is a multi-disciplinary practice of Chartered Surveyors and Architects providing in-house total design and management of all types and sizes of building project – from inception to completion.*

Provident House, 123 Ashdon Road
Saffron Walden, Essex CB10 2AJ
Tel: (01799) 513621
Fax: (01799) 514010
E-mail: info@wilbyburnett.co.uk

Specialising in education

SECONDARY SCHOOL

St Thomas More: (4703) Glendale Avenue, Wood Green N22 5HN
Tel: 020 8888 7122 Fax: 020 8826 9370 E-mail: stthomas.ss@connect.bt.com
Head Dr Colm Hickey **Chaplain** John Ravi, Siluvai Muth

LONDON BOROUGH OF HARROW (310)

PRIMARY SCHOOLS

St Anselm: (3501) Roxborough Park, Harrow HA1 3BE
Tel: 020 8422 1600 Fax: 020 8422 3564 E-mail: st.anselms.sch@harrow.gov.uk
Head Mr Andrew Rafferty (Harrow-on-the-Hill)

St Bernadette: (3500) Clifton Road, Kenton, Harrow Middx HA3 9NS Tel: 020 8204 8902 Fax: 020 8905 0738 E-mail: headteacher@stbernadettes.harrow.sch.uk
Head Mrs Tina Caulfield (Kenton)

St George: (3508) Sudbury Hill, Harrow HA1 3SBTel: 020 8422 1272 Fax: 020 8864 5540 E-mail: patmor4@hotmail.com **Head** Mr Pat Morrissey (Sudbury)

St John Fisher: (3505) (First & Middle) Melrose Road, Pinner HA5 5RA
Tel: 020 8868 2961 Fax: 020 8866 5882 E-mail: st.john.fisher.sch@harrow.gov.uk
Head Mrs Ann Lyons (Harrow North)

St Joseph: (3507) Dobbin Close, Belmont, Harrow, Middx HA3 7LT
Tel: 020 8863 8531 Fax: 020 8863 3341 E-mail: st.josephs.sch@harrow.gov.uk
Head Mr Philip Sutton (Wealdstone)

St Teresa: (3504) (First & Middle +N) Long Elmes, Harrow Weald, Middx HA3 6LE
Tel: 020 8428 8640 Fax: 020 8420 1571 E-mail: jfaint@st-teresas.harrow.sch.uk
Head Mrs Jane Faint (Headstone Lane)

SECONDARY SCHOOLS

Sacred Heart High: (4700) (Girls) 186 High St, Wealdstone, Harrow HA3 7AY
Tel: 020 8863 9922 Fax: 020 8861 5051 E-mail: sacred.heart.high.sch@harrow.gov.uk
Head Mrs Mary Waplington MA **Chaplain**

Salvatorian College: (5400) (Boys) High Road, Harrow Weald HA3 5DY Tel: 020 8863 2706 Fax: 020 8863 3435 **Head** Mr Andrew Graham MA **Chaplain** Fr Peter Preston (RO)

SIXTH FORM COLLEGE

St Dominic: (8600) Mount Park Avenue, Harrow-on-the-Hill, Middx HA1 3HX
Tel: 020 8422 8084 Fax: 020 8422 3759 E-mail: stdoms@stdoms.ac.uk
Principal Mr Patrick Harty **Chaplain** Fiona Mansford

LONDON BOROUGH OF HILLINGDON (312)

PRIMARY SCHOOLS

Botwell House: (3401) (+N) Botwell Lane, Hayes, Middx UB3 2AB
Tel: 020 8573 2229 Fax: 020 8569 0286 Head Mr Sean Reilly BEd Hons (Hayes)

Sacred Heart: (3405) (+N) Herlwyn Avenue, Ruislip, Middx HA4 6EZ
Tel: 01895 633240 Fax: 01895 625 772 Head Mr David Manley (Ruislip)

St Bernadette: (3402) (+N) 160 Long Lane, Hillingdon, Middx UB10 0EH
Tel: 01895 232298 Fax: 01895 230086 E-mail: stbernadette@lineone.net
Head Mrs Catherine Moss (Hillingdon)

St Catherine: (3403) (+N) Money Lane, West Drayton, Middx UB7 7NX
Tel: 01895 442839 Fax: 01895 442631 Head Miss Sara Benn (West Drayton)

St Mary: (3404) (+N) Rockingham Close, Uxbridge, Middx UB8 2UA
Tel: 01895 232814 Fax: 01895 235403 Head Miss Ann Shevling (Uxbridge)

St Swithun Wells: : (3400) (+N) Hunters Hill, South Ruislip, Middx HA4 9HS
Tel: 01895 671 960 Fax: 020 8845 1611 E-mail: ssrc@ebhill.gov.uk
Head Mr Tom Campbell (Ruislip South)

SECONDARY SCHOOL

The Douay Martrys: (5408) Edinburgh Drive, Ickenham, Uxbridge UB10 8QY
Tel: 01895 679400 Fax: 01895 679400 E-mail: tdmsickenh@aol.com
Head Mrs Geraldine Davies BSc Chaplain Louisa Foley

NON MAINTAINED SPECIAL SCHOOL

Pield Heath House: (7006) Pield Heath Road, Hillingdon, Middx UB8 3NW
Tel: 01895 258507 Fax: 01895 256497 E-mail: pieldheath@btconnect.com
Head Sister Julie Rose (RO)

LONDON BOROUGH OF HOUNSLOW 313

PRIMARY SCHOOLS

Our Lady & St John: (3502) (+N) Boston Park Road, Brentford, Middx TW8 9JF
Tel: 020 8560 7477 Fax: 020 8568 8806 E-mail: admin@stjohnrc.hounslow.sch.uk
Head Mrs Grainne Morland (Brentford)

St Lawrence: (3503) (+N) Victoria Road, Feltham TW13 4AF Tel: 020 8890 3878
Fax: 020 8883 1885 E-mail: rory.mccormack@st-lawrence.hounslow.sch.uk
Head Mr Rory McCormack BEd (Feltham)

St Mary: (3504) (+N) South Street, Isleworth TW7 6DL Tel: 020 8560 7166
Fax: 020 8232 8820 E-mail: head@st-marys-rc-pri-isleworth.hounslow.sch.uk
Head Mrs Myra Neves BA DipEd (Isleworth)

St Mary: (3505) (+N) Duke Road, Chiswick W4 2DF Tel: 020 8994 5606 Fax: 020 8742 7630
E-mail: SMPT:stmarys@intonet.co.uk Head Appointment pending (Chiswick)

St Michael's & St Martin's: (3507) (+N) Belgrave Rd, Hounslow TW4 7AG
Tel: 020 8572 9658 Fax: 020 8572 1982 E-mail: stmichaelandstmartin@hotmail.com
Head Mrs Eileen Mullarkey (Hounslow)

The Rosary: (3506) (Infants +N) Heston Road, Heston, Middx TW5 0RL
Tel: 020 8570 4942 Fax: 020 8570 8874 E-mail: angela.brennan@education.hounslow.gov.uk
Head Mrs Angela Brennan (Heston)

The Rosary: (3500) (Junior) 10 The Green, Heston, Middx TW5 0RL
Tel: 020 8581 0066 Fax: 020 8581 0065 E-mail: rosary@junschool.freeserve.co.uk
Head Mrs Jenny Bashford (Heston)

SECONDARY SCHOOLS

Gumley House: (5400) (Girls) Twickenham Road, Isleworth TW7 6PN
Tel: 020 8568 8692 Fax: 020 8758 2674 E-mail: general@gumley.hounslow.sch.uk
Head Sister Brenda Wallace FCJ BA PhD Chaplain Mary Ryan (RO)

Gunnersbury: (5401) (Boys) The Ride, Boston Manor Rd, Brentford TW8 9LB
Tel: 020 8568 7281 Fax: 020 8569 7946 E-mail: headteacher@gunnersbury.hounslow.sch.uk
Head Mr John Heffernan MA Chaplain Fr Gerard Quinn

St Mark: (4800) 106 Bath Rd, Hounslow TW3 3EJ Tel: 020 8577 3600 Fax: 020 8577 0559
E-mail: staffroom@stmarks.hounslow.sch.uk Head Paul Enright MA Chaplain Christy Davidson

LONDON BOROUGH OF ISLINGTON (206)

PRIMARY SCHOOLS

Blessed Sacrament: (3643) (+N) Boadicea Street N1 0UF
Tel: 020 7278 2187 Fax: 020 7278 0015 Head Mrs Norah Flatley (Copenhagen Street)

Christ the King: (3633) (+N) 55 Tollington Park N4 3QW
Tel: 020 7272 5987 Fax: 020 7272 7780 E-mail: christ_king@hotmail.com
Head Mr Paul Campbell(Tollington Park)

Sacred Heart: (3384) George's Road, N7 8JN
Tel: 020 7607 3407 Fax: 020 7606 4906 Head Mr John Lane (Holloway)

St Joan of Arc: (3631) (+N) Northolme Road, Highbury Park N5 2UX
Tel: 020 7226 3920 Fax: 020 7704 9220 E-mail: mail@st-joanofarc.islington.sch.uk
Head Miss Clare Campbell (Highbury)

St John the Evangelist: (3456) (+N) Duncan Street, Islington N1 8LB
Tel: 020 7226 1314 Fax: 020 7226 5563 E-mail: tina_oliva2002@yahoo.co.uk
Head Mrs Tina Oliva BSc (Hons) (Islington)

St Joseph: (3483) (+N) Highgate Hill N19 5NE
Tel: 020 7272 1270 Fax: 020 7272 9728 E-mail: school@st-joseph.islington.sch.uk
Head Mr Don Leavy BEd (Highgate) (RO)

St Peter & St Paul: (3575) (+N) Compton Street, Goswell Road EC1V 0EU
Tel: 020 7253 0839 Fax: 020 7336 7226 E-mail: sao@stpeterandstpaul.islington.sch.uk
Head Mr Daniel Keane BEd MA (Clerkenwell)

SECONDARY SCHOOLS

Mount Carmel Technology College: (4704) (Girls) Holland Walk, Duncombe Road N19 3EU
Tel: 020 7281 3536 Fax: 020 7281 0420 E-mail: office@mountcarmel.islington.sch.uk
Principal Mr Paul Kehoe **Chaplain** Fr Kevin McDevitt

St Aloysius: (4651) (Boys) Hornsey Lane, Highgate N6 5LY
Tel: 020 7263 1391 Fax: 020 7263 5757 E-mail: enquiries@staff.staloysius.islington.sch.uk
Head Mr Tom Mannion BA (Hons) MA **Chaplain** Dominic Herne

LONDON BOROUGH OF KENSINGTON AND CHELSEA (207)

PRIMARY SCHOOLS

Oratory: (3379) Bury Walk, Cale Street SW3 6QH
Tel: 020 7589 5900 Fax: 020 7581 5220 E-mail: info@oratory.kensington-chelsea.sch.uk
Head Mr Peter Ward BA (Oratory) (RO)

Our Lady of Victories: (5200) (+N) Clareville Street SW7 5AQ Tel: 020 7373 4491
Fax: 020 7244 0591 E-mail: madeline.brading@ourladyofvictories.kensington-chelsea.sch.uk
Head Mrs Madeline Brading BEd MA (Kensington)

Servite: (3613) (+N) 252 Fulham Road SW10 9NA
Tel: 020 7352 2588 Fax: 020 7351 4024 E-mail: info@servite.kensington-chelsea.sch.uk
Head Ms Kathleen Gale (Fulham Road) (RO)

St Charles: (5201) (+N) 83 St Charles Square W10 6EB
Tel: 020 8969 5566 Fax: 020 8960 4338 E-mail:stcharlesschool@hotmail.com
Head Mr Kevin Gallagher (St Charles Square)

St Francis of Assisi: (3437) (+N) **Treadgold Street W11 4BJ Tel: 020 7727 8523 Fax: 020 7229 2174 E-mail: paul.rincon@st-assisi.kensington-chelsea.sch.uk**
Head Mr Paul Rincon (Notting Hill)

St Joseph: (3477) (+N) **Cadogan Street SW3 2QT Tel: 020 7589 2438 Fax: 020 7581 9489 E-mail: info@st-josephs.kensington-chelsea.sch.uk Head** Mrs Ann Spragg BEd (Chelsea)

St Mary: (3542) (+N) **East Row W10 5AW Tel: 020 8969 0321 Fax: 020 8964 3122 E-mail: info@st-marys.kensington-chelsea.sch.uk Head** Mrs Ann Nugent (Kensal New Town)

Independent
St Philip's Preparatory: (6104) (Boys) **6 Wetherby Place SW7 4ND Tel: 020 7373 3944 Fax: 020 7244 9766 E-mail:info@stphilips.demon.co.uk**
Head Mr Harry Biggs-Davison MA (Kensington 2) (RO)

SECONDARY SCHOOLS

Cardinal Vaughan: (5402) (Boys) **89 Addison Rd W14 8BZ Tel: 020 7603 8478 Fax: 7602 3124 E-mail: mail@cvms.co.uk charles.eynaud@cardinalvaughan.kensington-chelsea.sch.uk**
Head Mr Michael Gormally BA ACP FRSA **Chaplain** Fr Dominic Allain

Sion Manning: (4801) (Girls) **St Charles Sq W10 6EL Tel: 020 8969 7111 Fax: 020 8969 5119 E-mail: info@sion-manning.kensington-chelsea.sch.uk**
Head Mrs Chrissie Leach **Chaplain** Sr Christine Edwards (North Kensington)

St Thomas More: (4861) **Cadogan Street, Chelsea SW3 2QS Tel: 020 7589 9734 Fax: 020 7823 7868 E-mail: info@st-thomasmore.kensington-chelsea.sch.uk**
Head Mr Gerry Connolly **Chaplain**

Independent
More House School: (6202) (Girls) **22 Pont Street SW1X 0AA Tel: 020 7235 2855 Fax: 020 7259 6782 E-mail: office@morehouse.org.uk**
Head Mrs Lesley Falconer **Chaplain** Canon Vincent Berry (RO)

SIXTH FORM COLLEGE

St Charles Catholic Sixth Form College: (8600) **74 St Charles Square W10 6EY Tel: 020 8968 7755 Fax: 020 8968 1061 E-mail: inquiries@stcharles.ac.uk**
Principal Mr Paul O'Shea **Chaplain** Mr Edward Pike (North Kensington)

LONDON BOROUGH OF RICHMOND (318)

PRIMARY SCHOOLS

Sacred Heart: (3320) **St Mark's Road, Teddington, Middx TW11 9DO Tel: 020 8977 6591 Fax: 020 8943 2449 E-mail: beall002@rgfl.org.uk**
Head Mr Michael Thompson (Teddington)

St Edmund: (3315) St Edmunds Lane, Nelson Road, Whitton, Middx TW2 7BB
Tel: 020 8894 7898 Fax: 020 8898 3032 E-mail: info@st-edmunds.richmond.sch.uk
Head Mrs Carmel Moreland (Whitton)

St James: (3316) (+N) 260 Stanley Road, Twickenham, Middx TW2 5NP
Tel: 020 8898 4670 Fax: 020 8893 3038 E-mail: st-james@rgfl.org.uk
Head Mrs Veronica Heffernan BA (Twickenham)

PRIMARY AND SECONDARY SCHOOL

Independent
St Catherine's Catholic School: (6008) (Girls) Cross Deep, Twickenham TW1 4QJ
Tel: 020 8891 2898 Fax: 020 8744 9629 E-mail: admissions@stcatherinesschool.co.uk
Head Mrs Zelma Braganza **Chaplain** Fr Ulick Loring (RO)

LONDON BOROUGH OF TOWER HAMLETS (211)

PRIMARY SCHOOLS

English Martyrs: (3619) (+N) St Mark Street E1 8DJ
Tel: 020 7709 0182 Fax: 020 7680 9395 E-mail: admin@englishmartyrs.towerhamlets.sch.uk
Head Ms Bronagh Nugent (Tower Hill)

Guardian Angels: (3346) Whitman Road, Mile End E3 4RB Tel: 020 8980 3939
Fax: 020 8983 4210 E-mail:admin@guardianangels.towerhamlets.sch.uk
Head Miss Elizabeth Worrell (Mile End)

Holy Family: (3667) (+N) Wade's Place E14 0DE
Tel: 020 7987 3066 Fax: 020 7538 8831 E-mail: admin@holyfamily.towerhamlets.sch.uk
Head Miss Julie Slack Poplar)

Our Lady: (3385) (+N) Copenhagen Place, Limehouse E14 7DA
Tel: 020 7987 1798 Fax: 020 7538 2682 E-mail: admin@ourlady.towerhamlets.sch.uk
Head Mr Matthew Ringham (Limehouse)

St Agnes: (3397) (+N) Rainhill Way, Bow E3 3ES
Tel: 020 8980 3076 Fax: 020 8983 1770 E-mail: admin@st-agnes.towerhamlets.sch.uk
Head Mrs Sue Chandler (Bow)

St Anne: (3411) (+N) Underwood Road E1 5AW
Tel: 020 7247 6327 Fax: 020 7377 5024 E-mail: head@st-anne.towerhamlets.sch.uk
Head Mrs Janet Sheehan BSc (Hons) (Underwood Road)

St Edmund: (3431) (+N) 297 West Ferry Road, Millwall E14 8RS
Tel: 020 7987 2546 Fax: 020 7538 0332 E-mail: head@st-edmund.towerhamlets.sch.uk
Head Ms Gail O'Flaherty (Millwall)

St Elizabeth: (2003) (+N) Bonner Road E2 9JY Tel: 020 8980 3964 Fax: 020 8983 3377 E-mail: admin2@st-elizabeth.towerhamlets.sch.uk **Head** Mr Richard Pickering (Bethnal Green)

St Mary & St Michael: (3507) (+N) Sutton St, Commercial Rd E1 0BD Tel: 020 7790 4986 Fax: 020 7790 9343 E-mail: admin@st-marymichael.towerhamlets.sch.uk
Head Mrs Sue Faulkner (Commercial Road)

SECONDARY SCHOOLS

Federation: Bishop Challoner Collegiate Schools
Bishop Challoner: (4726) (Girls) 1 Hardinge Street E1 0AB
Tel: 020 7790 3634 Fax: 020 7702 7398
E-mail: dbenson@bishop.towerhamlets.sch.uk
Head Mrs Catherine Myers BA DipEd **Chaplain** Awaiting appointment

Bishop Challoner: (4298) (Boys) 1 Hardinge Street E1 0AB
Tel: 020 7790 3634 Fax: 020 7791 9589
E-mail: dbenson@bishop.towerhamlets.sch.uk
Head Mrs Catherine Myers BA DipEd **Chaplain** Awaiting appointment

COUNTY OF SURREY (936)

PRIMARY SCHOOLS

Christ the King: (3482) (First) Falcon Drive, Stanwell, Staines, Middx TW19 7DS
Tel: 01784 257512 Fax: 01784 421878 E-mail: school@christ-the-king.surrey.sch.uk
Head Mrs Maureen Bermingham BEd (Hons) MEd (Stanwell)

Our Lady of the Rosary: (3461) Park Avenue, Staines, Middx TW18 2EF
Tel: 01784 453539 Fax: 01784 449485 E-mail: head@ourlady.surrey.sch.uk
Head Mr John Mescall (Staines)

St Ignatius: (3459) Green Street, Sunbury-on-Thames, Middx TW16 6QG
Tel: 01932 785396 Fax: 01932 771418 E-mail: admin@st-ignatius.surrey.sch.uk
Head Appointment pending (Sunbury)

St Michael: (3915) Feltham Hill Road, Ashford, Middx TW15 2DG
Tel: 01784 253333 Fax: 01784 240834 E-mail: info@stmichaels.surrey.sch.uk
Head Miss Ursula Beirne (Ashford)

SECONDARY SCHOOL

St Paul's College: (5411) The Ridings, Green St, Sunbury-on-Thames TW16 6NX
Tel: 01932 783811 Fax: 01932 786485 E-mail: info@stpauls-college.surrey.sch.uk
Principal Mr Simon Uttley **Chaplain** Miss U Morrisey

HERTFORDSHIRE (919)

PRIMARY SCHOOLS (ST ALBANS DEANERY)

St Adrian: (3389)(+N) Vesta Avenue, Watling View, St Albans, Herts AL1 2PB
Tel: 01727 852687 Fax: 01727 850822 E-mail: admin.stadrians@thegrid.org.uk
Head Mrs Yvonne Hawkes (St Albans South)

St Alban & St Stephen: (3362) (Infants +N) Vanda Crescent, St Albans AL1 5EX
Tel: 01727 854643 E-mail: admin.ssasinfants@thegrid.org.uk
Head Miss Paula Holden (St Albans)

St Alban & St Stephen: (3421) (Junior) Cecil Road, St Albans, Herts AL1 5EG
Tel: 01727 866668 Fax: 01727 810710 E-mail: admin.ssasjm@thegrid.org.uk
Head Mrs Helen Hill BEd (St Albans)

St Albert the Great: (3391) Acorn Rd, Rant Meadow, Hemel Hempstead HP3 8DW
Tel: 01442 264835 Fax: 01442 246418 E-mail: head.albertthegreat@thegrid.org.uk
Head Mr Robert Mundy BEd (Hemel Hempstead East)

St Bernadette: (3416) (+N) Walsingham Way, London Colney, Herts AL2 1NL
Tel: 01727 822489 Fax: 01727 823327 E-mail: head.stbernadette@thegrid.org.uk
Head Mrs Ann Cassidy (London Colney)

St Cuthbert Mayne: (3386) (Junior) Clover Way, Gadebridge, Hemel Hempstead HP1 3EA
Tel: 01442 253347 Fax: 01442 230320 E-mail: admin.stcuthbertmayne@thegrid.org.uk
Head Mrs Bernadette Quinn BEd (Hemel Hempstead)

St Dominic: (3401) (+N) Southdown Road, Harpenden, Herts AL5 1PF
Tel: 01582 760047 Fax: 01582 760047 E-mail: admin.stdominic@thegrid.org.uk
Head Appointment pending (Harpenden)

St John Fisher: (3403) Hazelmere Road, Marshalwick, St Albans, Herts AL4 9RW
Tel: 01727 861077 Fax: 01727 831163 E-mail: admin.sjfisher@thegrid.org.uk
Head Mr Charles McNerney (St Albans)

St Rose: (3409) (Infants +N) Green End Rd, Boxmoor, Hemel Hempstead HP1 1QW
Tel: 01442 398855 Fax: 01442 398835 E-mail: admin.stroses@thegrid.org.uk
Head Mrs Barbara Hancock (Boxmoor/Hemel Hempstead)

St Teresa: (3384) (+N) Brook Road, Borehamwood, Herts WD6 5HL
Tel: 020 8953 3753 Fax: 020 8381 5273 E-mail: admin@stteresaschool.co.uk
Head Miss Teresa McBride (Borehamwood)

St Thomas More: (3402) Greenway, Berkhamsted, Herts HP4 3LF
Tel: 01442 385060 Fax: 01442 385061 E-mail: adminstmore@thegrid.org.uk
Head Mrs Lisa Barton (Berkhamsted)

Independent
St Columba's College:(6136) (Boys) Preparatory School, 8 King Harry Lane, St Albans AL3 4AW
Tel: 01727 862616 Fax: 01727 892025 E-mail: headofprep@st-columbas.herts.sch.uk
Head Mr Edwin Brown (St Albans South) (RO)

PRIMARY SCHOOLS (WATFORD DEANERY)
Divine Saviour: (3410) (+N) Broomfield Rise, Abbots Langley, Herts WD5 0HW
Tel: 01923 265607 Fax: 01923 291632 E-mail: admin.divinesaviour@thegrid.org.uk
Head Mr Philip Gibbs (Abbots Langley)

Holy Rood: (3426) (Infant) Greenbank Road, Watford, Herts WD17 4FS
Tel: 01923 224480 Fax: 01923 240756 E-mail: head.holyrood@thegrid.org.uk
Head Appointment pending (Watford)

Holy Rood: (3412) (Junior) Greenbank Road, Watford, Herts WD17 4FR
Tel: 01923 227099 Fax: 01923 447644 E-mail: admin.holyroodjm@thegrid.org.uk
Head Mrs Evelyn Ward (Watford)

Sacred Heart: (3415) Merryhill Road, Bushey, Herts WD23 1SU
Tel: : 01923 493040 Fax: 01923 493041 E-mail: head.sacredheart.682@thegrid.org.uk
Head Mrs Rita Cooper (Bushey)

St Anthony: (3428) (+N) Croxley View, Watford, Herts WD18 6BW
Tel: 01923 226987 Fax: 01923 234645 E-mail: admin.stanthonys@thegrid.org.uk
Head Mrs Pauline Wilson (Watford)

St Catherine of Siena: (5211) Horseshoe Lane, Garston, Watford WD25 7HP
Tel: 01923 676022 Fax: 01923 893497 E-mail: admin.st-catherine@thegrid.org.uk
Head Ms Pauline Curran BA DipEd (Garston)

St John: (3398) Berry Lane, Mill End, Rickmansworth, Herts WD3 7HG
Tel: 01923 774004 Fax: 01923 710915
E-mail:
Head Mrs Paula Smith (Mill End)

St Joseph: (3383) (+N) Ainsdale Road, South Oxhey, Watford, Herts WD19 7DW
Tel: 020 8428 5371 Fax: 020 8421 0568
E-mail: head.stjosephs775@thegrid.org.uk
Head Appointment pending (Carpenders Park)

PRIMARY SCHOOLS (HATFIELD DEANERY)

Holy Family: (3404) (+N) Crookhams, Welwyn Garden City, Herts AL7 1PG
Tel: 01707 327419 Fax: 01707 327419 E-mail: admin.holyfamily@thegrid.org.uk
Head Mrs Catherine McMahon (Welwyn Garden City)

Our Lady: (3382) (+N) Woodhall Lane, Welwyn Garden City, Herts AL7 3TF
Tel: 01707 324408 Fax: 01707 391005 E-mail: admin.ourladys527@thegrid.org.uk
Head Mrs Julie Connolly (Welwyn Garden City/East)

Pope Paul: (3975) Baker Street, Potters Bar, Herts EN6 2ES
Tel: 01707 659755 Fax: 01707 659755 E-mail: admin.popepaul@thegrid.org.uk
Head Mrs Helen Lines (Potters Bar)

St Philp Howard: (3388) Woods Avenue, Hatfield, Herts AL10 8NN
Tel: 01707 263969 Fax: 01707 263969 E-mail: adminsthoward@thegrid.org.uk
Head Mrs Nuala Pawley BPhil DIPSIE (Hatfield)

PRIMARY SCHOOLS (STEVENAGE DEANERY)

Our Lady: (3399) Old Hale Way, Hitchin, Herts SG5 1XT
Tel: 01462 622555 Fax: 01462 622777 E-mail: admin.ourladys@thegrid.org.uk
Head Mrs Gaynor Eden (Hitchin)

St John: (3413) (+N) Providence Way, Baldock, Herts SG7 6TT
Tel: 01462 892478 Fax: 01462 892478 E-mail: head.stjohns4@thegrid.org.uk
Head Ms Alex Hanou (Baldock)

St Margaret Clitherow: (3397) Broadhall Way, Stevenage, Herts SG2 8RH
Tel: 01438 352863 Fax: 01438 352553 E-mail: admin.clitherow@thegrid.org.uk
Head Mrs Geraldine Cartwright BEd (Stevenage/Shephall)

St Mary: (5200) (+N) Melbourn Road, Royston, Herts SG8 7DB
Tel: 01763 242875 Fax: 01763 248825 E-mail: admin.smarys084@thegrid.org.uk
Head Mr Tony Carroll (Royston)

St Thomas More: (3400) Highfield, Letchworth, Herts SG6 3QB
Tel: 01462 620670 Fax: 01462 620670 E-mail: head.strcjmi@thegrid.org.uk
Head Mrs Mary Hewitson (Letchworth)

St Vincent de Paul: (3977) (+N) Bedwell Crescent, Stevenage, Herts SG1 1NJ
Tel: 01438 729555 Fax: 01438 358122 E-mail: admin.stvincent@thegrid.org.uk
Head Mrs Diann Ross (Stevenage)

ST. ELIZABETH'S
CENTRE

PRIMARY SCHOOLS (LEA VALLEY DEANERY)

Sacred Heart: (3424) Broadmeads, Ware, Herts SG12 9HY
Tel: 01920 461678 Fax: 01920 461418 E-mail: admin.sacredheart312@thegrid.org.uk
Head Miss Claire McDonnell (Ware)

St Augustine: (3345) (+N) Riversmead, Hoddesdon, Herts EN11 8DP
Tel: 01992 463549 E-mail: head.staugustines@thegrid.org.uk
Head Mrs Eileen Plunkett (Hoddesdon)

St Cross: (3318) Upper Marsh Lane, Hoddesdon, Herts EN11 8BN
Tel: 01992 467309 Fax: 01992 450362 E-mail: head.stcross@thegrid.org.uk
Head Appointment pending (Hoddesdon)

St Joseph: (3341) (+N) North Road, Hertford, Herts SG14 2BY
Tel: 01992 583148 Fax: 01992 550503 E-mail: head-stjosephs255@thegrid.org.uk
Head Miss Sheila McGee (Hertford)

St Joseph: (3327) (+N) Royal Avenue, Waltham Cross, Herts EN8 7EN
Tel: 01992 629503 Fax: 01992 628824 E-mail: head.stjosephs351@thegrid.org.uk
Head Miss Clare McFlynn (Waltham Cross)

St Joseph: (3318) (+N) Great Hadham Road, Bishops Stortford CM23 2NL
Tel: 01279 652576 Fax: 01279 466519 E-mail: head.stjosephs207@thegrid.org.uk
Head Mr Peter Coldwell (Bishop's Stortford)

St Paul: (3423) Park Lane, Cheshunt, Herts EN7 6LR Tel: 01992 635060
Fax: 01992 625215 E-mail: head.stpauls373@thegrid.org.uk
Head Mrs Sue Allen (Cheshunt)

St Thomas of Canterbury: (3367) High Street, Puckeridge, nr Ware, Herts SG11 1RZ
Tel: 01920 821450 Fax: 01920 822534 E-mail: head.stcanterbury@thegrid.org.uk
Head appointment pending(Old Hall Green/Puckeridge)

SECONDARY SCHOOLS (HERTFORDSHIRE)

John F Kennedy: (4619) Hollybush Lane, Hemel Hempstead, Herts HP1 2PJ
Tel: 01442 266150 Fax: 01442 200014 E-mail: admin.jfk@thegrid.org.uk
Head Mrs Bernadette Jenkins BA **Chaplain**

John Henry Newman: (5413) Hitchin Road, Stevenage, Herts SG1 4AE
Tel: 01438 314643 Fax: 01438 747882 E-mail: admin.jhnewman@thegrid.org.uk
Head Mr Michael Kelly BSc (Hons) MSc **Chaplain**

Loreto: (4620) (Girls) Hatfield Road, St Albans, Herts AL1 3RQ
Tel: 01727 856206 Fax: 01727 833794 Email: goringj53@thegrid.org.uk
Head Mrs Maire Lynch **Chaplain** Fr Manus (St Albans) (RO)

Nicholas Breakspear: (5412) Colney Heath Lane, St Albans, Herts AL4 0TT
Tel: 01727 860079 Fax: 01727 848912 E-mail:admin.nicholasbreakspear@thegrid.org.uk
Head Mr Philip Jakszta BA PGCE BNPQH **Chaplain** Fr Manus (St Albans)

St Joan of Arc: (5418) High Street, Rickmansworth, Herts WD3 1HG
Tel: 01923 773881 Fax: 01923 897545 E-mail: admin.joa@thegrid.org.uk
Head Mr Tony Sumner MSc FRSA **Chaplain** Miss Jennifer Whelan (Watford)

St Mary: (5422) Windhill, Bishop's Stortford, Herts CM23 2NQ
Tel: 01279 654901 Fax: 01279 653889 E-mail: info@stmarys.net
Head Mr Tony Sharpe BA MMus **Chaplain** (Lea Valley)

St Michael: (5417) High Elms Lane, Garston, Watford, Herts WD25 0SS
Tel: 01923 673760 Fax: 01923 680511 E-mail: admin.stmichaels719@thegrid.org.uk
Head Mr John Murphy STB MA BA(Psych) **Chaplain** Mr Ian Petrie (Watford)

Independent
St Columba's College: (6025) (Boys) King Harry Lane, St Albans AL3 4AW
Tel: 01727 855185 Fax: 01727 863997 E-mail: manager@st-columbas.herts.sch.uk
Head Mr Nick O'Sullivan **Chaplain** Fr Tim Edgar (RO) (St Albans)

NON MAINTAINED SPECIAL SCHOOL

St Elizabeth's School: (7006) Much Hadham, Herts SG10 6EW
Tel: 01279 843451 Fax: 01279 843903 E-mail: enquiries@stelizabeths.org.uk
Principal Mr Philip Poulton **Chaplain** Fr Paul Arnold (RO) (Lea Valley)

PRIMARY AND SECONDARY SCHOOL

Independent
St Edmund's College: (6115) Old Hall Green, Ware, Herts SG11 1DS
Tel: 01920 821504 Fax: 01920 823011 E-mail: enquiries@stedmundscollege.org.uk
Head Mr Christopher Long **Chaplain** Fr Michael Pinot de Moira (Lea Valley)

DIOCESAN STATISTICS

Priests of the Diocese

Working in the Diocese	230
Chaplains to the Forces	6
Further Studies	5
Others working outside the Diocese	24
Sick or on leave	15
Retired	87
Total	**367**

Priests of other Dioceses

From England & Wales	3
From Ireland	3
From other countries	15
Eastern Rites	5
Prelature of Opus Dei	8
Total	**34**

Priests of Religious Congregations & Societies of Apostolic Life

African Mission Society 4 Assumptionists 9; Augustinians 9; Augustinian Recollects 6; Benedictines (English) 17; Benedictines (Olivetan) 7; Camillians 2; Carmelites 3 Carmelites (Discalced) 6; Charity, Institute of, 1; Claretians 5; Columbans 7; Comboni Missionaries 4; Consolata Fathers 3; Divine Word Missionaries 8; Dominicans 12; Franciscans 2; Franciscans of the Atonement 1; Fransalians 3; John of God, Hospitallers 2; Holy Ghost Fathers 6; Jesuits 54; Lebanese Maronite 2; Marian Fathers 5; Marist Fathers 4; Mill Hill Missionaries 22; Missionaries of Africa 22; Montfort Missionaries 1; Oblates of Mary Immaculate 7; Oratorians 10; Pallottine Fathers 8; Passionists 9; Providence, Sons of Divine 3; Redemptorists 1; Sacred Heart, Missionaries of the 3; Sacred Hearts Community 4; Salvatorians 13; Scalabrini Fathers 1; Servites 5; Stigmatine 1; Vincentians 10; Xaverian Missionaries 5. **Total** **307**

Grand Total	**708**

Permanent Deacons	4
Parishes	216

Schools

Primary (Aided)	163
Secondary (Aided & Special Agreement)	38
Aided VI Form Colleges	2
Independent	18
Non-maintained Special	2

PARISH STATISTICS 2004

The following tables are compiled from the parish returns.
In the Parish Directory each parish has its deanery in brackets.
Mass attendance was counted during October 2004
Asterisk (*) indicates a previous year's figures where current return not available.
Mass attendance for 2006 will be counted over four Sundays in October.

Parish	Sunday Mass	Baptisms	Receptions	Marriages
Barnet Deanery				
Barnet	920	47	3	4
Burnt Oak	777	51	5	5
Cricklewood	1123	51	1	1
Edgware *	1080	32	4	6
Edgware (Broadfields)*	136	8	5	0
Finchley (Church End)	769	31	1	3
Finchley (East)	540	15	0	0
Finchley (North)	1088	35	4	3
Golders Green	771	29	2	6
Grahame Park *	300	5	0	0
Hendon *	485	25	0	7
Hendon (West)	477	23	2	0
Mill Hill	983	42	2	7
New Barnet *	474	25	0	7
Whetstone	734	20	0	3
Brent Deanery				
Dollis Hill	1002	53	3	7
Kensal Rise *	655	45	4	5
Kenton	1111	40	3	11
Kingsbury Green	1252	83	3	11
Neasden	386	27	0	2
Stonebridge	446	35	0	2
Sudbury	1414	64	12	11
Wembley 1	1305	72	1	8
Wembley 2	893	29	3	4
Wembley 3	409	6	1	0
Willesden *	843	58	0	3
Willesden Green	1219	102	1	8

Parish	Sunday Mass	Baptisms	Receptions	Marriages
Camden Deanery				
Camden Town *	560	49	3	6
Hampstead	509	38	5	4
Haverstock Hill	850	87	2	8
Kentish Town	735	40	1	3
Kilburn	1667	129	8	14
Kilburn (West) *	217	15	0	2
Laxton Place *	122	7	0	0
Lebanese Centre *	200	23	0	0
Somers Town	900	79	0	2
Swiss Cottage *	500	16	0	1
Ealing Deanery				
Acton	1193	61	1	3
Acton (East)	430	27	1	0
Acton (West)	277	10	0	3
Ealing	2204	143	6	22
Greenford *	2004	102	1	9
Hanwell	1268	70	1	7
Northfields	1300	81	7	3
Perivale	682	15	0	0
Polish Church*	177	18	0	2
Southall	850	58	0	8
Enfield Deanery				
Cockfosters *	830	22	2	4
Edmonton	1457	111	2	5
Enfield	2190	136	5	27
New Southgate	1441	55	4	9
Palmers Green	1405	78	3	11
Ponders End	1384	88	5	9
Hackney Deanery				
Clapton	611	89	5	8
Clapton Park *	360	27	0	2
Hackney	606	22	7	2
Homerton *	470	78	6	0
Hoxton	436	25	3	3
Kingsland	1408	114	5	21
Manor House	365	25	3	1
Stoke Newington *	565	51	3	5

Parish	Sunday Mass	Baptisms	Receptions	Marriages
Hammersmith & Fulham Deanery				
Brook Green	1048	89	4	16
Fulham	1198	78	1	10
Hammersmith	1119	62	1	5
Parsons Green	710	19	3	8
Polish (2)	1011	68	0	4
Shepherds Bush	742	40	7	4
Stephendale Road *	303	12	1	2
White City	535	20	0	1
Haringey Deanery				
Harringay *	150	3	0	0
Muswell Hill	937	40	4	1
Stamford Hill	1788	174	8	10
Stroud Green	790	43	3	10
Tottenham	1489	166	14	17
West Green	995	37	3	3
Wood Green	1234	49	1	6
Harrow Deanery				
Harrow-on-the-Hill	1120	58	2	15
Harrow (North)	1227	50	2	4
Harrow (South) & Northolt	1142	84	2	6
Headstone Lane	444	15	0	1
Pinner	555	21	1	4
Stanmore	388	20	0	1
Wealdstone & Harrow Weald	1837	155	2	27
Hatfield Deanery				
Cuffley *	328	11	0	1
Hatfield	388	27	0	1
Hatfield (South) *	296	12	1	0
Potters Bar	625	29	0	4
Welwyn Garden City	346	27	4	4
Welwyn Garden City (Digswell)	334	18	9	4
Welwyn Garden City (East)	421	29	0	2

Parish	Sunday Mass	Baptisms	Receptions	Marriages
Hillingdon Deanery				
Eastcote	512	34	3	4
Harefield *	135	5	0	0
Hayes *	1274	162	3	19
Hillingdon	682	76	1	5
London Airport	43	0	1	0
Northwood	685	18	0	4
Ruislip	1210	81	6	8
Ruislip (South)	685	30	2	4
Uxbridge	405	21	2	2
West Drayton *	470	20	3	5
Yeading	1089	51	0	7
Hounslow Deanery				
Brentford *	1007	25	0	0
Chiswick	1733	94	6	12
Cranford *	257	13	0	2
Feltham	918	64	5	2
Grove Park	191	9	0	0
Gunnersbury *	112	5	0	0
Heston *	600	7	2	2
Hounslow	1500	76	2	7
Isleworth *	680	47	3	6
Osterley *	569	17	5	4
Islington Deanery				
Bunhill Row	107	4	2	1
Clerkenwell	388	29	0	4
Copenhagen Street *	765	21	2	1
Highbury	750	50	3	2
Highgate	966	2	2	24
Holloway **	547	57	1	2
Islington	888	83	7	7
Polish Church (Islington) *	600	38	0	10
Tollington Park *	472	91	6	7
Upper Holloway	1009	21	2	2

** HMP Holloway/Pentonville	120			

Parish	Sunday Mass	Baptisms	Receptions	Marriages
Kensington and Chelsea Deanery				
Chelsea (1)	707	52	0	11
Chelsea (2)	1074	43	3	13
Fulham Road	913	23	11	16
Kensington (1)	1576	50	4	2
Kensington (2)	1273	40	4	1
Oratory	2355	102	24	32
Lea Valley Deanery				
Bishop's Stortford	734	67	3	6
Buntingford	142	13	0	0
Cheshunt	508	34	0	2
Hertford *	563	35	2	7
Hoddesdon	645	66	1	10
Much Hadham*	76	11	2	5
Old Hall Green & Puckeridge	130	7	0	5
Sawbridgeworth *	187	13	0	1
Waltham Cross	1008	71	5	12
Ware	256	17	1	9
Marylebone Deanery				
Farm Street	688	117	0	61
Marylebone	706	28	4	0
Ogle Street*	539	26	0	3
St John's Wood	1405	100	8	7
Spanish Place	876	37	1	14
University	211	8	2	1
North Kensington Deanery				
Bayswater	1013	42	9	4
Harrow Road *	415	32	0	0
Kensal New Town	716	37	0	5
Notting Hill	1100	101	8	9
Paddington	209	11	1	0
Queensway *	850	30	0	5
St Charles Square	628	0	0	3
St Albans Deanery				
Berkhamsted	522	27	0	0
Borehamwood	293	21	0	3
Borehamwood (North)	162	27	0	2
Harpenden	675	45	0	14
Hemel Hempstead (Boxmoor)	587	48	1	10

Parish	Sunday Mass	Baptisms	Receptions	Marriages
Hemel Hempstead (East)	642	13	4	4
Hemel Hempstead (North)	317	23	1	0
Hemel Hempstead (West)	275	15	0	0
London Colney *	561	43	6	8
Radlett	219	12	2	0
Redbourn	139	11	0	1
St Albans	1291	123	4	15
St Albans (South) *	592	48	3	9
Shenley	106	4	0	0
Tring	253	19	0	6
Wheathampstead	202	11	0	1
Stevenage Deanery				
Baldock	321	15	2	2
Hitchin	658	29	2	3
Knebworth	366	12	0	1
Letchworth	811	31	1	3
Royston	298	12	0	3
Stevenage (Bedwell)	607	30	2	1
Stevenage (Old Town)	422	30	4	3
Stevenage (Shephall)	380	30	4	4
Tower Hamlets Deanery				
Bethnal Green	307	34	2	4
Bow	398	38	1	1
Commercial Road *	577	39	4	2
German Church *	53	23	3	3
Limehouse	238	20	0	2
Lithuanian Church	220	87	0	7
Mile End	444	43	0	1
Millwall	259	20	3	2
Poplar	468	77	4	2
Tower Hill	160	1	0	2
Underwood Road	800	38	0	2
Vietnamese*	528	47	0	2
Wapping	230	22	1	4
Upper Thames Deanery				
Ashford	652	72	3	28
Hampton Hill	537	41	2	1
Hampton-on-Thames	378	17	1	1
St Margarets-on-Thames	530	49	3	2
Shepperton	221	9	1	0

Parish	Sunday Mass	Baptisms	Receptions	Marriages
Staines	300	30	4	0
Stanwell	198	19	0	3
Sunbury-on-Thames	410	35	0	5
Teddington	368	22	1	4
Twickenham	559	48	5	10
Whitton	910	61	0	7
Watford Deanery				
Abbots Langley	384	60	2	2
Bushey & Oxhey	750	47	3	6
Carpenders Park	256	39	0	2
Chipperfield *	238	17	0	6
Chorleywood	86	4	0	-
Croxley Green	257	18	0	1
Garston	821	31	9	6
Mill End & Maple Cross *	272	18	2	0
Rickmansworth	527	30	3	14
Watford	1032	67	3	8
Watford (North)	350	46	0	4
Westminster Deanery				
Cathedral	4123	136	8	16
Ely Place	167	74	2	55
French Church	585	95	2	5
Italian Church	650	128	0	36
Lincoln's Inn Fields	829	60	11	9
Maiden Lane	252	9	0	4
Moorfields	80	12	2	9
Pimlico **	647	54	2	8
** Melkite Church *	120	19	19	71
Soho Square	704	3	3	4
Warwick Street	125	11	0	5
Ukrainian Cathedral*	150	0	0	9
TOTAL FOR DIOCESE	**151,692**	**9,511**	**537**	**1,363**

CATHOLIC SOCIETIES AND ORGANISATIONS

Organisations listed in this section must have:

1. A fundamental commitment to the teaching and practice of the Catholic Church, particularly as expressed by the documents of the Second Vatican Council and the *Catechism of the Catholic Church.*
2. A membership widely distributed in the Diocese of Westminster.

AFRICA-EUROPE FAITH & JUSTICE NETWORK

International group of Catholic missionary congregations and societies working at grass roots level in Africa and 9 European countries for the establishment of peace and the conditions required for a dignified livelihood for the people of Africa.
33 Lyonsdown Rd, New Barnet EN5 1JG Tel: 020 8449 9244 E-mail: aefjnuk@lineone.net

AFRICAN CATHOLIC CHAPLAINCY

Recognised by Bishops' Conference bringing together all African Catholic Communities in Britain to provide for their spiritual and pastoral care and foster links with the Church in Britain and Africa. **Chaplain/Director** Rev Joseph Baffour-Awuah,
132 Shernhall Street E17 9HU Tel: 020 8521 2359 E-mail; africath@clara.co.uk

AID TO THE CHURCH IN NEED

1 Times Square, Sutton SM1 1LF Tel: 020 8642 8668 Fax: 020 8661 6293
E-mail: acn@acnuk.org Director Neville Kyrke-Smith **Appeals Co-ordinator** Mike Cowie

APOSTLESHIP OF THE SEA

Part of international network of AOS agencies of Catholic Church working to support seafarers. Outreach involves spiritual, pastoral, practical welfare, education and campaigning work in support of all seafarers, regardless of their nationality, colour or creed. Supports seafarers through a network of chaplains and ship visitors visiting seafarers on ships offering friendship; runs ecumenical drop-in centres in ports where seafarers can relax and contact families by phone/e-mail; accompany seafarers on voyages as seagoing chaplains.
Director Commodore Chris York **Tel: 020 7588 8285 Fax: 020 7588 8280**
E-mail: londonoffice@aposmar.net AOS Herald Hse, Lamb's Passage, Bunhill Row EC1Y 8LE

ARCHCONFRATERNITY OF ST STEPHEN

For altar servers **Secretary** Michael O'Leary
Archconfraternity of St Stephen, PO Box 568, London WC1A 1YT

ASCENT MOVEMENT (VIE MONTANTE INTERNATIONALE)

Helping and encouraging Christians in middle and later life grow spiritually and to take up their responsibilities as members of the Church through friendship, spirituality and mission.

National President: Miss Margaret Snowden
National Secretary: Mrs Kathleen Venting **44 Edgeworth Close NW4 4HN**
E-mail: ascent@tiscali.co.uk

ASSOCIATION FOR LATIN LITURGY

To promote the use of Latin texts and music in the approved rites of the Church.
Edward Barrett, **14 Connaught Mans, Prince of Wales Drive SW11 4SA Tel: 020 7978 5676**
E-mail: Edward.Barrett@Latin-Liturgy.org
Website: www.Latin-Liturgy.org

ASSOCIATION FOR THE PROPAGATION OF THE FAITH (APF)

The APF ensures every bishop in the new churches has the necessary funds for building churches and schools. The APF 'red boxes' and the World Mission Sunday collection enable every diocese of this country to support the spreading of the Gospel in each of the 1092 mission dioceses of the world. Members play a vital role in building up the Church through their prayers and offerings.

Diocesan Director Fr Kevin McDevitt **Tel: 020 7272 8195**
Mill Hill Appeals Organiser Fr John Pharro **Tel: 020 8959 8254**

ASSOCIATION FOR PRIESTS OF AFRICAN OR ASIAN DESCENT

The Association meets twice a year to give support to clergy from ethnic minorities. Working closely with Catholic Association for Racial Justice who sponsor the association.
Secretary Uzo Agyare-Klimi **9 Henry Road N4 2LH Tel: 020 8802 8080**

ASSOCIATION OF BLIND CATHOLICS

To enable blind Catholics to participate more fully in the life of the Church
Secretary Paul Questier **58 Oakwood Rd, Horley, Surrey RH6 7BU Tel: 01293 772104**

ASSOCIATION OF CATHOLIC WOMEN

Under the patronage of Our Lady and St Joseph, it unites supporters from all parts of the country who find joy and fulfilment in giving glad assent to the Church's teachings.
Chair Mrs Josephine Robinson.
Secretary Mrs Ruth Real **22 Surbiton Hill Park, Surbiton, Surrey KT5 8ET Tel: 020 8399 1459**
E-mail: ACWReview@aol.com

ASSOCIATION OF MARY HELP OF CHRISTIANS

To promote personal devotion to, and public honour of Our Lady under the title 'Help of Christians'. A prayer meeting is held on the fourth Saturday of each month at 4pm at **36 Adolphus Road N4 2AY**. Contact: Mother Eugenia Pantalleresco **Tel: 020 8800 5228**

ASSOCIATION OF NURSING RELIGIOUS OF GREAT BRITAIN

Open to all religious in nursing and caring professions. For the promotion of the professional and pastoral service of its members to the sick. **Contact** Sr Catherine Lehane, **Pield Heath House School, Pield Heath Road, Uxbridge UB8 3NW Tel: 01895 233092**

ASSOCIATION OF SEPARATED AND DIVORCED CATHOLICS.

A federation of lay support groups to provide mutual help and spiritual support to those who have experienced the pain of marriage breakdown. For details of diocesan groups **contact** Frank Hacklett, **164 Whitmore Road, Harrow, Middlx HA1 4AQ**
Tel: 020 8422 1591
E-mail: frankhacklett@btinternet.com

ASSOCIATION OF SRI LANKAN CATHOLICS

To promote spiritual advancement, reconciliation and understanding among all Sri Lankans and work for peace.
SS Michael & Martin, 94 Bath Road, Hounslow TW3 3EH
President Mr P Vincent Paul Perera BSc Cert Ed **Chaplain** Fr Nimal Ponweera
Joint Secretaries: Dr Christopher Perera, Mr Glen Kroon **Tel: 020 8426 4565**

ASSUMPTION LAY VOLUNTEER PROGRAMME

For young people, married or single, 20-40 years, who would like to live and work with marginalised communities around the world. One year minimum. Inspired by the call to build bridges between cultural, national and other divides. Professional qualifications not essential.
Volunteer Co-ordinator, 23 Kensington Square W8 5HN Tel: 020 7361 4752
E-mail: cburns@rayouth.freeserve.co.uk Website: www.alvp.org.uk

BANNEUX ND. INTERNATIONAL UNION OF PRAYER

To promulgate the message given by Our Lady at Banneux under the title 'Virgin of the Poor' by film shows, all-night vigils, retreats and pilgrimages.
Secretary Mrs Maria Hare **10 Bramble Close, Hillingdon UB8 3QE Tel: 01895 420753**
Website: www.banneux-nd.org.uk

BEGINNING EXPERIENCE

A healing peer group ministry to those suffering grief due to widowhood, separation or divorce. **Contact** Joan Thompson **Tel: 020 8809 3844**

CAFOD

Official overseas development agency of the Church. Works through organisations in developing world, supporting over 1000 long-term self-help projects in 75 countries and supported by Church members and individuals. Has a network of volunteers. Regional Volunteers work specifically with parishes, schools, the campaign and youth. **Romero Close, Stockwell Road SW9 9TY Tel: 020 7733 7900**

Regional Organiser Dermott McNulty, **CAFOD Westminster 29 Bramley Rd N14 4HE Tel: 020 8449 6970 E-mail: westminster@cafod.org.uk**

CARITAS CHRISTI

An international secular institute open to single women and widows who remain where they are, living the Gospel in the ordinary circumstances of life.

Contact Sandra Sowls, **31 Chestnut Avenue, Stonehouse, Gloucestershire GL10 2HW**

CARMELITE SECULAR INSTITUTE (THE LEAVEN)

A secular institute for women, single or widowed. **Contact** Miss Patricia Edwards, **17 Pioneer Way W12 0EZ Tel: 020 8749 1919 E-mail: leaven@ouvip.com**

CARMELITE SECULAR ORDER (DISCALCED) (3RD ORDER)

An association of lay people and secular priests who wish to be members of the discalced Carmelite family, observing a modified form of its rule - a contemplative apostolic life in the world, in the spirit of Carmel. Meetings: men 2nd Wed 6.30pm; women 2nd Sun 11am.

Contact Carmelite Priory, 41 Kensington Church Street W8 4BB

CATENIAN ASSOCIATION

For Catholic professional and business men. Non-political with a world-wide membership of over 10,000 and over 290 groups in the UK. Meets at least once a month.

8 Chesham Place SW1X 8HP Tel: 020 7235 6671 E-mail: catena@dial.pipex.com

Province No 2 (City of London) **Secretary** B Noakes

24 Petersfield, Broomfield, Chelmsford CM1 4EP Tel: 01245 441247

Province No 8 (West London, Herts, Middx) **Secretary** O Steed

2 The Laurels, Potten End, Berkhamstead. HP4 2SP Tel: 01442 875544

Province No 14 (Westminster, North London, Herts) **Secretary** J. A.Reynolds,

38 Whitmore Rd Harrow HA1 4AD Tel: 020 8422 1547

CATHOLIC AGENCY TO SUPPORT EVANGELISATION (CASE)

To support and resource Catholic communities and individuals in England and Wales to offer the Gospel; to promote dialogue between gospel and culture; and to offer information on the Catholic faith through the **Catholic Enquiry Office**.
Chair of Executive Committee: Bishop Declan Lang **Director** Mgr Keith Barltrop Clare Ford, Fr Philip Knights, Clare Ward **114 West Heath Road NW3 7TX**
Tel: 020 8458 3316 / 020 8455 9871 Fax: 020 8905 5780
E-mail: cms@cms.org.uk Website: www.cms.org.uk

CATHOLIC ARCHIVES SOCIETY

Promotes and advises on the care, management and preservation of records of dioceses, religious foundations, institutions and societies of the Church. Does not store or collect archives.
Chair Sr Barbara Jeffrey RSM **98 Hunters Road, Handsworth, Birmingham B19 1EB**
Secretary: Margaret Harcourt Williams
Innyngs House, Hatfield Park, Hatfield AL9 5PL
Website: www.catholic-history.org

CATHOLIC BIBLICAL ASSOCIATION

To promote knowledge and love of the Bible. **Hon Secretary** Sr Marie Therese Roberts MMM
PO Box 6201, Edgbaston, Birmingham, W Midlands B16 9LB Tel: 0121 472 3040

CATHOLIC CENTRAL LIBRARY

Based at Farnborough Abbey, Hampshire
Librarian Mrs Joan Bond **E-mail: librarian@catholic-library.org.uk**
Website: www.catholic-library.org.uk

CATHOLIC CHARISMATIC RENEWAL

Information and resource centre for the National Service Committee: contacts with prayer groups and communities in Britain and abroad. Bi-monthly magazine: 'Goodnews'
Allen Hall 28 Beaufort Street SW3 5AA Tel: 020 7352 5298 Fax: 020 7351 4486
E-mail: ccruk@ontel.com Website: www.ccr.org.uk

CATHOLIC EDUCATION SERVICE FOR ENGLAND AND WALES

Represents the Bishops' Conference, Hierarchy and Catholic bodies in all Educational Matters.
Chair Archbishop Vincent Nichols. **Chief Executive** Oona Stannard, **39 Eccleston Sq SW1V 1BX**
Tel: 020 7901 4880 Fax: 020 7901 4893
E-mail: general@cesew.org.uk Website: www.cesew.org.uk

CATHOLIC ENQUIRY OFFICE

To interest non-Catholics in the belief and practice of Catholics and reach out to those who no longer practise their Faith, by means of advertising and the distribution of free literature.
The Chase Centre, 114 West Heath Road NW3 7TX
Tel 020 8458 3316 Fax: 020 8905 5780
E-mail: catholic.enquiry.office@cms.org.uk

CATHOLIC EVANGELISATION SERVICES

Helping Catholics respond to the challenge of a New Evangelisation through using videos in small groups. Catholic Faith Exploration (CaFE)
PO Box 333 St Albans, Herts AL2 1EL Tel: 01727 822837
E-mail: info@faithcafe.org Website: www.faithcafe.org

CATHOLIC EVIDENCE GUILD

For the training and provision of public speakers on the Catholic Faith.
Enquiries Mr Phil Gough 84 Grove Green Road E11 4EL

CATHOLIC FAMILY HISTORY SOCIETY

To encourage research and preserve the memory of those who suffered for the Faith.
Secretary Mrs M Bowery
9 Snow Green Rd, Shotley Bridge, Consett, Co Durham DH8 0HD

CATHOLIC FUND FOR HOMELESS AND DESTITUTE PEOPLE

St Martin of Tours HA, 318-320 St Pauls Road N1 2LF
Tel: 020 7704 3850

CATHOLIC GUIDE GUILD (WESTMINSTER)

Chair Kathleen Mulvey, 18 Fawcett Estate, Clapton Common E5 9DG
Tel: 020 8806 1712

CATHOLIC INSTITUTE FOR INTERNATIONAL RELATIONS (CIIR)

Research, information & education on international justice and Third World development. Recruits skilled/qualified people for projects as part of its overseas programme.
Director Christine Allen Unit 3, Canonbury Yard, 190a New North Road N1 7BJ
Tel: 020 7354 0883 Fax: 020 7359 0017
E-mail: ciir@ciir.org Website: www.ciir.org

CATHOLIC MISSIONARY UNION OF ENGLAND AND WALES.

The national forum and information centre of the mission societies and other agencies working for the Church overseas.
Secretary Br Leo Labbe SC **8 King Harry Lane, St Albans AL3 4AW**
E-mail: llabbesc@hotmail.com Website: www.cmu.org.uk

CATHOLIC ORGAN FORUM

Is available to give informed advice, free from commercial interest, on the installation, restoration and maintenance of organs to parishes, communities and schools, etc.
Secretary Dr John Rowntree, **Tel: 01635 44630**
The Cottage, 2 Burys Bank, Greenham Common North, Thatcham, Berks RG19 8BZ
Local Representative Mr Patrick Russil, **Brompton Oratory.**

CATHOLIC PEOPLE'S WEEKS

Residential weeks and weekends for exploration of the faith; some are for families (with or without children), some are for adults only. Annual programme available each January.
Secretary Clare Walker **1 Hazel Close, Chandlers Ford, Eastleigh, Hants SO53 5RF.**
Tel: 02380 260121 E-mail: ccrhdw@btinternet.com Website: www.c-p-w.ic24.net

CATHOLIC POLICE GUILD

An association of serving and retired Catholic police officers and civilian staff.
Chair Andrew Bayes **15th Floor, Empress Buildings, Lillie Road SW6 1TR**

CATHOLIC RECORD SOCIETY

To publish the historical sources for post-Reformation Catholic history in England and Wales. **President** Bishop Daniel Mullins (Menevia Emeritus).
Chair Professor V A McClelland. **Secretary** Dr L Gooch,
12 Melbourne Place, Wolsingham, Co Durham DL13 3EH Tel: 01388 527747
Website: www.catholic-history.org.uk

CATHOLIC SOCIAL WORKERS GUILD

A fellowship of present and former social workers providing a forum for discussion of ethical and professional issues encountered in social work practice in the light of Catholic teaching.
Chaplain Fr Theodore Davey CP. (Heythrop College)
Chair Mrs Anne Dodwell **40 Westcroft Road, Carshalton SM5 2TG**

CATHOLIC STAGE GUILD

To cater for the spiritual and temporal needs of Catholics engaged in the Theatre, Film, Television, Radio and allied arts including performers, writers and technicians. Associate Membership open to all. **Chaplain**: Canon J McDonald.
Secretary Molly Steele **1 Maiden Lane WC2E 7NB Tel: 020 7240 1221**
E-mail: mollysteele@talk21.com

CATHOLIC TRUTH SOCIETY

To explain the faith, teaching and life of the Church by reliable publication and dissemination of low-priced books & booklets; by retail sale of books & religious articles; and by publishing documents of the Holy See,
Chair Archbishop Peter Smith (Cardiff) **General Secretary** Fergal Martin LLB, LLM
Publishing Office & Distribution, 40-46 Harleyford Road SE11 5AY
Tel: 020 7640 0042 Fax: 020 7640 0046 E-mail: info@cts-online.org.uk
Bookshop Tel: 020 7834 1363 Fax: 020 7821 7398 Website: www.cts-online.org.uk

CATHOLIC UNION OF GREAT BRITAIN

A non-political association of members of the Catholic laity to watch over Catholic interests, in collaboration with Christians and others of like mind, especially in matters arising from Government action, proposed legislation or the activities of local authorities and other public bodies. **Ecclesiastical Adviser** Bishop Howard Tripp
Secretary Peter Higgs, **St Maximilian Kolbe House, 63 Jeddo Road W12 9EE**
Tel: 020 8749 1321 Fax: 020 8735 0861
E-mail: phiggs@cathunion.fsnet.co.uk Website:www.catholicunion.org

CATHOLIC WOMEN'S LEAGUE

For the promotion of religious, educational and social welfare and to represent Catholic women's interests on national and international bodies.
Branch President Maureen Anderson, **5 Hornbeams, Bricket Wood, St Albans AL2 3SP**
Tel: 01923 404250

CATHOLIC WOMEN'S NETWORK

A national network of women who believe that the Gospel speaks about freedom from oppression and calls women to full participation in all aspects of life and the church as a matter of justice. The Network aims to empower women to grow and mature in their spiritual life, encourage and enable them to engage in theology and develop new ways of worshipping together. CWN is a member of the National Board of Catholic Women. Publishes quarterly journal 'Network'. **National Contact** Mary Warrener
31 Homeway Road, Evington, Leicester LE5 5RH Website: www.cwnetwork.org.uk

CATHOLIC WRITERS' GUILD (THE KEYS)

For Catholics in journalism, writing, publishing, advertising or public relations.
President H. E. Cardinal Cormac Murphy-O'Connor **Master** Anthony Tyler OBE.
Chaplain Fr Christopher Cunningham IC. MBE **Administrator** Rosemary Nibbs,
14 Ely Place, Holborn Circus EC1N 6RY Tel: 020 7405 1061 Fax: 020 7405 7440

CATHOLIC YOUTH SERVICES

Youth Service Agency of the Bishops' Conference. A central resource for all engaged in informal youth provision within the Church. **Contact** Miss H Bardy
CYS, 39 Eccleston Square SW1V 1BX Tel: 020 7901 4870 Fax: 020 7901 4273
E-mail: cys@cbcew.org.uk Website: www.catholicyouthservices.org.uk

CHRISTIAN LIFE COMMUNITY

Small groups of Christians who meet regularly to help each other deepen their life of prayer. CLC's special characteristic is the spirituality of St Ignatius, helping members to integrate prayer with action in their daily lives. **National Chaplain** Fr A Nye SJ
Diocesan Representative Anne Shelley MHM. Website: www.clcew.org.uk
St Joseph's College, Lawrence St NW7 4JX Tel: 020 8959 8254

CIEL.UK

An international organisation pursuing the research and publication of scholarly works and resources on the Liturgy. Holds an annual 3-day International Liturgical Conference. Annual Mass and 1-day Conference held in London in May. Publishes annual *Proceedings* and quarterly *Chronicle*. **President** Fra Fredrick Crichton-Stuart
Chair Lt Cdr Neville J McNally RN CIEL UK, FREEPOST LON 15936, London SE19 2BR
E-mail: Chairman@CIEL-UK.org Website: www. CIEL-UK.org

CONSTANTINIAN ORDER OF ST GEORGE

Internationally recognised ancient and charitable Catholic Order of Knighthood under the custodianship of the Royal House of Bourbon Two Sicilies.
The British and Irish delegation:
Delegate HE Mr Anthony Bailey KCSS, KHS, KCMCO, KCFO,
Prior HE Cardinal Cormac Murphy-O'Connor GCJCO
Vice-Delegate & Chancellor Senator Donal Lydon KCSG, KM, KGCHS, KCMCO
Contact
26 Prince Consort Road SW7 2EE
Tel: 020 7594 0275 Fax: 020 7594 0265
E-mail: info@constantinian.org.uk Website: www.constantinian.org.uk

COR CHRISTI TRINITATE

Association of those seeking to foster a greater awareness of God's presence in daily life, especially in business and administration.
Contact Alexandra de Koranyi **Tel: 020 7245 1045**

COUPLES FOR CHRIST (CFC)

Founded in Manila in 1981, CFC is an international and recognised movement in 127 countries for the renewal of Christian family life in all its stages and states.
UK Head Rene Garcia MBE **Tel: 01628 783237 Mobile: 07900 901343**
Head of Family Ministries Romeo Mendozo **Tel: 020 8924 4675 Mobile: 07879 428083**
Websites: www.cfcglobal.org and **www.singlesforchrist.co.uk**

COUNCIL FOR THE MARIST WAY

The lay branch of the Marist Family bringing together those who wish to participate in the life and mission of the Church in the 'Spirit of Mary' envisaged by Jean-Claude Colin, founder of the Society of Mary.
Contact Mrs Agnes McGrogan **Tel: 01642 281408**
12 Harrow Rd, Linthorpe, Middlesborough TS5 5PD
E-mail: agnes.mcgrogan@ntlworld.com

DOMINICAN LAITY

Men and women called to spread the Gospel in the tradition of St Dominic. London Fraternity meets monthly at Haverstock Hill.
Chaplain Fr Dominic Noel OP
Secretary Stephen White, **10 St Simon's Avenue SW15 6DU**

DOMINICAN SECULAR INSTITUTE

A life consecrated to God through vow, offering challenge and mutual support, helping to develop our apostolate and service to others.
Moderator Miss Janet Wiltshire **19 Broomfield Place, Earlsdon, Coventry CV5 6GY**
E-mail: Janetwilts@aol.com

DYMPNA CENTRE

Offers person-to-person consultancy for spiritual direction, counselling, psychotherapy, or vocation discernment. Primarily for those in Church ministry or consecrated life.
Contact Fr Terry McGrath **Tel: 01423 817515**
Website: www.thedympnacentre.co.uk

EDUCATION FOR PARISH SERVICE

Offers a number of pathways in partnership with information for parish ministry at degree, diploma and certificate level in partnership with University of Wales (Lampeter)
Course Director Patricia Carroll, **Christian Education Centre, 21 Tooting Bec Road SW17 8BS**
Tel: 020 8767 4445 E-mail: eps@tootingbec.org.uk

ENCOURAGE

Support network for Catholics experiencing homosexual attraction wishing to live according to the teaching of the Church. Regular meetings and Newsletter. **PO Box 3745 N2 8LW**
E-mail: encouragelondon@yahoo.co.uk Website: www. encouragetrust.org.uk

ENGLISH CATHOLIC HISTORY ASSOCIATION

Aims to advance the education of the public in English Catholic history, including promoting interest and encouraging research into the Catholic history of England and Wales and helping to preserve relevant documents. Regular meetings and visits are arranged and members receive a quarterly newsletter. **Secretary** Miss Toni Eccles,
6 Townside, Church St, Tisbury, Salisbury, Wilts SP3 6AX Tel: 01747 871070
E-mail: toni.eccles@btinternet.com Website: www. echa.org.uk

EMMANUEL COMMUNITY

One of the new movements in the Church, includes lay people, priests and men and women consecrated to the celibate life who together live a life founded on prayer and the sacraments, committed to the graces of Adoration, Compassion and Evangelisation. It is recognised by the Holy See as an Association of the Lay faithful.
Contact Nicholas and Susan Rodger
40 Grafton Road W3 6PB Tel: 020 8993 9914
E-mail: nrodger@osteopath.fsnet.co.uk Website: www.emmanuel.info

FOCOLARE MOVEMENT

An international ecclesial movement started by Chiara Lubich in 1943 in Trentino, Italy. Its main aim is to contribute towards the fulfilment of the prayer of Jesus 'May they all be one'. Engages in dialogue with those who want to work for peace and unity.
Residential Conference Centre
69 Parkway, Welwyn Garden City, Herts AL8 6JG
Tel: 01707 323620 Fax: 01707 336413
Website: www.@focolare.org

FRIENDS OF THE HOLY FATHER

To pray for the Holy Father's intentions, study his teaching and make it more widely known as well as supporting a fund to assist in defraying the rising expenses incurred in furthering his Apostolic Ministry. **Chair** Colin Edwards FCA, KCSG,KC*HS
Secretary Dr Michael Straiton MB, KCSG,
Vaughan House, 46 Francis Street SW1P 1QN

GHANA CATHOLIC ASSOCIATION

The Societies in the UK Ghana Catholic Chaplaincy co-ordinating the welfare of Ghanaians are: Area Communities, St Theresa, St Bernadette's, Knights & Ladies of Marshall, Christian Mothers, Knights & Ladies of St John.
212 Sangley Road SE6 2JS Tel: 020 8355 8360 Fax: 020 8698 5037
Chaplain Fr James K. Enin MIC **E-mail: james.enin@ntlworld.com**
Vice Chair Mr H A A Miezah **Tel: 020 8809 4420**
Secretary Mr A K Dwomoh **Tel: 079 5193 7769**

GOOD COUNSEL NETWORK

Catholic pregnancy counselling organisation, consecrated to Our Lady, offering information & support to women in crisis pregnancies to enable them to avoid abortion. Faithful to the Church's teaching on contraception and abortion; provides speakers on chastity for schools and parishes. Organises post-abortion retreats in conjunction with the Franciscan Friars of the Renewal.
Director Clare McCullough **PO Box 46679 London NW9 8ZT**
Tel: 020 7723 1740 E-mail: info@goodcounselnetwork.freeserve.co.uk

GRAIL, THE

A society of married couples, associates, young adults and a family network. Within it is a Secular Institute for single women and widows, some living in their own homes and others in a small community at Pinner where they run a day conference centre, and retreat hermitages. The Grail is about bringing God into our world; about the quest for the meaning of life, the treasure of great price that heals and enlivens. It is about empowering ordinary men and women and building community by drawing others into this search and by reflecting the essentials of Christian belief in a relevant and creative way.
President Miss Claire Davidson **The Grail Centre, 125 Waxwell Lane, Pinner HA5 3ER Tel: 020 8866 2195 Community E-mail: waxwell@compuserve.com Business and Centre E-mail: grailcentre@compuserve.com Website: www.grailsociety.org.uk**
Diocesan representative Pat Edwards **26 Thrush Green, Woodlands, N.Harrow HA2 6EZ Tel: 020 8429 4663**

GUILD OF CATHOLIC DOCTORS

For Catholic members of the medical profession. **Hospital of St John and St Elizabeth, 60 Grove End Rd, NW8 9NH Tel: 020 7266 4246 Master of Westminster Branch:** Dr Michael Jarmulowicz **6 St Andrews' Road NW10 2QS Tel: 020 8459 8572 E-mail: enquiries@catholicdoctors.org.uk Website: www.catholicdoctors.org.uk**

GUILD OF OUR LADY OF RANSOM

For the conversion of England & Wales by prayer; appreciation of our Catholic Heritage, publications, historical pilgrimages, etc; financial support for rural and inner-city parishes **Master** Mgr Anthony Stark KCHS **31 Southdown Road, Wimbledon SW20 8QJ Tel: 020 8947 2598 Fax: 020 8944 6355 E-mail: MgrAGS@aol.com**

GUILD OF ST AGATHA

Catholic Association of Bellringers **Guild Office 1 Albert Road, Bournemouth BH1 1BZ. Diocesan Rep** Fr Shaun Lennard **39 Duncan Terrace N1 8AL Tel: 020 7226 3277**

GUILD OF ST STEPHEN AND ST GREGORY

Those who serve in Westminster Cathedral. **Contact Cathedral Clergy House, 42 Francis Street SW1P 1QW Tel: 020 7798 9055** or Simon Jennings **Tel: 07860 493718**

HOLY CHILDHOOD

One of the Pontifical Mission Societies. Through its project Mission Together it encourages children to be concerned with Mission through prayer, learning activities and fund-raising. Church's official overseas charity for children. Its motto is 'children helping children'. For free materials or to arrange a school assembly contact **Diocesan Director** Fr Michael Markey **Tel: 01784 252230**

HOUSETOP CENTRE

Evangelisation through the modern media. Adult Faith Formation. John Wijngaards, **Housetop, 111A High Street, Rickmansworth, Herts WD3 1AN Tel: 01923 779446 E-mail: john.nmw@ntlworld.com**

HOUSING JUSTICE

(Formerly Catholic Housing Aid Society) Information, campaigning and advice. **Chief Executive** Robina Rafferty **209 Old Marylebone Road NW1 5QT Tel: 020 7723 7272 Fax: 020 7723 5943 E-mail: info@housingjustice.org.uk Website: www.housingjustice.org.uk**

INTERNATIONAL CATHOLIC SOCIETY FOR GIRLS (ACISJF)

Founded 1929, cares for young adults travelling/living temporarily away from home. Advice & information on accommodation, Au Pair placements, social activities and other services, in the UK and on the Continent. **Contact** (enclosing sae) Andrea Watson
8 Farm Lane, Croydon CR0 8AQ Tel: 020 8777 8371 Website: www.aupairadvice.org.uk

IRISH CENTRE (PART OF IRISH CHAPLAINCY SCHEME)

Irish Welfare, Housing, Employment, Social & Day Care Centre for the elderly with a range of outreach services and social facilities. **50-52 Camden Square NW1 9XB Tel: 020 7916 2222 Fax: 020 7916 2638 E-mail: irishchaplaincy@btconnect.com**

KNIGHTS OF ST COLUMBA

Fraternal order of Catholic men supporting the mission of the Church and the spiritual, intellectual and material welfare of its members and their families. Working for the moral and social welfare of the country; helping young people develop in the likeness of Christ.
Provincial Grand Knights: Province 11 John Boniface, **44 Woodstock Avenue W13 9UG**
Province 29 Andy McKie, **218 Knella Road, Welwyn Garden City, Herts AL7 3NW**
Province 30 Bertie M Grogan, **98 Burket Close, Norwood Green, Middx UB2 5NT**

LATIN MASS SOCIETY

For the preservation of the traditional Roman Rite. **11-13 Macklin Street WC2B 5NH**
Tel: 020 7404 7284 Fax: 020 7831 5585
E-mail: thelatinmasssociety@snmail.co.uk Website: www.latin-mass-society.org

LAY CARMELITE THIRD ORDER

Forming praying communities at the service of God's people. For details **contact** Charmaine Jayasuriya **Tel: 01442 267035** or Maureen Beck **Tel: 020 7834 9684**

LAY MISSIONARY AND VOLUNTEER NETWORK

Collaborative partnership within missionary and volunteer groups, working to share resources and expertise. **Contact LMVN, 23 Kensington Square W8 5HN**

LEGION OF MARY

Worldwide organisation based on the ideals of Vatican II's Decree on the Lay Apostolate. For the spiritual formation of members through prayer & action under ecclesiastical guidance. **The President, Frank Duff House, 16 Northdown Street N1 9BG Tel: 020 7837 2371**

LINACRE CENTRE FOR HEALTHCARE ETHICS

A research and education centre established in 1977 under a charitable trust formed by the Catholic Archbishops of England and Wales.
Director Dr Helen Watt **60 Grove End Road NW8 9NH**
Tel: 020 7806 4088 Fax: 020 7266 5424
E-mail: admin@linacre.org Website: www.linacre.org

LITTLE WAY ASSOCIATION (THE)

Association of Lay Volunteers who assist Missionaries to spread the Faith by prayer and active work and promote the Message of St Thérèse of Lisieux.
President Mary Doohan.
All communications to **119 Cedars Road SW4 0PR Tel: 020 7622 0466**

MALTA, ORDER OF (BRITISH ASSOCIATION)

The Order of Malta, a religious order of the Church, supports the Hospital of St John and St Elizabeth in London and other hospitaller work, including pilgrimages to Lourdes and Walsingham. **President** Prince Rupert Zu Loewenstein
Chancellor Charles Weld
Brampton House, 60 Grove End Road NW8 9NH
Tel: 020 7286 1414 Fax: 020 7289 3243

MARRIAGE ENCOUNTER

Provides weekends where couples and priests can enrich their lives through improving communication; also weekends for engaged couples preparing for marriage.
Contact Tony and Margaret Hunt
213 Chambersbury Lane, Hemel Hempstead HP3 8BQ Tel: 01442 393838
Website: www.wwme.org.uk
Priest Fr Teddy O'Brien MSC **Tel: 01926 632214**

MARRIAGE CARE (FORMERLY CMAC)

Professionally trained marriage counsellors offer counselling for those with marital and relationship difficulties, and short courses for couples preparing for marriage. Specially trained facilitators act as a resource for teachers and others responsible for delivering personal health and social education to young people.
National telephone helpline - 0845 660 6000 - operates Monday - Friday between 10 - 4pm.
National Office **Clitherow House, 1 Blythe Mews, Blythe Road W14 0NW**
Tel: 020 7371 1341 Fax: 020 7371 4921
Website: www.marriagecare.org.uk

MARY POTTER CENTRE

Offering counselling, talks, courses and workshops (basic and post basic) to enable the individual to build self-understanding, confidence, deal with stress, difficult relationships, help deal with loss, bereavement, anxiety, emotional distress. Workshops include The Myers Briggs Type Indicator and the Enneagram. Courses: Awareness and Self Worth; Assertiveness Training.

Director Sr Josephine Bugeja LCM, MA, RGN, RMN
33 Mattock Lane W5 5BH Tel: 020 8840 4313
E-mail: jbugeja@aol.com Website: http://members.aol.com/jbugeja

MING-AI (LONDON) INSTITUTE

A life-long education institute having close links with Caritas Hong Kong. Wide range of leisure, cookery, health, business and Oriental language classes. Promotes links between our diocese and the Church in Hong Kong and China. **Director** Dr Therese Shak, Denver House, 1 Cline Road N11 2LX Tel: 020 8361 7161 Fax: 020 8361 4207

MISSIONARY UNION

One of the Pontifical Mission Societies. Through its quarterly magazine Mission Outlook, the Missionary Union stimulates the interest of priests, religious and laity in the missionary work of the Church and developments in the younger churches.
E-mail: director@missio.org.uk
Website: www.missio.org.uk

MOVEMENT OF CHRISTIAN WORKERS

To promote Gospel values of equality, social justice & solidarity. Works through small groups which exist to help people relate faith to their daily lives; provides positive support to those who are working in their local communities, in the labour movement & in the Church to build the Kingdom of God.
National HQ St Joseph's, off St Joseph's Grove NW4 4TY
Tel: 020 8203 6290 Fax: 020 8203 6291 E-mail: mcworkers@aol.com

NATIONAL BOARD OF CATHOLIC WOMEN

A consultative body to the Bishops' Conference of England & Wales with consultative status within the United Nations, with representatives from 32 Catholic organisations and the dioceses. A forum in which women are enabled to share their views and concerns and make recommendations at all levels. Quarterly newspaper *Catholic Omnibus.*
Contact Angela Perkins 12 Worsall Rd, Yarm, Cleveland TS15 9DF
Tel/Fax: 01642 791840 E-mail: enquiries@nbcw.org Website: nbcw.org

NATIONAL COUNCIL FOR LAY ASSOCIATIONS (ENGLAND AND WALES).

A consultative body to the Bishops' Conference, consisting of lay apostolic national organisations, 8 liaison representatives, advisors & executive. **Adviser** Bishop Terence Brain. **Secretary** Mrs Rita Forster **21 Bassett Crescent West, Bassett, Southampton SO16 7EB**

NEWMAN ASSOCIATION

A national association of Catholic laity & clergy which aims to help Catholics develop their understanding of their Faith in the context of the contemporary world. Local circles
London Therese & Anthony Havery, **27 Southfields NW4 4LX**
Ealing Mrs Anne Riley, **17 Mount Pleasant Rd W5 1SG**
Herts Alasdair Archivot, **28 Beechfield Close, Redbourne, St Albans AL3 7EG**

OUR LADY'S CATECHISTS

An association of men and women qualified to give religious instruction. Postal courses include: 'Sowing the Seed' for training parish catechists leading to a certificate; or as an adult developmental course. The Diploma Course provides a more academic training, the Children's Course for those unable to attend Catholic schools, the Duke of Edinburgh Award Scheme 'Service through Religious Education-Roman Catholic' at Silver & Gold levels, & Young Parish Helpers programme for youth to assist in parish catechesis.
Secretary Charmaine Jayasuriya **21 Charlesworth Close, Hemel Hempstead HP3 9EW**
Tel: 01422 267035 E-mail: DCharmaineJ@aol.com
Website: www.ourladyscatechists.co.uk

PAPAL ORDERS IN GREAT BRITAIN

An association of holders of Pontifical Orders of Knighthood in Great Britain.
Chair Rt Hon Sir Swinton Thomas PC KCSG **Secretary** Leo Simmonds KCSG KCHS
5 Sheen Park, Richmond TW9 1UN Tel: 020 8940 1030

PAX CHRISTI

International Catholic Movement for Peace, promoting a greater sense of Christian responsibility on the issues of war and peace. **National President** Bishop Malcolm McMahon
General Secretary Patricia Gaffney **St Joseph's, Watford Way NW4 4TY**
Tel: 020 8203 4884 Fax: 020 8203 5234
E-mail: paxchristi@gn.apc.org Website: www.paxchristi.org.uk

PIONEER TOTAL ABSTINENCE ASSOCIATION OF THE SACRED HEART

A lay organisation whose primary aim is the promotion of sobriety and temperance through prayer and self-sacrifice. **20 Parkfields Avenue NW9 7PE**

PONTIFICAL MISSION SOCIETIES

PMS comprise the following: Association for the Propagation of the Faith (APF); Holy Childhood (Mission Together); Pontifical Missionary Union; Society of St Peter the Apostle. **See separate entries for each.** Together they form the principal organisation for providing spiritual and financial support for missions overseas.

PONTIFICAL MISSIONARY UNION

Through its quarterly review *Mission Outlook* (£8 pa) stimulates interest in the missionary work of the Church and in developments in the younger churches.
National Director 23 Eccleston Square SW1V 1NU Tel: 020 7821 9755

PONTIFICAL SOCIETY OF ST JOHN CHRYSOSTOM

Founded in 1926 to promote unity & encourage greater knowledge of Eastern Churches. Publishes *Chrysostom.* **Chair** Rev ATJ Salter **1 St James Close, Bishop Street N1 8PH**

PRISON ADVICE AND CARE TRUST

(formerly The Bourne Trust). Provides counselling, advice and support to prisoners and their families, and education for parishes and schools about imprisonment.
Director Myra Fulford **Lincoln House, 1-3 Brixton Road SW9 6DE**
Tel: 020 7582 1313 (Administration) 020 7582 6699 (Counselling) Fax: 020 7735 6077
E-mail: info@thebournetrust.org.uk Website: www.imprisonment.org.uk

PROVIDENCE ROW

Working with the Sisters of Mercy and Providence Row Housing Association. A range of services for homeless people and those living in poverty. **41 Spelman Street E1 5LQ**

PUERI CANTORES FEDERATION OF GREAT BRITAIN

The Church's official organisation for choirs of young people. It achieves its aims particularly through choir exchanges & congresses, at diocesan, national & international levels. **President** Michael Landers **7 Keats Close, Newport NP9 3JU Tel/Fax: 01633 213049**

RADIANT LIGHT

Seeking to encourage people to grow in holiness by believing and living the Catholic faith in its fullness. Founded by Elizabeth Wang and inspired by her writings, paintings and spirituality. **Contact Radiant Light, 25 Rothamsted Avenue, Harpenden AL5 2DN**
E-mail: mail@radiantlight.org.uk Website: www.radiantlight.org.uk

REGNUM CHRISTI APOSTOLIC LAY MOVEMENT

Active in over 30 countries seeking to serve and contribute to local needs of the Church through social development, youth education and family programmes. Lay movement of the Legionaries of Christ founded by Fr Marcial Maciel **Contact** Tom Wingate
Tel: 020 7313 4649 E-mail: tmjwingate@hotmail.com

ST BARNABAS SOCIETY

(successor to The Converts' Aid Society). For the assistance of needy former clergy and religious received into the Catholic Church. **Secretary** Fr Robin Sanders
4 First Turn, Wolvercote, Oxford OX2 8AH Tel: 01865 513377
E-mail: secretary@StBarnabasSociety.org.uk Website: www.StBarnabasSociety.org.uk
Diocesan Rep Daniel Gibbons **3 Court Close, Twickenham TW2 5JH Tel: 020 8898 5859**

ST FRANCIS LEPROSY GUILD

Supporting leprosy hospitals & centres, helping rehabilitate people who have had leprosy, caring for the elderly affected by leprosy in need of residential care.
President Mrs Gwen Sankey **Spiritual Director** Fr Provincial, OFM
Admin Officer Eric Williams **Secretaries** Sr Eleanor Marshall FMM, Sr Anne Curtin MMM
73 St Charles Square W10 6EJ Tel: 020 8969 1345 Fax: 020 8969 3272
E-mail: enquiries@stfrancisleprosy.org. Website: www.stfrancisleprosy.org

ST FRANCIS OF ASSISI CATHOLIC RAMBLERS CLUB

Regular Sunday walks in Home Counties; also walking holidays, weekends & social events.
Contact Helen Hunt **157 Coteford Street SW17 8NT Tel: 020 8767 6956**
E-mail: HelenHunt@freeda.com Website: www.stfrancisramblers.org.uk

ST JOSEPH'S SOCIETY FOR THE RELIEF OF THE AGED POOR

To provide sheltered accommodation for elderly Catholics of limited means.
Secretary S. Dolan **St Joseph's House, 42 Brook Green W6 7BW Tel: 020 7603 9817**

SECULAR CLERGY COMMON FUND

Chief Administrator Canon John McDonald **St Mary's Cemetery, Harrow Road NW10 5NU**
Tel: 020 8969 1145 Fax: 020 8969 1153

SECULAR CLERGY NEW COMMON FUND

Chief Administrator, 38 Hartlands Road, Fareham, Hants PO16 0NL Tel: 01329 239584

SECULAR FRANCISCAN ORDER

Men and women who make a solemn profession to follow Christ in the spirit of St Francis, living the Gospel in contemporary society by observing the SFO Rule.
Contact Rubie Masse, **66 Springfield Road N15 4AZ Tel: 020 8808 0230**

SERRA CLUBS OF LONDON

Branches of an international organisation of laity, to encourage and foster vocations to the priesthood & religious life and develop its members' understanding of the faith of the Church.
Secretary (London) Sheila Berkery-Smith DSG. **20 Clifton Gardens N15 6AP Tel: 020 8800 4980**
Secretary (South Herts) Eric R H Selley **9 Home Farm Road, Rickmansworth WD3 1JU Tel: 01923 776304 E-mail: erhs@globalnet.co.uk**

SERVITE SECULAR INSTITUTE

A life of service to God and his people through consecration lived by vows of chastity, poverty and obedience in union with others of like mind, remaining in their own circumstances. Women of prayer living in the world as Servants of Mary.
Contact Eileen Healy **39 Wellington Row E2 7BB Tel: 020 7729 5183**
E-mail: eileen.healy@tiscali.co.uk Website: www.ssi.org.uk

SION CENTRE FOR DIALOGUE & ENCOUNTER ♿

For study of other faiths and inter-religious dialogue focussing on the relationship between Christianity & Judaism. Resources, library, day conference area, regular study programme, outreach staff. **34 Chepstow Villas W11 2QZ Tel: 020 7727 3597/020 7313 8286**
Fax: 020 7313 8281 E-mail: sioncde@yahoo.co.uk Website: sistersofsion.org

SOCIETY OF CATHOLIC ARTISTS

Aims to encourage high standards in church art, to assist prospective patrons in the selection of suitable artists and craftsmen and to provide fellowship to those who have the arts and Catholicism in common. **Website: www.catholicartists.co.uk**
Chair Mary Davey **Secretary** Patrick Pike **46 Waterlow Rd N19 5NH Tel: 020 7272 5458**
E-mail: ralderson@ukonline.co.uk

SOCIETY OF OUR LADY OF LOURDES

To promote devotion to Our Lady, organise services and pilgrimages to Lourdes and assist sick pilgrims, financially and otherwise, to go there.
St Joseph's College, Lawrence Street NW7 4JX Tel: 020 8959 7171 Fax: 020 8959 7189
E-mail: soll@btinternet.com Website: www.soll-lourdes.com

SOCIETY OF ST AUGUSTINE OF CANTERBURY

To assist in the maintenance of the official residence of the Archbishop of Westminster.
Secretary M Milbourn **The River House, St Mary's Lane, Hertingfordbury, Hertford SG14 2LF**

SOCIETY OF ST GREGORY

National Society working to assist priests and people celebrate the liturgy worthily. It encourages study and active participation through study days, conferences and an annual summer school for all concerned with music/worship. Publishes journal *'Music and Liturgy'*. Meetings arranged for composers. **Contact** John Ainslie, **76 Great Bushey Drive N20 8QL**
E-mail: westminster@ssg.org.uk Website: www. ssg.org.uk

SOCIETY OF ST PETER THE APOSTLE (SPA)

The Church's official fundraising body for the training of clergy and religious in mission countries. Through prayer and finance SPA members and contributors help the younger churches provide their own priests and religious. For more information please contact
National Director, Pontifical Mission Societies, 23 Eccleston Square SW1V 1NU
Tel: 020 7821 9755

SOCIETY OF ST VINCENT DE PAUL

For all willing to work in a spirit of justice and peace with people in need.
Diocesan Council President Siobhan Garibaldi **Chaplain** Fr Paul McAleenan
St Vincent de Paul Centre, 24 George Street W1U 3QZ Tel: 020 7935 7625
Fax: 020 7371 2644 Website: www.svp.org.uk

TEAMS OF OUR LADY (EQUIPES NOTRE DAME)

An international movement for Christian married couples of all ages in which groups of 4-6 couples, with a chaplain, form teams and meet monthly in each other's homes to support each other in their daily lives, to pray and to discuss live interests in the Church today.
Contact Kevin & Rachel Pugh **Cornerstone, Highfield Ave, Bishops Stortford CM23 5LS**
Tel: 01279 465187 E-mail: pugh3@btopenworld.com
Website: www.teamsofourlady.org.uk

THE CATHOLIC FUND

A Catholic charity working in a Vincentian spirit to give help and support to people in extreme need and help them to re-establish themselves. Works in close co-operation with the St Martin of Tours HA.
318-320 St Paul's Road N1 2LF
Tel: 020 7704 3850 Fax: 020 7704 3832

THE TWENTYSOMETHINGS AND THE THIRTYSOMETHINGS - PROJECT 2030

Groups for Catholics in their 20s/30s, getting together at social/spiritual levels. Walks, meals, evenings out, Masses & retreats. International visits. Sponsored by the Dehonians (Sacred Heart Fathers) **Contact** Fr Hugh Hanley SCJ
Project 2030 Office, St Joseph's, Malpas SY14 7DD Tel: 01614 763234
E-mail: hugh@project2030.fsnet.co.uk Website: www.project2030.org.uk

TRAVELLING MISSION TO THE TRAVELLING PEOPLE

Responsible for the catechesis and pastoral needs of the Travelling People and Gypsies in England and Wales.
Contact Sr Margaret Begley
St Joseph's House, 18 Leopold Street, Oxford OX4 1PS Tel: 01865 240325

UNION OF CATHOLIC MOTHERS

A national organisation of Catholic women for the preservation of the family and sanctification of the home. **Diocesan President** Valerie Gould
Spiritual Director Fr David Irwin **Secretary** B Hegarty
6a Rutland Park Gardens NW2 4RG E-mail: brigidhegargy@hotmail.com

UNITED SERVICES CATHOLIC ASSOCATION

To develop the work of the Lay Apostolate within the Armed Forces and to help Catholics serving in HM Forces to practise their religion.
AGPDO, Middle Hill, Aldershot, Hants GU11 1PP

VINCENTIAN VOLUNTEERS

A challenging and fulfilling Gap Year. 18-30, spends a year living in small communities serving the poor in the spirit of St Vincent de Paul. **Contact** Sr Pauline Gaughan DC
39 Marlsford Street, Liverpool L6 6AX Tel: 0151 261 0225
E-mail: director@vincentvols.freeserve.co.uk
Website: www.vincentianvolunteers.org

VOCATIONS GROUP

A group of young adults in their 20s and 30s searching for their path in life and meeting on a monthly basis for prayer, mutual support and talks from guest speakers.
Website: www.vocationsgroup.org.uk
Contact Camilla Tel: 020 7247 5658 or 01277 373959
E-mail: Eccomi2000@vocationsgroup.org.uk

VOLUNTEER MISSIONARY MOVEMENT

Recruits, prepares and sends Christians with educational, technical or medical skills to share their skills, lives, faith and friendship with the people of Africa and Central America for two years or more.

VMM, Liverpool Hope University, Hope Park, Liverpool L16 9JD
Tel: 0151 291 3438
E-mail: VMM@hope.ac.uk
Website: www.vmm.cjb.net

WALSINGHAM ASSOCIATION

Supports National Shrine & promotes pilgrimages.

London Representative Mr M. A. Whelton
Flat 15, Cholmeley Lodge, Cholmeley Park N6 5EN
Tel: 020 8340 9698

WESTMINSTER ECCLESIASTICAL EDUCATION FUND (WEEF)

Fund for training of candidates for the Priesthood.

Chair Mgr John Arnold
Archbishop's House, Ambrosden Avenue Tel: 020 7391 6062
E-mail: johnarnold@rcdow.org.uk

YOUNG CHRISTIAN WORKERS AND IMPACT!

A movement for young people between the ages of 16-30. Through a programme of enquiry in small groups, the YCW educates and trains young people for their mission of Christian service and apostolate in everyday life.

St Joseph's, off St Joseph's Grove NW4 4TY
Tel: 020 8203 6290 Fax: 020 8203 6291
E-mail: ycworkers@aol.com

YOUTH 2000

A spiritual initiative aimed primarily at young people between 15 & 35. It exists as a response to the call of Pope John Paul II for a new evangelisation and seeks to draw young people into the heart of the Church through a programme of prayer festivals and regular prayer groups. In Westminster the prayer group meets every Wednesday at 7.30pm in Corpus Christi, Maiden Lane WC2. For more information visit

Website: www.youth2000.org
or contact **Youth 2000** on **Tel: 020 7370 0211**
or **E-mail: youth2000_london@hotmail.com**

LISTED BUILDINGS 2005/6

In order of Parish, Dedication, Address, Local Authority and Grade

Cathedral Most Precious Blood Victoria Street, SW1 City of Westminster I
Bayswater St Mary of the Angels Moorhouse Road, W2 City of Westminster II
Bethnal Green Our Lady of the Assumption Victoria Park Sq., E2 Tower Hamlets II
Bishops Stortford St Joseph and the English Martyrs Windhill, CM23 East Herts II
Brook Green Holy Trinity Brook Green, W6 Hammersmith & Fulham II*
Buntingford St Richard of Chichester Station Road, SG9 East Herts II
Chelsea St Mary Cadogan Street SW3 Kensington & Chelsea II*
Chelsea Most Holy Redeemer & St Thomas More SW3 Kensington & Chelsea II
Chiswick Our Lady of Grace & St Edward W4 Hounslow II
Chorleywood St John Fisher Shire Lane, WD3 Three Rivers II
Clerkenwell Ss. Peter & Paul Amwell Street, EC1 Islington II*
Commercial Road St Mary & St Michael E1 Tower Hamlets II
Ealing Abbey Church of St Benedict Charlbury Grove, W5 Ealing II
Ely Place St Etheldreda Holborn Circus, EC1 Camden I
Farm Street The Immaculate Conception Farm Street, W1 City of Westminster II*
French Church Notre Dame de France Leicester Place, WC2 City of Westminster II
Fulham St Thomas of Canterbury Rylston Road, SW6 Hammersmith & Fulham II
Fulham Road Our Lady of Dolours Fulham Road, SW10 Kensington & Chelsea II
Hampstead St Mary Holly Place, NW3 Camden II*
Harrow on the Hill Our Lady and St Thomas of Canterbury HA1 Harrow II
Haverstock Hill St Dominic Southampton Road, NW5 Camden II*
Hertford Immaculate Conception & St Joseph St John's Street, SG14 East Herts II
Highgate St Joseph Highgate Hill, N19 Islington II*
Holloway Sacred Heart of Jesus Eden Grove, N7 Islington II
Hoxton St Monica Hoxton Sq, N1 Hackney II
Islington St John the Evangelist Duncan Terrace N1 Islington II
Italian Church St Peter Clerkenwell Road, EC1 Camden II
Kensal New Town Our Lady of the Holy Souls Bosworth Road, W10 Kensington & Chelsea II
Kensington Our Lady of Mount Carmel & St Simon Stock W8 Kensington & Chelsea II
Kentish Town Our Lady Help of Christians Lady Margaret Road, NW5 Camden II
Lincolns Inn Fields SS. Anselm & Cecilia Kingsway, WC2 Camden II
London Colney All Saints Pastoral Centre St Albans II*
Maiden Lane Corpus Christi Maiden Lane, WC2 City of Westminster II
Marylebone Our Lady of the Rosary Old Marylebone Road, NW1 City of Westminster II
Mile End Guardian Angels Mile End Road, E3 Tower Hamlets II
Moorfields St Mary Eldon Street. EC2 Hackney II
Notting Hill St Francis of Assisi Pottery Lane, W11 Kensington & Chelsea II*
Ogle Street St Charles Borromeo Ogle Street, W1 City of Westminster II
Oratory Immaculate Heart of Mary Brompton Road, SW7 Kensington & Chelsea II*

Polish Church Our Lady of Czestochowa Devonia Road, N 1 Islington II
Poplar St Mary & St Joseph E14, Tower Hamlets II
Queensway, Our Lady Queen of Heaven W2 City of Westminster II
St Johns Wood Our Lady Lisson Grove, NW8 City of Westminster II
St Margarets St Margaret St Margaret's Rd TW1 Richmond II
Soho Square St Patrick Soho Square, W1 City of Westminster II*
Spanish Place St James W1 City of Westminster II*
Stamford Hill St Ignatius High Road, N15 Haringey II
Sudbury St George Harrow Road, HA0 Brent II
Tollington Park St Mellitus N4 Islington II
Tower Hill English Martyrs Prescot Street, El Tower Hamlets II
Ukrainian Cathedral Holy Family in Exile Duke Street, W1 City of Westminster II
Underwood Road St Anne El Tower Hamlets II*
Wapping St Patrick Dundee Street El Tower Hamlets II
Warwick Street Our Lady of the Assumption & St Gregory W1 City of Westminster II*
Watford Holy Rood Market Street, WD1 Watford I
Willesden Our Lady of Willesden Acton Lane, NW10 Brent I

HISTORIC CHURCHES COMMITTEE

www.rcdow.org.uk/hcc/

Under the ecclesiastical exemption provision of the Town and Country Planning Act, listed Churches are exempt from the requirement to obtain from their local authority Listed Building Consent for works of repair and refurbishment, providing they obtain approval from the local Historic Churches Committee. These regulations have been confirmed by the Bishops Conference of England and Wales in their 1999 'Directory on the Ecclesiastical Exemption from Listed Building Control'.

Chair Fr Peter Harris **Tel 020 7987 4114**
Secretary Mr Chris Fanning **Tel 020 8202 2695**

GUIDE TO LONDON CHURCHES

CENTRAL LOCATIONS

Services in the Churches listed will be found in the Parish Directory section, under the entry indicated here in bold and italic.

CITY (I) St Mary Moorfields, Eldon Street EC2 *north of Finsbury Circus, near Liverpool Street stn & Moorgate stn* Tel 020 7247 8390 ***(Moorfields)***
CITY (II) The English Martyrs, Prescot Street E1 *off Mansell Street, near Tower of London* Tel 020 7488 4654 ***(Tower Hill)***
CITY (III) St Joseph, Lamb's Buildings *off Bunhill Row, near Barbican Centre* Tel 020 7628 0326 ***(Bunhill Row)***

HOLBORN CIRCUS St Etheldreda, Ely Place EC1 *off Charterhouse Street, beside Holborn Circus* Tel 020 7405 1061 ***(Ely Place)***
KINGSWAY St Anselm and St Cecilia, Kingsway WC2 *east side by Holborn Underground stn* Tel 020 7405 0376 ***(Lincoln's Inn Fields)***
LEICESTER SQUARE Notre Dame de France, Leicester Place WC2 *north side of Leicester Square* Tel 020 7437 9363 ***(French Church)***
MAYFAIR Immaculate Conception, Farm Street W1 *entrance also in Mount Street, between South Audley Street and Berkeley Square* Tel 020 7493 7811 ***(Farm Street)***
PICCADILLY CIRCUS The Assumption, Warwick Street W1R 3PA *close to Piccadilly Circus* Tel 020 7437 1525 ***(Warwick Street)***
SOHO St Patrick, Soho Square W1 *in angle between Oxford Street and Charing Cross Road; near Tottenham Court Road stn* Tel 020 7437 2010 ***(Soho)***
STRAND Corpus Christi, Maiden Lane WC2 *off Southampton Street on north side of the Strand; near Covent Garden* Tel 020 7836 4700 ***(Maiden Lane)***
VICTORIA Westminster Cathedral, Ashley Place SW1 *south side of Victoria Street, close to Victoria stn* Tel 020 7798 9097 ***(Westminster)***
WEST END (I) St Charles Borromeo, Ogle Street W1 *off eastern end of New Cavendish Street, behind Middlesex Hospital* Tel 020 7636 2883 ***(Ogle Street)***
WEST END (II) St James, George Street W1 *eastern end i.e. between Baker Street and Marylebone High Street* Tel 020 7935 0943 ***(Spanish Place)***
WEST END (III) Our Lady of the Rosary, Marylebone Road *off Edgware Road, opposite Sussex Gardens* Tel 020 7 723 5101 ***(Marylebone)***
WEST END (IV) Tyburn Convent, 8 Hyde Park Place W2 *in Bayswater Road, close to Marble Arch* Perpetual Exp. of the Bl. Sacrament. Tel 020 7723 7262 ***(Marylebone)***

AIRPORT CHAPELS

Gatwick Airport Chapel in Main Terminal Building (Diocese of Arundel & Brighton) For times of services **Tel: 01293 503851**

HEATHROW AIRPORT (TERMINALS 1, 2 & 3) St George's Chapel
opp. Car Park No 2
Sun M: 12.30 Hds M: 7.30, 12.30 and 6pm.
For further information **Tel: 020 8745 4261** See Parish Directory **London Airport**

CHURCHES NEAR RAILWAY STATIONS

CANNON STREET; FENCHURCH STREET; LONDON BRIDGE;
The English Martyrs, 26 Prescot Street. *(Tower Hill)*
CHARING CROSS; Corpus Christi, 1 Maiden Lane *(Maiden Lane)*
EUSTON; ST PANCRAS; KING'S CROSS; St Aloysius, Phoenix Road *off Eversholt Street* *(Somers Town)*
HOLBORN St Etheldreda's, Ely Place, Holborn Circus *(Ely Place)*
LONDON BRIDGE Our Lady of La Salette & St Joseph 14 Melior Street SE1
Tel: 020 7407 1948 *(Diocese of Southwark)*
KING'S CROSS; The Blessed Sacrament, 165 Copenhagen Street *off York Way* *(Copenhagen Street)*
LIVERPOOL STREET; St Mary Moorfields, 4-5 Eldon Street *(Moorfields)*
MARYLEBONE; PADDINGTON; Our Lady of the Rosary, 211 Old Marylebone Road *(Marylebone)*
VICTORIA; Westminster Cathedral, Victoria Street
WATERLOO; St Patrick's, 26 Cornwall Road, Waterloo *(Diocese of Southwark)* Tel 020 7928 4818

POSTAL DISTRICTS

Parishes are listed according to the postal address of the church or presbytery; postal district numbers following the name of a parish indicate that parts of those districts also are within the parish. Postal districts south of the River Thames (Diocese of Southwark) or east of the River Lea (Diocese of Brentwood) are not included.

N1	Copenhagen Street
N1	Hoxton E2, EC2, EC1
N1	Islington EC1
N1	Kingsland N5, N16, E8
N1	Polish Church
N2	Finchley (East) N3, N6, N12, NW11
N3	Finchley (Church End) N12, NW11, NW7
N4	Manor House
N4	Harringay N8
N4	Tollington Park N7, N19
N5	Highbury N4
N7	Holloway N5, N19
N8	Stroud Green N4, N19
N9	Lower Edmonton N13, N18, N21
N10	Muswell Hill N2
N11	New Southgate N13, N14, N20, N22
N12	Finchley (North) N3, N20
N13	Palmers Green N14, N21
N14	Cockfosters N21
N15	Stamford Hill N16, E5
N15	West Green N8, N17, N22
N16	Stoke Newington N4
N17	Tottenham
N19	Highgate N6, N8, NW5
N19	Upper Holloway
N20	Whetstone N12
N22	Wood Green N8, N11, N17
NW1	Somers Town WC1
NW1	Laxton Place
NW1	Marylebone W1, W2
NW1	Camden Town N1, N7
NW2	Cricklewood NW3, NW11, NW6
NW2	Dollis Hill NW10

NW3	Hampstead
NW3	Swiss Cottage NW6, NW8
NW4	Hendon NW7, NW9
NW5	Haverstock Hill NW3, NW1
NW5	Kentish Town NW1, N7, N19
NW6	Kilburn NW2, NW8
NW6	Kilburn West
NW7	Mill Hill
NW8	St John's Wood NW1, W2, W9
NW9	Grahame Park
NW9	Hendon (West) NW4
NW9	Kingsbury Green
NW10	Kensal Rise NW6
NW10	Neasden
NW10	Stonebridge
NW10	Willesden
NW10	Willesden Green NW2, NW6
NW11	Golders Green NW3, N2
E1	Commercial Road
E1	German Church
E1	Tower Hill EC3
E1	Underwood Road E2
E1	Wapping
E2	Bethnal Green E1
E2	Lithuanian Church
E3	Bow
E3	Bow Common E14
E3	Mile End E1
E5	Clapton E8, N16
E5	Clapton Park E9
E9	Hackney E8
E9	Homerton E5
E14	Limehouse
E14	Millwall
E14	Poplar
EC1	Bunhill Row
EC1	Clerkenwell WC1, N1
EC1	Ely Place EC4
EC1	Italian Church
EC2	Moorfields EC1, EC3, EC4, E1
SW1	Westminster Cathedral
SW1	Pimlico
SW3	Chelsea (St Mary) SW1
SW3	Chelsea (Holy Redeemer) SW10
SW6	Fulham
SW6	Parsons Green
SW6	Stephendale Road
SW7	Oratory SW1, SW3, W2, W8
SW10	Fulham Road SW3, SW5, SW7
W1	Farm Street SW1
W1	Ogle Street WC1
W1	Soho Square EC1, WC2
W1	Spanish Place
W1	Ukrainian Cathedral
W1	Warwick Street SW1
W2	Bayswater W11
W2	Paddington
W2	Queensway
W3	Acton
W3	East Acton NW10, W10, W12
W3	West Acton W5
W3	Gunnersbury W5
W4	Chiswick
W4	Grove Park
W5	Ealing W13
W5	Polish Church
W6	Brook Green W12, W14
W6	Hammersmith SW6
W7	Hanwell W13
W8	Kensington (O.L.V.) SW5, W11, W14
W8	Kensington (Carmelites) SW5, SW7, W11
W9	Harrow Road
W10	Kensal New Town W9
W10	St Charles Square
W11	Notting Hill W10
W12	Polish Church
W12	Shepherd's Bush W3, W6
W12	White City
W13	Northfields W5, W7
WC2	French Church
WC2	Lincoln's Inn Fields EC4, WC1
WC2	Maiden Lane SW1

Fr Philip Dayer RIP

Fr Philip Dayer died on 30 January 2005 at Nazareth House, Hammersmith. Born on 27 June 1912 in Brondesbury to Richard and Jane he was one of three sons and is survived by his brothers. He was educated at the Haberdashers Askes School from 1923 to 1930 and after attending St Edmund's, Ware, he was ordained priest by Cardinal Hinsley on 6 June 1937 in Westminster Cathedral where he had his first appointment. Mobilised into the Territorial Army in August 1939 just days before the declaration of war he was involved in both the Dunkirk Evacuation and the Normandy Invasion. Unfortunately he had been wounded and had to be brought back to Scotland. After 7 years he was demobilised and returned to the Cathedral. He was appointed assistant priest at Our Most Holy Redeemer, Chelsea in 1947 and in September 1958 he was instrumental in the building of the new parish of St Gregory the Great, South Ruislip, remaining there as parish priest until his retirement in 1984. He had hoped to write something of the parish's history but sadly his health deteriorated before he was able to do this. His Funeral Mass took place at Our Lady and St Benedict, Wooton Wawen, Warwickshire and Fr Patrick Sayles SSC was the chief celebrant. May he rest in peace.

Fr John Taylor, RIP

Fr John Taylor died on 28 February 2005. Born on 1 January 1930 in Preston he was one of five children to George and Elizabeth. Bertram, his twin brother, five minutes younger, is a priest of the Lancaster Diocese. He was educated at the English Martyrs School, Preston and attended the Junior Seminary at St Mary's College, Grange over Sands until 1949, moving to the Novitiate in Clermont, France and St Joseph's Seminary, Upton Hall, Newark where he was ordained for the Holy Ghost Fathers on 30 October 1955 He was incardinated into the Westminster Diocese in 1990.

From 1956 to 1985 he served in the missions in Nigeria. He was Sub Novice Master and Bursar at St Joseph's Novitiate and teacher and Rector of St James' Seminary in Makurdi. In 1979 he was appointed Administrator to the Holy Ghost Cathedral, Makurdi. In 1986 he was recalled to the Provincial House at Bickley, Kent where he was assigned to the work of 'Appeals'. His first appointment in Westminster was as assistant priest at St Agnes Cricklewood under Fr Bert Haines. In 1992 he became parish priest at Our Lady of Willesden fostering a great devotion to Our Lady and renovating the Shrine Chapel. In 2000 he moved to Baldock where he remained until retirement in 2003. An extremely kind and courteous person he was an exemplary pastoral priest with a good sense of humour. His Funeral Mass was on 9 March at St Thomas of Canterbury and the English Martyrs, Preston, Bishop Alan Hopes was the chief celebrant and preacher. There was a Memorial Mass on 12 March at Our Lady of Willesden at which Bishop George Stack was chief celebrant and Fr Terry Tastard preached. May he rest in peace.

Fr Charles Connor RIP

Fr Charles Connor died on 17 March 2005 at Nazareth House, Hammersmith. Born in Bow on 10 November 1912 to David and Miriam he was ordained after training at Allen Hall, Ware on 29 June 1936 serving at Golders Green, Millwall, Westminster Cathedral and East Finchley. In 1957 he became Administrator at Isleworth and was then parish priest of Shepperton from 1969 until his retirement in 1986. He celebrated his Golden Jubilee of Ordination in 1986 at Westminster Cathedral with the other Jubilarians. He was a priest of good humour, ease of manner and great courtesy with a record of devoted service to the Diocese. His Funeral Mass during the week of Easter was held at Our Lady of Sorrows and St Bridget of Sweden, Isleworth, celebrated by Bishop James O'Brien. May he rest in peace.

Fr Charles Mercer, RIP

Fr Charles Mercer died at St Raphael's Nursing Home, Danehill, East Sussex on 10 May 2005. Born on 7 December 1924 in Bermondsey he was educated at St James School, Finchley where he later served as a school governor on two occasions. He studied for the priesthood in Lisbon and Allen Hall, Ware and was ordained on 17 July 1949 by Archbishop Myers. He served as assistant priest at Bow, Wembley, Welwyn Garden City and Bushey and in 1967 was appointed parish priest of Cranford where he was instrumental in the design and building of the parish. During his time there he was also part time chaplain at London Airport. In 1978 he became parish priest of Willesden Green, followed in 1981 by Cheshunt, in 1982 by Grahame Park and 1987 by Isleworth. In 1996 he moved to West Drayton where he is remembered as having taken Holy Communion daily to the sick and housebound. From 1999 to 2003 he was Chaplain at Nazareth House, Isleworth. Due to the burden of advancing years he then moved to St Raphael's Nursing Home where, because of his lack of mobility, he was enabled to get around the grounds on an electric scooter provided by Fr James Mallon. Always a social person with a great sense of humour he used to quote Cardinal Hume's words to him that his faults were known publicly but the Cardinal's were between him and God! His Funeral Mass was at St George's Retreat, Burgess Hill (followed by burial there) on 19 May. Bishop George Stack was the chief celebrant and Fr Mallon preached. A Memorial Mass was held at Cranford on 5 July when Bishop Alan Hopes was chief celebrant. May he rest in peace.

Father David Roderick, RIP

Fr David Roderick died on 27 July 2005. He had been ill for over a year, suffering from prostate cancer and a heart condition bearing both with courage and cheerfulness. Born in 1937 in Kingsbury of an Irish mother and a Welsh father he was educated at Finchley Catholic Grammar School and Lincoln College, Oxford, where he read English. He went to St Edmund's, Ware, in 1960 and was ordained priest by Cardinal Heenan in the College chapel on 4 June 1966. He served at St John's Wood, Willesden (1970) and East Acton and then worked for five years in the London University Catholic Chaplaincy until 1979. Between 1980 and 1990 he lectured in Church History at Allen Hall, helping also at St Francis de Sales, Tottenham and occasionally lecturing at the Mill Hill Institute. After a year at Bunhill Row he spent fourteen years as assistant priest at St Ignatius, Sunbury. He wore his knowledge lightly and was unassuming as a person with a deep sensitivity especially towards the sick and housebound. His body was received into St Ignatius Sunbury where Bishop Hopes was the chief celebrant at the evening Mass. The Funeral Mass was held on the following day (9 August) when Bishop Stack was the chief celebrant. Fr David is survived by his sister Mrs Pat Suckling. May he rest in peace..

Canon Herbert Veal, RIP

Canon Bert Veal died on 22 July 2005 after a long and courageous struggle with Motor Neurone Disease. He was cared for by Fr Willie Skehan and the parishioners of St Joan of Arc, Highbury before being admitted to St Joseph's Hospice and then Nazareth House, Hammersmith for the final months of his life. Born near Harrogate in 1920, the family moved to Mill Hill in 1931. He was an Officer in the Royal Navy and, after the war, received the DSC for his outstanding contribution. He also served on board the Royal Vanguard. He studied for the priesthood at the Beda College in Rome and was ordained on 17 March 1956 to be assistant at SS Peter and Paul, Northfields. He was a Chaplain at Westminster Cathedral and was appointed Headmaster of the Choir School where he was held in high esteem by succeeding generations of pupils. In 1968, a time of great expansion in the number of new Catholic Schools and fast changing legislation in education, he became Diocesan Director of schools. He was appointed to the Cathedral Chapter in 1976 and also parish priest of Enfield where he was a hardworking priest who affirmed the laity in their ministry. His warmth and humanity as a pastor is still remembered as is his outreach to young people, especially to the pupils of St Ignatius College and St Anne's School, Palmers Green. Canon Bert had always had a desire to serve in Africa and in 1981 Cardinal Hume allowed him to travel to Freetown in Sierra Leone where he remained for the next ten years founding a Diocesan Youth programme in the poorer parts of the country. When he returned to England to be parish priest of St Mary's, Chelsea he continued to maintain his interest in and support for the developing world. He retired in 1996 but continued to serve in St John's Brentford, The Holy Name of the Sacred Heart and finally in Highbury. His body was received into St Joan of Arc's Church on 2 August when Bishop Bernard Longley was chief celebrant at the Mass. Bishop James O'Brien was chief celebrant at the Funeral Mass on the following day before Canon Bert's burial at Mill Hill Cemetery. May he rest in peace.

Fr Peter Latham, RIP

Fr Peter Latham died on 16 August 2005. Born to Peter and Anne on 25 February 1931 he had a brother Michael and sister Anne. He was a pupil at Cardinal Vaughan School from 1942 to 1949 and then studied at the Venerable English College and the Gregorian in Rome until 1956 attaining a Licentiate in Philosophy and was a Bachelor of Theology. Following ordination to the priesthood in Rome on 27 November 1955 he was then Assistant at South Harrow, Our Lady of Lourdes, Acton (1961-1965), Our Lady of Victories, Kensington and Lincoln's Inn Fields (1969-1973). He was then Parish Priest at Clapton Park, St Joseph's, Wembley (1977-1993), Ruislip (1993-2002) and then latterly Dean of Hillingdon. His other ministries were Chaplain of CMAC (1977-1995), Chair and Pilgrimage Director of the Society of Our Lady of Lourdes (1980-1993), Westminster Director of the Archconfraternity of St Stephen (1977-1984) becoming National Director in 1984.

Fr Peter's body was received into the Church of the Most Sacred Heart, Ruislip on 24 August and the Funeral Mass took place the following day. Bishop George Stack was the chief celebrant. Cremation was at Brakespear Crematorium. May he rest in peace.

Deacon Syd Adams, RIP

Syd Adams was ordained Deacon by Bishop Gerald Mahon at Our Lady of Apostles, Heston on 5 December 1976, one of a small group of men in the Diocese who were called to this ministry following the restoration of the Permanent Diaconate after the Second Vatican Council. Syd was born in Bow on 28 July 1912. A life-long friend of his from schooldays and a great influence was Charles Mercer who was later ordained a priest in the Diocese. Syd was received into the Church as a teenager. After the Second World War, when he served as a gunner, he married Pat; though they had no children Pat's support was immense. They moved to Heston where Syd's skills as an accountant were put to the service of the White Fathers and subsequently in assisting Canon Moore, the new Parish Priest. Syd was active in training and organising the altar servers with whom he had an easy rapport. On taking early retirement he was asked by Canon Moore to consider becoming a Permanent Deacon and began full-time training at Allen Hall. He continued his ministry at Heston until increasing frailty of both he and Pat led to a move to Nazareth House, Isleworth, where Fr Mercer was Chaplain. Following Pat's death and the closure of the home, Syd spent his last years peacefully and happily at the Maryville Care Home, run by the Servants of the Mother of God. There he was held in much affection and on key days was able to put on his dalmatic and stole and take part in the liturgies. He died on 28 July 2005. May he rest in peace.

Fr Bernard Lang, RIP

Fr Bernard Lang died on 26 September 2005 whilst out for his usual jog in the local park. He suffered a massive heart attack and was found by local police but because he had no identification on him it was ten days before his body was identified. He was 74 years old. Ordained by Bishop David Konstant on 13 December 1980 he had served as Assistant at Barnet (1980), Ware Carmel as Chaplain (1983), Garston (1984), St Elizabeth's Convent, Much Hadham as Chaplain (1985), Hatfield as Parish Priest (1989), Lincoln's Inn Fields and Maiden Lane (1992), Clapton (1993), Parishes in Yorkshire (1994), Muswell Hill (1996) and Our Lady of Willesden (1997). He had a strong personality and forthright character with a well informed mind and stimulating conversation. A gifted preacher with a passion for justice, he was very musical with an excellent singing voice. As a private person he enjoyed his own company and was fascinated by astronomy – even setting up a telescope on the stairway at Allen Hall when he was a student. He loved his native Yorkshire and his holidays in Scotland. He retired in 2004 and supplied throughout the Diocese, looking after the community at Broadfields until just after Easter 2005. His Funeral Mass was at St Monica's, Palmers Green (near where he lived in a warden controlled flat) on 18 October. Bishop George Stack was the chief celebrant. May he rest in peace.

Fr Ben Morgan, RIP

Fr Ben died peacefully on 22 October 2005 in the Tonbridge Wells Nursing Home where he had been living. His brother, Douglas, and sister, Llyan, were with him. Born on Christmas Day 1928 to John and Elizabeth he attended the local Church of England School and then the Grammar School in the Wirral where the family had moved in 1938. He studied medicine at Liverpool University where under the influence of the Jesuit chaplain he decided to become a Catholic. He was received by Fr John Lang at Farm Street in 1955 and began to consider a vocation to the priesthood. Encouraged by Fr Wilfred Gayne at Bayswater he joined the Oblates of St Charles. He studied for the priesthood at the Franciscan Study Centre in East Bergholt and was ordained in Westminster Cathedral by Cardinal Godfrey on 27 May 1961. He served at Bayswater (1961- 1968), Paddington (1969-1974) and Kingsway (1975-1980). He joined the Catholic Missionary Society in 1975 and became its Director in 1977. He became Spiritual Director at Allen Hall in 1981 and Parish Priest at Willesden in 1984. Sadly Fr Ben suffered a series of strokes which proved a serious hindrance to pastoral ministry causing him to resign in 1992 but he continued supply and retreat work in the Diocese. In 1997 and 2002 further strokes left him blind and severely disabled. He bore increasing infirmity with patience and faith. A gentle, sensitive, intelligent and dedicated priest he was cared for by his brother and sister and the priests and people around the Nursing Homes in Kent where he resided. His Funeral Mass was on 31 October at St Augustine's, Tonbridge Wells. Bishop George Stack was the chief celebrant and Fr Brian Ward preached. May he rest in peace.

DIOCESAN CLERGY ANNIVERSARIES

JANUARY

1	Cardinal Francis Bourne (1935) Fr Brendan Soane (2000)
2	Fr Sidney Dommersen (1970) Fr Alexander Wells (1970) Fr Cyril Wilson (1988)
3	Fr Samuel Reddy (1958) Fr Donald Campbell (1985) Fr Denis Cantwell (1995)
4	Fr Bernard Canham (1990) Fr William Brown (2001)
6	Fr Thomas McNamara (1976) Fr Thomas Anderson (1974)
7	Fr John T Carberry (1988)
8	Fr John Kearsey (2004)
10	Mgr Ernest T Bassett (1990) Fr William Kahle (1993)
11	Mgr Eustace Bernard (1972)
12	Fr Arthur P Mintern (1993)
13	Fr Francis Dent (1963)
14	Cardinal Henry Manning (1892) Fr Peter Lyons (1998)
15	Canon James Hathway (1976)
16	Fr Edward Hinsley (1976)
17	Fr George O'Connor (1989) Fr Edward Dering Leicester (1977)
18	Fr Gerry Ennis (2000)
19	Fr Oldrich Trnka (2003)
20	Mgr George Leonard (1993) Fr Thomas Gardner (1995)
21	Preb Ronald Pilkington (1975)
22	Cardinal William Godfrey (1963)
23	Fr Derek Jennings (1995)
25	Canon William Heffernan (1965) Fr Bernard Fisher (1990)
26	Bishop Patrick Casey (1999)
29	Fr Frederick Vincent (1973)
30	Fr Joseph Fehrenbach (1985) Fr Patrick Howard (2000) Fr Philip Dayer (2005)

FEBRUARY

1	Fr Harold Gadsden (1972) Mgr Edward Dunderdale (2001)
2	Fr Charles Lowe (1978) Bishop Philip Harvey (2003)
3	Fr Hugh Bishop (1984)
6	Fr Patrick McEvoy (1974) Canon William Ward (1993) Canon Daniel Kay (2003)
7	Fr Bernard Ferry (1970) Fr George Haines (2000) Fr Harold Riley (2003)
9	Canon George Groves (1997)
11	Fr Alan Body (1988)
12	Fr Joseph Francis (1984) Canon Edward Armitage (1987) Mgr Canon Francis Bartlett (1992)
13	Fr Patrick O'Callaghan (1970) Mgr Canon Maurice Kelleher (1994)
15	Cardinal Nicholas Wiseman (1865) Fr Richard Wakeling (1988) Fr Leo Straub (2000)
16	Mgr Bernard Chapman (1999) Fr John Kirwin (2003)
20	Fr Joseph Scholles (1983)
21	Fr Michael Hollings (1997) Canon Peter Bourne (2001)
23	Canon John O'Callaghan (1981)
24	Mgr Canon Arthur Rivers (1978)
25	Fr Charles McMenemy (1976) Fr Archibald Bardney (1985) Fr Andrew Clancy (1986)
27	Fr Nicholas Lambert (1976) Canon Michael Richards (1997)
28	Fr Joseph Gilligan (1990) Fr John Taylor (2005)
29	Fr Frank Rochla (1992)

MARCH

6	Mgr Frederick Row (1974) Mgr Canon Clement Parsons (1980)
7	Fr Henry Dodd (1992) Fr Harold Riley (2003)
8	Fr Thomas Nobbs (1977)
9	Fr Paul Lenihan (1992)
13	Fr Patrick English (1971)
14	Bishop David Cashman (1971) Canon Jeremiah Galvin (1973) Fr Reginald Watt (1975)
15	Bishop George Craven (1967) Fr Walter Donovan (1981)
17	Cardinal Arthur Hinsley (1943) Fr Michael Buckley (1993) Fr Lionel Keane (1997) Fr Charles Connor (2005)
20	Canon Desmond Swan (1995) Fr Edward Bushey (1996)
21	Fr James de Felice (1978)
22	Fr Edward Higgs (1988)
24	Fr John Gill (1985)
25	Mgr Richard Kenefeck (1982)
30	Fr William Hutchinson (1984)

APRIL

3	Fr Francis Kenney (1987)
4	Fr Peter Dunn (1974)
5	Fr Albert Parisotti (1970) Fr David Evans (1989)
7	Fr John Keep (2002)
9	Fr Thomas Hookham (1998) Fr Ronald Cox (1994) Fr James Wooloughan (2003)
10	Mgr Canon John MT Barton (1977) Fr Brian Laycock (2004)
11	Fr John Bebb (1975)
12	Fr John Mills (1975)
13	Fr Albert Davey (1987)
14	Fr Michael Hendry (1994)
16	Mgr Canon Lancelot Long (1978) Fr Clement Tigar (1976) Fr Bernard McGuinness (1978)
17	Canon Lionel Dove (1971)
19	Fr Joseph McEntee (1978) Canon Harold Winstone (1987)
20	Fr Patrick Smyth (1978)
22	Fr Herbert Crees (1974) Fr Robert Tollemach (1998) Fr John Robson (2000)
23	Canon Frank Martin (2002)
24	Canon Clement Rochford (1978) Fr Derek McClughen (1991)
25	Canon Francis Hegarty (2004)
27	Fr Stanley Harrison (1973) Mgr John F. McDonald (1992)
28	Canon John Longstaff (1986)
29	Fr Michael Moriarty (1996)

MAY

2	Fr John Coughlan (1997) Fr John Farrelly (1990) Fr Francis Finnegan (1999)
4	Fr Peter Lowry (1972) Fr Raymond Tomalin (1996)
5	Canon Herbert Welchman (1982) Fr Denys Lucas (1995)
6	Fr John Hathway (1995) Fr Anthony Potter (2003)
7	Fr Alastair Russell (1997)
9	Fr Bernard Lagrue (1995)
10	Fr Patrick Keegan (1992) Canon Denis Britt-Compton (2002) Fr Charles Mercer (2005) Mgr Canon Oliver Kelly (1995)
11	Fr Thomas Kean (1981)
13	Mgr Stephen Shaw (1998)
14	Fr Peter Boshell (1993)
15	Fr William O Brien (2004)
18	Fr Kenneth Dale Roberts,
20	Fr Stanislaus Savage (1975)
22	Fr Ronald Richardson (1999) Fr Charles MacMahon (2003)
23	Fr Bernard Bussy (1992) Fr Hugh McAleese (1994)
24	Fr Denis Ward (1978) Fr Michale Garvey (2002) Fr Denis Nottingham (2002) Fr Philip Rogers (1995)
25	Mgr Canon John Bagshawe (1971) Mgr Denis McGuinness (1993) Fr John Oldland (1995)
26	Canon Patrick J Murphy (1974) Fr John Murray (1995)
30	Fr Albert Purdie (1976)
31	Canon Reginald Crook (1990) Fr John Luke (2003) Fr Kevin Greene (2004)

JUNE

1	Fr Philip Carpenter (1992) Bishop Victor Guazzelli (2004)
2	Fr Stephen Finnegan (1993) Fr Damien McManus (1997)
7	Fr John O'Connell (1970)
11	Fr Vincent McCarthy (1974) Fr Francis Davis (2003)
13	Canon Alfonso de Zulueta (1980)
14	Fr George Lee (1987)
17	Cardinal Basil Hume OSB (1999)
19	Cardinal Herbert Vaughan (1903)
21	Fr J Brian Campbell (1983)
22	Fr Anthony Turbett (2000)
26	Fr John Moran (1988) Mgr Canon Roderick More O'Ferrall (1991)
27	Fr Raleigh Addington, (1980)
28	Fr Cuthbert Boddy (1970) Canon Denis Crowley (1980)
30	Fr Edmund R J Henry, (1971) Fr William Anderson (1972)

JULY

3	Fr William M. Brown (1989)
4	Fr Joseph Anthony Carr (1999)
7	Canon Alfred Cuming (1978) Fr John Power (2002) Fr Frank Morrall (1995)
8	Fr Joseph Gardner (1992)
9	Fr Christopher Pemberton (1983) Fr John Norton (1989)
10	Fr Peter Harris (1976) Fr Thomas Kelly (1983)
12	Fr Daniel Higgins (1996)
14	Mgr Canon Joseph Williams (1991)
15	Fr Christopher McKenna (2003)
16	Fr Michael Giffney (1987) Canon John McKenzie (1988)
19	Fr Peter Pearson (1971)
21	Fr Anthony O'Sullivan (1997) Canon Philip Moore (1976) Fr Norman Kersey (1999) Canon Herbert Veal (2005)
26	Fr George Fonseca (1998) Fr David Roderick (2005)
27	Fr Graham Feint (2000)
28	Fr Ralph Gardner (1976) Fr Patrick Whyte (1988) Rev Sydney Adams (2005)
30	Fr Calum MacLean (1982) Fr Vincent Commerford (1997)
31	Fr Albert Vaughan (1995)

AUGUST

1	Fr Richard Johnson (1992) Fr Ignatius Tonna (1993)
2	Fr Thomas Stack (1984)
3	Mgr Canon John Mostyn (1981)
5	Fr William Lynagh (1977)
9	Fr John Greene (1980)
11	Fr Laurence Allan (1981)
12	Fr Roderick Cuming (1981) Fr Wilfrid Soggee (1990) Fr Joseph Finnegan (2002) Fr John Milne (2001)
14	Fr Philip Dwerryhouse (1986)
15	Fr John Adam (1979) Fr Bernard Mortimore (1980)
16	Canon Denis O'Sullivan (1983) Fr Peter Latham (2005)
19	Canon George Davey (1986) Fr Leslie Cole (1997)
20	Cardinal Bernard Griffin (1956) Fr Joseph McVeigh (1977) Fr Desmond Mullin (1988)
21	Fr Percival Fielden (1990)
25	Fr James Gunston (1972) Mgr Canon Herbert Haines (2004)
26	Fr Thomas Kilcoyne (1972) Fr Peter Keenan (1984)
27	Mgr John Coonan (1979)
29	Fr Edward Fowler (1973) Fr Michael Lynam (1984)
31	Fr William Rees (1984) Canon Maurice O'Leary (1997)

SEPTEMBER

2	Fr Gerard Strain (1980)
4	Fr John O'Neil (1971)
6	Canon Michael Roberts (2004)
7	Canon John F Marriott (1977)
11	Mgr Cuthbert Collingwood (1980) Fr William Erby (1974) Fr James Whitehead (1983)
12	Fr Leslie Wood (1984)
13	Archbishop Edward Myers (1956)
14	Fr William Ruhman (1978) Fr Leonard Collingwood (1985)
15	Fr Brian Connaughton (1979)
16	Canon Nicholas Kelly (1988)
17	Fr Frederick Thomas (1986) Fr John Pakenham (1987)
18	Canon John L Wright (1978)
20	Bishop Christopher Butler OSB (1986)
21	Fr George Ingram (1992)
23	Fr Godfrey Wilson (1998)
26	Fr James Loughnane (1993) Fr Bernard Lang (2005)
28	Fr Robert Newbery (1981) Fr Gerard Barry (1998)
30	Fr Michael O'Dwyer (1977)
30	Fr Joseph Murray (1989)

OCTOBER

2	Canon Des Sheehan (2004)
5	Fr John Fleming (1974) Fr Walter Meyjes (1987)
6	Fr Denis Murphy (1999)
7	Fr Thomas Daniel (1984)
8	Fr Thomas Allan (1982)
10	Fr Norman Fergusson (1986)
11	Fr Joseph Davey (1970)
12	Fr James Finn (1977) Canon John P. Murphy (1989)
14	Fr Henry Bryant (1972) Fr John Woods (2002)
16	Mgr Canon Terence Keenan (1984)
18	Fr John Eveleigh Woodruff (1976) Fr John Murphy (2005)
19	Fr John Farrell (1983)
21	Fr Richard Berry (1989)
22	Fr David Cullen (1974) Fr Herbert Keldany (1988) Fr Ben Morgan (2005)
23	Fr Joseph O'Hear (1970) Fr Joe Gibbons (2002)
24	Fr John Halvey (1990)
25	Fr Andrew Moore (1994)
26	Fr John Clayton (1992) Fr George Talbot (2004)
27	Fr Colin Kilby (1985)
29	Canon Leo Ward (1970) Fr Joseph Eldridge (1993)
30	Canon William Gordon (1976)

NOVEMBER

1	Fr Horace Tennant (2000)
2	Mgr Canon George Tomlinson (1985) Fr Terence Brady (1989)
5	Fr Eric Chadwick (1993)
6	Fr Peter Geraerts (1980)
7	Cardinal John Heenan (1975) Canon Charles Carr (1985) Fr Raymond Geraerts (1995)
8	Fr Jeremiah Ryan (2001)
9	Fr George Barringer (1978) Fr James Ethrington (1981)
10	Fr Richard M. Sutherland (1974) Fr John Spencer (1980)
12	Fr James R. Coughlan (1974) Fr Peter Johnson (2000)
14	Fr Maurice Ryan (1983) Canon Louis Marteau (2002)
15	Fr James Stephenson (1970)
16	Fr Ian Dommerson (1996)
17	Fr Samuel Steer (1996)
22	Mgr Reginald Butcher (1976) Fr Christopher Fullerton (1980)
24	Canon Edmund Hadfield (1982)
25	Fr Joseph Doyle (1978) Canon Joseph Geraerts (1979)
26	Fr James Woodward (1976) Fr William Wood (1986)
27	Fr Joseph Scally (1995)
30	Canon Arthur Welland (1978)

DECEMBER

3	Fr Harold Purney (1983)
4	Fr John Simcox (1972) Fr Peter Allen (1978) Fr Benedict Westbrook (1989) Mgr Wilfrid Purney (1987)
6	Fr John Harper-Hill (1998) Mgr Alexander Groves (1998)
11	Fr Dalton Haughey (1991)
12	Fr Laurence Kingseller (1975)
13	Fr Jeremiah Daly (1974)
15	Fr Francis Donovan (1983)
16	Mgr George Tancred (2002)
18	Canon Bernard George (1980)
19	Canon John Shaw (1981) Fr Edward Gwilliams (1981) Fr William Campling (1996) Fr Edward Scanlan (1992)
21	Fr Clive Godwin (1974)
24	Fr Manoel Gomes (1989)
26	Fr Alan O'Connor (1992) Fr Bernard Lavin (1999)
27	Fr Andrew Morley (1993)
28	Mgr Canon Joseph Collings (1978) Fr Gerard Mulvahey (1996)
29	Fr Robert Bradley (1976)
30	Canon Alexander Stewart (1976)
31	Fr Wilfrid Trotman (1976) Fr Stephen Rigby (1978) Fr George Swanton (1979) Fr Dennis Skelly (1996) Fr Michael Ware (1998)

May they rejoice for ever in the vision of the mysteries
which they have faithfully ministered here on earth.

Obituaries from previous Year Books
and dates for those who died before 1970
are all on our website
www.westminsteryearbook.org.uk

Open the Doors

This parish-based Diocesan Festival will show our Diocese as a single body, which thinks together, works together and plans its future together.

His Eminence Cormac Murphy-O'Connor
Archbishop of Westminster

The year 2006 will be a great opportunity for the whole Diocese to unite and celebrate the life of our parishes and communities. It will give us the opportunity to look back, with joy, on the journey we have made so far as well as looking confidently ahead at what we are invited to become. The whole year will encourage the Diocese to embrace our common vision, which we will begin to discover in the White Paper, and in which we all have our part to play. The Cardinal is asking every parish to use **Lent 2006** as a time to look at the principles that will underlay the White Paper. Booklets will be available to help everyone get involved.

The ***Open the Doors*** festival will be a weekend of activity, outreach and celebration for the whole Diocese. We will show the life of our parishes/communities to the wider community so that together we can more deeply discover the richness of the Catholic Faith.

Your parish or community is invited to take part in the festival by hosting an event during the weekend of 14th-16th July (or in the week preceding). Events may include themed liturgies, talks, prayer, plays, out reach projects, exhibitions, music evenings - to name but a few examples.

Preparation is a major reason for having the festival itself. Use this festival as a way of building stronger relationships with other parishes, schools and communities of the Diocese.

- Parishes can work together in their Deaneries
- Parishes can work with local schools and religious communities
- Parishes can welcome other parishes to use their facilities
- Parishes and Communities can draw on the talents of the ecclesial movements, agencies and organisations in our Diocese.

Altogether this is a great opportunity to strengthen the bonds of communion between individuals, parishes, deaneries and across the whole Diocese. If we can do that well, we offer a powerfully united witness to the rest of society around us.

Let us ***Open the Doors*** this year to let the world know the gifts we have in abundance!

THE CYCLE OF PRAYER

The liturgical year has been divided into six periods. We are asked to use the intentions during the current period, both corporately and in personal prayer, as well as on specific Days of Prayer. Parish Priests are asked to make the Cycle known by displaying and distributing copies in their churches, and to issue a reminder when a new period of the Cycle begins. When a Day of Special Prayer occurs on a Sunday, it is sufficient at Mass to announce the Day during the opening remarks and to include a suitable petition in the General Intercessions.
Photocopiable prayer leaflets are available from
Liturgy Office, 39 Eccleston Square SW1V 1PL Tel: 020 7821 0553 Fax: 020 7630 5166

ADVENT/CHRISTMAS 2005

We are asked to pray for these intentions:
Openness to the Word of God; Migrants and Refugees; Expectant Mothers.

Migrants' Day	Saturday	3 December
Bible Sunday	2nd Sunday of Advent	4 December
Expectant Mothers	especially on 4th Sunday of Advent	18 December

ORDINARY TIME: WINTER 2006

We are asked to pray for these intentions:
Peace on Earth, Christian Unity, The Sick and those who care for them;
Students and Teachers; The Unemployed

Peace Day	(2nd Sunday of the Year)	15 January
Octave of Prayer for Christian Unity	18 – 25 January	
World Day for the Sick	Saturday 11 February	
Education Day	3 Sundays before Lent	12 January
Europe	Tuesday 14 February (SS Cyril & Methodius)	
Day for the Unemployed	Sunday before Lent	26 February

LENT 2006

We are asked to pray for these intentions:
Candidates for the Sacraments, (especially on the Sundays of Lent); Women;
The Needy and Hungry of the World; Penitents and Wanderers.

Women's World Day of Prayer	1st Friday in March	3 March
CAFOD Lent Fast Day	Friday, 1st Week of Lent	10 February

EASTER 2006

We are asked to pray for these intentions:
New Members of the Church; Vocations; The Right Use of the Media; the Church;
Human Work.

Europe	Saturday	29 April (St Catherine of Siena)
St Joseph the Worker	Saturday	1 May
World Day of Prayer for Vocations	4th Sunday of Easter	7 May
World Communications Day	Sunday after Ascension	28 May
The Church	especially at Pentecost	4 June

ORDINARY TIME: SUMMER 2006

We are asked to pray for these intentions:
A Deeper Understanding between Christians and Jews; Those who suffer Persecution, Oppression and Denial of Human Rights; Europe; Human Life; Seafarers.

Those who suffer Persecution, Oppression and Denial of Human Rights on:

	SS John Fisher & Thomas More	22 June
Europe on	St Benedict	11 July
	St Bridget of Sweden	23 July
	St Teresa Benedicta of the Cross	9 August
A deeper understanding between Christians and Jews		
	St Teresa Benedicta of the Cross	9 August
Day for Life	1st Sunday in July	2 July
Sea Sunday	2nd Sunday in July	9 July

ORDINARY TIME: AUTUMN 2006

We are asked to pray for these intentions:
The Spread of the Gospel; The Harvest; the Fruits of Human Work, and the Reverent Use of Creation; Justice and Peace in the World; All Victims of War; Young People; Prisoners and their Families.

Racial Justice Day	2nd Sunday in September	10 September
Home Mission Day	3rd Sunday in September	17 September
World Mission Day	penultimate Sunday in October	22 October
The Harvest	Sunday 22–28 September or whenever harvest festivals are held	24 September
Harvest Fast Day	1st Friday in October	6 October
Remembrance Sunday	2nd Sunday in November	12 November
Prisoners' Week	9 – 15 November	
Day of Prayer for Prisoners and their Dependants		
	3rd Sunday in November	19 November
Youth Day	Christ the King	26 November

ADVENT/CHRISTMAS 2006

We are asked to pray for these intentions: Openness to the Word of God; Migrants and Refugees; Expectant Mothers.

Migrants' Day	Sunday	3 December
Bible Sunday	2nd Sunday of Advent	10 December
Expectant Mothers	especially on 4th Sunday of Advent	24 December

The six periods of the Cycle of Prayer for the year are each repeated in the Liturgical Calendar below at the point in the year when the relevant period begins.
Dated Days of Prayer are repeated against the relevant date; the symbol § indicates a reference to the Cycle of Prayer.

LITURGICAL CALENDAR

Variations from the Universal Calendar

(1) New Proper Calendar for England

This has now received Recognitio from the Holy See (June 5, 2000). Recognitio has not yet been received for the Proper, but the Liturgy Office of the Bishops' Conference has prepared a booklet of biographical notes and suggested Commons, price £2.

In the Introduction to that booklet we read:

'The National Calendar for England was approved by our Bishops' Conference in 1993 and received Recognitio from the Holy See in June 2000. This expanded Calendar completely replaces the previous National Calendar of 1971. Though it is now a long time since there was a wide consultation of dioceses, this Calendar is the fruit of that process. There was a clear desire to produce a Calendar that was at the same time more representative of the rich English heritage of Saints and, following the wishes of the Holy See, was more restrained in the ranking of celebrations. It was also widely recognised that this was a heritage we shared with other denominations and so there was a desire, where possible, to harmonise calendars with them as an example of shared witness.

There is one Solemnity - St George - and the original intention was for only the Patrons of Ireland, Scotland and Wales to be Feasts. The bishops, after consultation with Rome, wished to raise SS Thomas More and John Fisher to the rank of Feast. The Holy See has since decided that all the Patrons of Europe be included in each National Calendar, and that each be celebrated as a Feast. The traditional date for some celebrations, such as St George, has necessitated the transfer or reclassification of some celebrations in the Universal Calendar.'

Where no indication of rank is given, the celebration is an optional memorial.

January 12	St Aelred of Rievaulx, Abbot		
January 19	St Wulstan, Bishop		
February 14	SS Cyril, Monk and Methodius, Bishop	Patrons of Europe	Feast
March 1	St David, Bishop,	Patron of Wales	Feast
March 17	St Patrick, Bishop	Patron of Ireland	Feast
April 21	St Anselm, Bishop & Doctor		
April 23	ST GEORGE, Martyr	Patron of England	Solemnity
April 24	St Adalbert, Bishop & Martyr		
	St Fidelis of Sigmaringen, Priest & Martyr		
April 29	St Catherine of Siena, Virgin & Doctor,	Patron of Europe	Feast
May 4	The English Martyrs		Memorial
May 19	St Dunstan, Bishop		
May 25	St Bede the Venerable, Priest & Doctor		Memorial
May 27	St Augustine of Canterbury		Memorial
June 5	St Boniface, Bishop & Martyr		Memorial
June 9	St Columba, Abbot		

June 16	St Richard of Chichester, Bishop		
June 20	St Alban, Protomartyr		Memorial
June 22	SS John Fisher & Thomas More, Martyrs		Feast
June 23	St Etheldreda (Audrey), Abbess		
July 1	St Oliver Plunkett, Bishop & Martyr		
July 11	St Benedict, Abbot	Patron of Europe	Feast
July 23	St Bridget, Religious	Patron of Europe	Feast
August 9	St Teresa Benedicta of the Cross (Edith Stein) Virgin & Martyr Patron of Europe		Feast
August 26	Blessed Dominic of the Mother of God, Priest		
August 30	SS Margaret Clitherow, Anne Line & Margaret Ward, Virgin, Martyrs		
August 31	St Aidan, Bishop, & the Saints of Lindisfarne		
September 3	St Gregory the Great, Pope & Doctor		Memorial
September 4	St Cuthbert, Bishop		
September 19	St Theodore of Canterbury, Bishop		
September 24	Our Lady of Walsingham		Memorial
October 10	St Paulinus of York, Bishop		
October 12	St Wilfrid, Bishop		
October 13	St Edward the Confessor		
October 26	SS Chad & Cedd, Bishops		
November 3	St Winefride, Virgin		
November 7	St Willibrord, Bishop		
November 16	St Edmund of Abingdon, Bishop St Margaret of Scotland		
November 17	St Hilda, Abbess St Hugh of Lincoln, Bishop St Elizabeth of Hungary, Religious		
November 30	St Andrew, Apostle,	Patron of Scotland	Feast
December 29	St Thomas Becket, Bishop & Martyr		

(2) Diocesan

In addition to the above, the following celebrations are observed in the Diocese of Westminster:

February 3	SS Laurence, Dunstan, Theodore, Archbishops of Canterbury	Memorial
April 19	St Alphege, Bishop	Memorial
April 24	SS Erkenwald & Mellitus, Bishops	Memorial
June 27	St John Southworth, Priest & Martyr	Memorial
July 1	Dedication of the Cathedral	Feast
October 13	St Edward the Confessor	Feast
October 29	Blessed Martyrs of Douai College	Memorial
November 16	St Edmund, Bishop	Memorial

(3) Recent Additions

The celebrations inserted into the General Calendar up to 1996 have already been taken account of in previous editions of the Westminster Year Book. The Calendar incorporated into the new Latin edition of the Missal has in addition the following celebrations, all optional memorials:

3 January	Most Holy Name of Jesus
8 February	St Josephine Bakhita, Virgin
13 May	Our Lady of Fatima
21 May	St Christopher Magallanes, Priest, & Companions, Martyrs
22 May	St Rita of Cascia, Religious
9 July	SS Augustine Zhao Rong, Priest, & Companions, Martyrs
20 July	St Apollinaris, Bishop & Martyr
24 July	St Charbel Makhluf, Priest
9 August	St Teresa Benedicta of the Cross, Virgin & Martyr (Feast in Europe)
12 August	St Jane Frances de Chantal (formerly 12 December)
12 September	Most Holy Name of Mary
25 November	St Catherine of Alexandria
9 December	St John Diego Cuahtlatoatzin
12 December	Our Lady of Guadalupe

(4) Local

Each church celebrates as a Solemnity its Feast of Title, and, if it is consecrated, the Anniversary of Dedication. These celebrations may, for pastoral reasons, be transferred to an ordinary Sunday or other suitable day.

Holydays of Obligation

currently observed in England and Wales are:

Epiphany, January 6

Ascension, Thursday in sixth week of Eastertide

Corpus Christi, Thursday after Trinity Sunday

SS Peter & Paul, June 29

Assumption of Our Lady, August 15

All Saints, November 1

Christmas Day, December 25

The Bishops' Conference has legislated that when a Holyday, other than Christmas, falls on a Saturday or a Monday, it shall be transferred to the Sunday.

Eucharistic Fast

Whoever is to receive the blessed Eucharist is to abstain for at least one hour before Holy Communion from all food and drink, with the sole exception of water and medicine. (Canon 919.1)

A priest who, on the same day, celebrates the blessed Eucharist twice or three times may consume something before the second or third celebration, even though there is not an hour's interval. (Canon 919.2)

The elderly, and those who are suffering from some illness, as well as those who care for them, may receive the blessed Eucharist even if within the preceding hour they have consumed something. (Canon 919.3)

Reception of the Eucharist a Second Time on the Same Day
In accordance with Canon 917 of the Code of Canon Law it is permitted to receive Holy Communion twice on one day provided this takes place during the celebration of Mass. This provision is to be observed except in the case of Viaticum for the dying.

Fasting and Abstinence
Statement by the Bishops of England and Wales on Canons 1249-1253 (24 Jan 1985)

1. The new Code of Canon Law reminds us that all of Christ's faithful are obliged to do penance. The obligation arises in imitation of Christ himself and in response to his call. During his life on earth, not least at the beginning of his public ministry, Our Lord undertook voluntary penance. He invited his followers to do the same. The penance he invited would be a participation in his own suffering, an expression of interior conversion and a form of reparation for sin. It would be a personal sacrifice made out of love for God and our neighbour. It follows that if we are to be true, as Christians, to the spirit of Christ, we must practise some form of penance.

2. So that all may be united with Christ and with one another in a common practice of penance, the Church sets aside certain penitential days. On these days the faithful are to devote themselves in a special way to prayer, self-denial and works of charity. Such days are not designed to confine or isolate penance but to intensify it in the life of the Christian right through the year.

3. Lent is the traditional season of renewal and repentance in Christ. The New Code reaffirms this. It also prescribes that Ash Wednesday and Good Friday are to be observed as days of fast and abstinence. Fasting means that the amount of food we eat is considerably reduced. Abstinence means that we give up a particular kind of food or drink or form of amusement. Those over eighteen are bound by the law of fasting until the beginning of their sixtieth year, while all over fourteen are bound by the law of abstinence. Priests and parents are urged to foster the spirit and practice of penance among those too young to be the subjects of either law.

4. Because each Friday recalls the crucifixion of Our Lord, it too is set aside as a special penitential day. The Church does not prescribe, however, that fish must be eaten on Fridays. It never did. Abstinence always meant the giving up of meat rather than the eating of fish as a substitute. What the Church does require, according to the new Code, is that its members abstain on Fridays from meat or from some other food or that they perform some alternative work of penance laid down by the Bishops' Conference.

5. In accordance with the mind of the Universal Church, the Bishops of England and Wales remind their people of the obligation of Friday penance, and instruct them that it may be fulfilled in one or more of the following ways:

a) by abstaining from meat or some other food
b) by abstaining from alcoholic drink, smoking or some form of amusement
c) by making the special effort involved in family prayer, taking part in the Mass, visiting the Blessed Sacrament or praying the Stations of the Cross
d) by fasting from all food for a longer period than usual and perhaps giving what is saved in this way to the needy at home and abroad
e) by making a special effort to help somebody who is poor, sick, old or lonely.

6. The form of penance we adopt each Friday is a matter of personal choice and does not have to take the same form every Friday. Failure to undertake this penance on a particular Friday would not constitute a sin. However, penance is part of the life of every Christian and the intention to do penance on Friday is of obligation. We are confident that the faithful of England and Wales will take this obligation to heart in memory of the passion and death of Our Lord.

Funeral Mass

A Funeral Mass may be celebrated on any day, except solemnities which are holydays of obligation, the last three days of Holy Week, and the Sundays of Advent, Lent, and Eastertide.

Masses for the Dead, Nuptial Masses, Ritual Masses, Masses and Prayers for Various Needs and Occasions, Votive Masses

For a detailed description of when these are permitted and of the texts to be used, see pages 14 - 20 of 'Order for the Celebration of Mass and the Liturgy of the Hours according to the Roman General Calendar, Liturgical Year 2005-2006', published by Centro Liturgico Vincenziano, Rome, 2005.

Choice of Eucharistic Prayer

Eucharistic Prayer IV has its own preface; together they form one integral text and so cannot be separated. Therefore any Mass with a proper preface precludes the use of Eucharistic Prayer IV.

Fulfilment of Obligation

The obligation of participating in the Mass is satisfied by one who assists at Mass wherever it is celebrated in a Catholic rite, either on the holyday itself or on the evening of the previous day. (Canon 1248.1)

Ranks of Celebration

There are three ranks of celebration: Solemnity, Feast, Memorial. These are indicated in the calendar by the typeface used, thus:

SOLEMNITY FEAST Memorial

Abbreviations

B	Black
G	Green
P	Purple
R	Red
RP	Rose Pink
W	White

\+ indicates Holy Day of Obligation

Ps on right of page = week of psalter

§ indicates reference to Cycle of Prayer

TABLE OF MOVEABLE FEASTS

	2006	**2007**	**2008**	**2009**	**2010**
Lectionary (Sunday/Weekday)	**B/II**	**C/I**	**A/II**	**B/I**	**C/II**
First Sunday of Advent	27 November 2005	3 December 20006	2 December 2007	30 November 2008	20 November 2009
Epiphany	6 January	7 January	6 January	6 January	6 January
Ash Wednesday	1 March	21 February	6 February	25 February	17 February
Easter Sunday	16 April	8 April	23 March	12 April	4 April
Ascension	25 May	17 May	1 May	21 May	13 May
Pentecost	4 June	27 May	11 May	31 May	23 May
The Body and Blood of Christ	15 June	7 June	22 May	11 June	3 June
St Peter & St Paul	29 June	29 June	29 June	29 June	29 June
Assumption	15 August	15 August	15 August	16 August	15 August
All Saints	1 November	1 November	2 November	1 Novembr	31 October
First Sunday of Advent	3 December	2 December	30 November	29 November	28 November

- **Bold entries** denote Holydays of Obligation in England and Wales. According to a decision of the Bishops' Conference Holydays which fall on Saturday or Monday are transferred to the Sunday.

- Table supplied by Liturgy Office for England and Wales: www.liturgyoffice.org.uk

NOVEMBER/DECEMBER 2005

§ CYCLE OF PRAYER – ADVENT/CHRISTMAS

We are asked to pray for these intentions:
Openness to the Word of God; Migrants and Refugees; Expectant Mothers.

Migrants' Day		Saturday 3 December
Bible Sunday		Sunday 4 December 2nd Sunday of Advent
Expectant Mothers	especially on	18 December 4th Sunday of Advent

Lectionary for Sundays and Feasts: Year B

NOVEMBER 2005

Date	Colour	Celebration	
27 Sun	P	+FIRST SUNDAY OF ADVENT *Creed, Advent Preface I*	*Ps Week I*
28 Mon	P	Advent feria	
29 Tues	P	Advent feria	
30 Wed	R	ST ANDREW, Apostle Patron of Scotland *Gloria, Preface of Apostles*	*national*

DECEMBER 2005

Date	Colour	Celebration	
01 Thurs	P	Advent feria	
02 Fri	P	Advent feria	
03 Sat	W	St Francis Xavier, Priest § Migrants' Day	
04 Sun	P	+ SECOND SUNDAY OF ADVENT *Creed, Advent Preface I* § Bible Sunday	*Ps Week 2*
05 Mon	P	Advent feria	
06 Tues	P W	Advent feria *or* St Nicholas, Bishop	

DECEMBER 2005		
07 Wed	W	St Ambrose, Bishop & Doctor
08 Thurs	W	**IMMACULATE CONCEPTION OF THE BLESSED VIRGIN MARY** *Gloria, Creed, Proper Preface*
09 Fri	P W	feria *or* St John Diego Cuahtlatoatzin
10 Sat	P	Advent feria
11 Sun	RP or P	+THIRD SUNDAY OF ADVENT (Gaudete Sunday) *Ps Week 3* *Creed, Advent Preface I*
12 Mon	P W	Advent feria *or* Our Lady of Guadalupe
13 Tues	R	St Lucy, Virgin & Martyr
14 Wed	W	St John of the Cross, Priest & Doctor
15 Thurs	P	Advent feria
16 Fri	P	Advent feria
		Memorials which occur on days between 17 and 31 December may if wished be commemorated at Mass by using the collect of the saint in place of the collect of the Mass of the day.
17 Sat	P	Advent feria Advent Preface II from today
18 Sun	P	+ FOURTH SUNDAY OF ADVENT *Ps Week 4* *Creed, Advent Preface II* Announce Holyday of Obligation § Expectant mothers
19 Mon	P	Advent feria
20 Tues	P	Advent feria
21 Wed	P	Advent feria (St Peter Canisius)
22 Thurs	P	Advent feria

DECEMBER 2005/JANUARY 2006

23 Fri	P	Advent feria (St John of Kanty)
24 Sat	P	Advent feria
evening	W	First Vespers and Mass of the Vigil of Christmas On Christmas night, it is appropriate that before the Midnight Mass a solemn vigil be kept by celebrating the Office of Readings.
25 Sun	W	**+ NATIVITY OF THE LORD – CHRISTMAS DAY** *Gloria, Creed – genuflect at* Incarnatus, *Proper Preface &* Communicantes. All priests may celebrate three Masses today, provided that they are celebrated at their proper time.
26 Mon	R	ST STEPHEN, Protomartyr *Gloria, Preface &* Communicantes *of Christmas*
27 Tues	W	ST JOHN, Apostle & Evangelist *Gloria, Preface &* Communicantes *of Christmas*
28 Wed	R	HOLY INNOCENTS, Martyrs *Gloria, Preface &* Communicantes *of Christmas*
29 Thurs	W	FIFTH DAY IN THE OCTAVE OF CHRISTMAS *Gloria, Preface &* Communicantes *of Christmas* (St Thomas Becket, Bishop & Martyr) *national*
30 Fri	W	HOLY FAMILY OF JESUS, MARY & JOSEPH *Gloria, Preface &* Communicantes *of Christmas*
31 Sat	W	SEVENTH DAY IN THE OCTAVE OF CHRISTMAS *Gloria, Preface &* Communicantes *of Christmas* (St Sylvester I, Pope)
evening	W	First Vespers and Mass of Mary, Mother of God
		JANUARY 2006
01 Sun	W	**+ OCTAVE DAY OF CHRISTMAS** **SOLEMNITY OF MARY, MOTHER OF GOD** *Gloria, Creed, Preface of B.V. Mary I 'as we celebrate the motherhood…',* Communicantes *of Christmas* Announce Holyday of Obligation
02 Mon	W	SS Basil the Great & Gregory Nazianzen, Bishops & Doctors *Ps Week 2*

JANUARY 2006

Date	Colour	Celebration
03 Tues	W W	Christmas feria *or* Most Holy Name of Jesus *Readings from this Votive Mass in Lectionary volume III*
04 Wed	W	Christmas feria
05 Thurs	W	Christmas feria
evening	W	First Vespers and Mass of the Epiphany *The* Missale Romanum, editio typica tertia, *gives texts for a Vigil Mass of the Epiphany different from those of the Mass of the day.*
06 Fri	W	**+ EPIPHANY OF THE LORD** *Gloria, Creed, Proper Preface &* Communicantes *At today's Mass, after the Gospel, the announcement may be made of moveable feasts according to the formula given in the Roman Pontifical, and on page 1247 of the* Missale Romanum, editio typica tertia
07 Sat	W W	Christmas feria *or* St Raymond of Penyafort
08 Sun	W	+ BAPTISM OF THE LORD *Gloria, Creed, Proper Preface*

§ CYCLE OF PRAYER – ORDINARY TIME: WINTER

During Ordinary Time (Winter) i.e. up to Lent, we are asked to pray for these intentions: Peace on Earth; Christian Unity; The Sick and those who care for them; Students and Teachers; The Unemployed

Peace Day	Sunday 15 January (2nd Sunday of the Year)
Octave of Prayer for Christian Unity	18 – 25 January
World Day for the Sick	Saturday 11 February
Education Day	Sunday 12 February (3 Sundays before Lent)
Europe	Tuesday 14 February (SS Cyril & Methodius)
Day for the Unemployed	Sunday 26 February (Sunday before Lent)

The weekday Lectionary for Mass is taken from	Year 2
Lectionary for Sundays and Feasts:	Year B

Date	Colour	Celebration	
09 Mon	G	feria, First Week of the Year	*Ps Week I*
10 Tues	G	feria	
11 Wed	G	feria	
12 Thurs	G W	feria *or* St Aelred of Rievaulx, Abbot	 *national*

JANUARY 2006			
13 Fri	G W	feria *or* St Hilary, Bishop & Doctor	
14 Sat	G W	feria *or* Saturday Mass of the Blessed Virgin Mary	
15 Sun	G	+ SECOND SUNDAY OF THE YEAR *Gloria, Creed, Preface of Sundays of the Year* § Peace Day	*Ps Week 2*
16 Mon	G	feria	
17 Tues	W	St Anthony, Abbot	
		§ from 18-25 January is held the Octave of Prayer for Christian Unity	
18 Wed	G	feria	
19 Thurs	G W	feria *or* St Wulstan, Bishop	*national*
20 Fri	G R R	feria *or* St Fabian, Pope & Martyr *or* St Sebastian, Martyr	
21 Sat	R	St Agnes, Virgin & Martyr	
22 Sun	G	+THIRD SUNDAY OF THE YEAR *Gloria, Creed, Preface of Sundays of the Year*	*Ps Week 3*
23 Mon	G	feria	
24 Tues	W	St Francis de Sales, Bishop & Doctor	
25 Wed	W	CONVERSION OF ST PAUL, Apostle *Gloria, Preface of Apostles*	
26 Thurs	W	SS Timothy & Titus, Bishops *Proper readings*	
27 Fri	G W	feria *or* St Angela Merici, Virgin	
28 Sat	W	St Thomas Aquinas, Priest & Doctor	

JANUARY/FEBRUARY 2006

Date	Colour	Celebration	
29 Sun	G	+FOURTH SUNDAY OF THE YEAR *Gloria, Creed, Preface of Sundays of the Year*	*Ps Week 4*
30 Mon	G	feria	
31 Tues	W	St John Bosco, Priest	

FEBRUARY 2006

Date	Colour	Celebration	
01 Wed	G	feria	
02 Thurs	W	PRESENTATION OF THE LORD *Blessing of candles with procession or solemn entry* *Gloria, 1st or 2nd reading, Proper Preface*	
03 Fri	W	SS Lawrence, Dunstan, & Theodore, Bishops *The blessing of St Blaise on throats may be given*	*diocesan*
04 Sat	G W	feria *or* Saturday Mass of the Blessed Virgin Mary	
05 Sun	G	+ FIFTH SUNDAY OF THE YEAR *Gloria, Creed, Preface of Sundays of the Year* Announce special collection	*Ps Week 1*
06 Mon	R	SS Paul Miki and Companions, Martyrs	
07 Tues	G	feria	
08 Wed	G W W	feria *or* St Jerome Emiliani *or* St Josephine Bakhita, Virgin	
09 Thurs	G	feria	
10 Fri	W	St Scholastica, Virgin	
11 Sat	G W	feria *or* Our Lady of Lourdes § World Day for the Sick	
12 Sun	G	+ SIXTH SUNDAY OF THE YEAR *Gloria, Creed, Preface of Sundays of the Year* Collection for Catholic Education Service § Education Day	*Ps Week 2*

FEBRUARY 2006

Date	Colour	Celebration
13 Mon	G	feria
14 Tues	W	SS CYRIL, Monk, & METHODIUS, Bishop, Patrons of Europe *Gloria, Preface of Pastors* § Europe
15 Wed	G	feria
16 Thurs	G	feria
17 Fri	G W	feria *or* Seven Holy Founders of the Servite Order
18 Sat	G W	feria *or* Saturday Mass of the Blessed Virgin Mary
19 Sun	G	+ SEVENTH SUNDAY OF THE YEAR *Ps Week 3* *Gloria, Creed, Preface of Sundays of the Year*
20 Mon	G	feria
21 Tues	G W	feria *or* St Peter Damian, Bishop & Doctor
22 Wed	W	CHAIR OF ST PETER, Apostle *Gloria, Preface of Apostles*
23 Thurs	R	St Polycarp, Bishop & Martyr
24 Fri	G	feria
25 Sat	G W	feria *or* Saturday Mass of the Blessed Virgin Mary
26 Sun	G	+ EIGHTH SUNDAY OF THE YEAR *Ps Week 4* *Gloria, Creed, Preface of Sundays of the Year* Announce Ash Wednesday, Day of Fast and Abstinence Announce Lenten Alms § Day for the Unemployed
27 Mon	G	feria
28 Tues	G	feria

MARCH 2006

§ CYCLE OF PRAYER: LENT

We are asked to pray for these intentions:
Candidates for the Sacraments, (especially on the Sundays of Lent); Women; The Needy and Hungry of the World; Penitents and Wanderers.

Women's World Day of Prayer	Friday 3 March (1st Friday in March)
CAFOD Lent Fast Day	Friday 10 March (Friday 1st Week of Lent)

The season of Lent is a preparation for the celebration of Easter. The liturgy prepares the catechumens for the celebration of the paschal mystery by the various stages of Christian initiation: it also prepares the faithful, who recall their baptism and do penance in preparation for Easter.
Memorials which occur on a weekday may be commemorated, if wished, only by using the collect of the saint in place of the collect for the Mass of the Day.
The Alleluia is always omitted, both in the Liturgy of the Hours & Mass.
It is not permitted to adorn the altar with flowers, and the organ and other instruments may only be played for the purpose of sustaining the singing. An exception is made for Laetare Sunday, and for solemnities and feasts.
For the celebration of marriages, the parish priest should alert spouses to the need to take account of the particular penitential character of this season.

MARCH 2006

01 Wed P — ASH WEDNESDAY Fast & Abstinence — *Ps Week 4*
Penitential rite omitted, blessing and distribution of ashes after the homily, Lenten Preface IV

02 Thurs P — Lent feria

03 Fri P — Lent feria

04 Sat P — Lent feria
(St Casimir)

05 Sun P — + FIRST SUNDAY OF LENT — *Ps Week 1*
Creed, Preface of First Sunday of Lent
Announce Lent Fast Day
Rite of Election in the Cathedral
§ Candidates for the Sacraments

MARCH 2006

Date	Colour	Celebration	
06 Mon	P	Lent feria	
07 Tues	P	Lent feria (SS Perpetua and Felicity)	
08 Wed	P	Lent feria (St John of God)	
09 Thurs	P	Lent feria (St Frances of Rome)	
10 Fri	P	Lent feria § Lent Fast Day	
11 Sat	P	Lent feria	
12 Sun	P	+ SECOND SUNDAY OF LENT *Creed, Preface of Second Sunday of Lent* Collect Lent Fast Day offerings for CAFOD § Candidates for the Sacraments	*Ps Week 2*
13 Mon	P	Lent feria	
14 Tues	P	Lent feria	
15 Wed	P	Lent feria	
16 Thurs	P	Lent feria	
17 Fri	W	ST PATRICK, Bishop, Patron of Ireland *Gloria, Preface of Pastors*	*national*
18 Sat	P	Lent feria (St Cyril of Jerusalem)	
19 Sun	P	+ THIRD SUNDAY OF LENT *Creed, Preface of Third Sunday of Lent* RCIA – First Scrutiny § Candidates for the Sacraments	*Ps Week 3*
20 Mon	W	**ST JOSEPH, Husband of the Blessed Virgin Mary** *Gloria, Creed, Proper Preface*	
21 Tues	P	Lent feria	

MARCH/APRIL 2006

Date	Colour	Celebration
22 Wed	P	Lent feria Anniversary of the Installation of Cardinal Cormac Murphy O'Connor, Tenth Archbishop of Westminster (2000)
23 Thurs	P	Lent feria (St Turibius of Mogrovejo)
24 Fri	P	Lent feria
25 Sat	W	ANNUNCIATION OF THE LORD *Gloria, Creed – genuflect at* Incarnatus, *Proper Preface*
26 Sun	RP or P	+FOURTH SUNDAY OF LENT (Laetare Sunday) *Ps Week 4* *Creed, Preface of Fourth Sunday of Lent* RCIA – Second Scrutiny § Candidates for the Sacraments
27 Mon	P	Lent feria
28 Tues	P	Lent feria
29 Wed	P	Lent feria
30 Thurs	P	Lent feria
31 Fri	P	Lent feria

APRIL 2006

Date	Colour	Celebration
01 Sat	P	Lent feria The practice of covering crosses and images in the church may be observed. Crosses remain covered until the end of the Celebration of the Lord's Passion on Good Friday; images until the beginning of the Easter Vigil.
02 Sun	P	+ FIFTH SUNDAY OF LENT *Ps Week I* *Creed, Lenten Preface I or II* RCIA – Third Scrutiny *Anniversary of the Death of Pope John Paul II* § Candidates for the Sacraments
03 Mon	P	Lent feria

APRIL 2006

Date	Colour	Celebration
04 Tues	P	Lent feria (St Isidore)
05 Wed	P	Lent feria (St Vincent Ferrer)
06 Thurs	P	Lent feria
07 Fri	P	Lent feria (St John Baptist de la Salle)
08 Sat	P	Lent feria
		HOLY WEEK In Holy Week the Church celebrates the mysteries of salvation accomplished by Christ in the last days of his earthly life, from his messianic entry into Jerusalem, until his blessed Passion and glorious Resurrection. Lent continues until Maundy Thursday.
09 Sun	R	**+ PALM SUNDAY OF THE LORD'S PASSION** *Ps Week 2* *Blessing of palms and Procession or solemn entrance before principal Mass; the latter may be repeated before another Mass. Simple entrance before other Masses. Narrative of Lord's Passion, Creed, Proper Preface.* Announce Good Friday (Fast & Abstinence) Announce Good Friday collection. § Candidates for the Sacraments
10 Mon	P	MONDAY OF HOLY WEEK *Preface of the Passion II*
11 Tues	P	TUESDAY OF HOLY WEEK *Preface of the Passion II* Chrism Mass in the Cathedral
12 Wed	P	WEDNESDAY OF HOLY WEEK *Preface of the Passion II*
13 Thurs	P	MAUNDY THURSDAY *Holy Communion may be distributed to the faithful only during the Mass of the Lord's Supper. The sick may receive Communion at any hour of the day. The celebration of Mass without a congregation is prohibited today.*

APRIL 2006

THE EASTER TRIDUUM

W **Evening Mass of the Lord's Supper**
Gloria, during which the bells rung.
Washing of feet may be carried out.
Proper Preface, and insertions in the Roman Canon.
Procession & Reposition of the Blessed Sacrament, only if the Celebration of the Lord's Passion is to take place in the Church.
Watching before the Altar of Repose may take place with solemnity until midnight.

14 Fri **GOOD FRIDAY** Fast & Abstinence
Holy Communion is distributed to the faithful only during the Celebration of the Lord's Passion, but may be taken at any time to the sick who are unable to take part in this liturgy. Only the Sacraments of Penance and of the Anointing of the Sick may be celebrated. It is highly appropriate that the Office of Readings and Lauds be celebrated in solemn fashion with the people.

R **Celebration of the Lord's Passion**
in the afternoon, at around 3.00 pm, according to the prescriptions of the liturgical books. No one should introduce changes on his own initiative.
Collection for the Holy Places

15 Sat P **HOLY SATURDAY**
The Church today abstains completely from the celebration of Mass. Holy Communion may only be given in the form of viaticum. Only the Sacraments of Penance and of the Anointing of the Sick may be celebrated.
It is highly appropriate that the Office of Readings and Lauds be celebrated in solemn fashion with the people.

W **The Easter Vigil**
The whole celebration of the Easter Vigil should take place at night, so that it begins after night has fallen and concludes. before daybreak. The celebration of a Mass without the rites of the Easter Vigil is not allowed.
Gloria, Proper Preface & insertions in the Roman Canon.
Double alleluia *added to* Ite, missa est

The Paschal candle should be placed near the ambo or altar, and kept there for the whole Easter season until the end of Pentecost Sunday. It should be lit for the more solemn liturgical celebrations during this time.

APRIL 2006

16 Sun W

+EASTER SUNDAY

In place of the penitential rite, all are sprinkled with water blessed on Easter night to recall their Baptism.
Gloria, Sequence, Creed or Renewal of Baptismal Promises, Proper Preface & insertions in the Roman Canon; Double alleluia *added to* Ite, missa est.

Throughout the Easter season, the Angelus *is replaced by* Regina Coeli.

§ CYCLE OF PRAYER: EASTER

During Easter we are asked to pray for these intentions:
New Members of the Church; Vocations; The Right Use of the Media; the Church; Human Work.

Europe	Saturday 29 April (St Catherine of Siena)
St Joseph the Worker	Monday 1 May
World Day of Prayer for Vocations	Sunday 7 May (4th Sunday of Easter)
World Communications Day	Sunday 28 May (Sunday after Ascension)
The Church	especially at Pentecost, 4 June

17 Mon W

MONDAY WITHIN THE OCTAVE OF EASTER

Gloria, Sequence ad lib *Proper Preface & insertions in the Roman Canon, double* alleluia *added to* Ite, missa est

18 Tues W

TUESDAY WITHIN THE OCTAVE OF EASTER

Gloria, Sequence ad lib *Proper Preface & insertions in the Roman Canon, double* alleluia *added to* Ite, missa est

19 Wed W

WEDNESDAY WITHIN THE OCTAVE OF EASTER

Gloria, Sequence ad lib *Proper Preface & insertions in the Roman Canon, Double* alleluia *added to* Ite, missa est

Anniversary of the Election of Pope Benedict XVI

Being within the Octave of Easter, the Mass for the anniversary of the election of the Pope is not celebrated this year. But at all Masses a special intention for the Holy Father should be inserted into the Prayer of the Faithful.

20 Thurs W

THURSDAY WITHIN THE OCTAVE OF EASTER

Gloria, Sequence ad lib *Proper Preface & insertions in the Roman Canon, double* alleluia *added to* Ite, missa est

21 Fri W

FRIDAY WITHIN THE OCTAVE OF EASTER

Gloria, Sequence ad lib. *Proper Preface & insertions in the Roman Canon, double* alleluia *added to* Ite, missa est

APRIL/MAY 2006		
22 Sat	W	**SATURDAY WITHIN THE OCTAVE OF EASTER** *Gloria, Sequence* ad lib *Proper Preface & insertions in the Roman Canon, double* alleluia *added to* Ite, missa est
23 Sun	W	+ **OCTAVE DAY OF EASTER** SECOND SUNDAY OF EASTER (Divine Mercy Sunday) *Gloria, Creed, Proper Preface & insertions in the Roman Canon, double* alleluia *added to* Ite, missa est
24 Mon	R	**ST GEORGE, Martyr, Patron of England** *national* *Gloria, Creed, Preface of Martyrs*
25 Tues	R	ST MARK, Evangelist *Gloria, Preface of Apostles II*
26 Wed	W	Easter feria *Ps Week 2*
27 Thurs	W	Easter feria
28 Fri	W R W	Easter feria *or* St Peter Chanel, Priest & Martyr *or* St Louis Marie Grignion de Montfort, Priest
29 Sat	W	ST CATHERINE OF SIENA, Virgin & Doctor Patron of Europe *Gloria, Preface of Holy Men and Women* § Europe
30 Sun	W	+ THIRD SUNDAY OF EASTER *Ps Week 3* *Gloria, Creed, Preface of Easter* Announce Special Collection
		MAY 2006
01 Mon	W W	Easter feria *or* St Joseph the Worker
02 Tues	W	St Athanasius, Bishop & Doctor
03 Wed	R	SS PHILIP & JAMES, Apostles *Gloria, Preface of Apostles*
04 Thurs	R	The English Martyrs *national*
05 Fri	W	Easter feria

MAY 2006

Date	Colour	Celebration
06 Sat	W	Easter feria
07 Sun	W	+FOURTH SUNDAY OF EASTER *Ps Week 4* *Gloria, Creed, Preface of Easter* Collection for WEEF § World Day of Prayer for Vocations
08 Mon	W	Easter feria
09 Tues	W	Easter feria
10 Wed	W	Easter feria
11 Thurs	W	Easter feria
12 Fri	W R R	Easter feria *or* SS Nereus & Achilleus, Martyrs *or* St Pancras, Martyr
13 Sat	W W	Easter feria *or* Our Lady of Fatima
14 Sun	W	+FIFTH SUNDAY OF EASTER *Ps Week I* *Gloria, Creed, Preface of Easter*
15 Mon	W	Easter feria
16 Tues	W	Easter feria
17 Wed	W	Easter feria
18 Thurs	W R	Easter feria *or* St John I, Pope & Martyr
19 Fri	W	Easter feria *(The proper Calendar for England gives St Dunstan as an optional memorial for today, but in the Diocese of Westminster February 3rd is an obligatory memorial for St Dunstan, along with SS Lawrence & Theodore.)*
20 Sat	W W	Easter feria *or* St Bernardine of Siena, Priest
21 Sun	W	+SIXTH SUNDAY OF EASTER *Ps Week 2* *Gloria, Creed, Preface of Easter* Announce Holyday of Obligation Announce Special Collection

MAY/JUNE 2006		
22 Mon	W W	Easter feria *or* St Rita of Cascia, Religious
23 Tues	W	Easter feria
24 Wed evening	W W	Easter feria First Vespers and Vigil Mass of the Ascension *The* Missale Romanum, *editio typica tertia, gives texts for a Vigil Mass of the Ascension different from those of the Mass of the day.*
25 Thurs	W	**+ASCENSION OF THE LORD** *Gloria, Creed, Proper Preface &* Communicantes
26 Fri	W	St Philip Neri, Priest
27 Sat	W	St Augustine of Canterbury, Bishop *national*
28 Sun	W	+SEVENTH SUNDAY OF EASTER *Ps Week 3* *Gloria, Creed, Preface of Easter* Collection for Catholic Communications § World Communications Day
29 Mon	W	Easter feria
30 Tues	W	Easter feria
31 Wed	W	VISITATION OF THE BLESSED VIRGIN MARY *Gloria, 1st or 2nd reading, Preface of the B. V. Mary*
		JUNE 2006
01 Thurs	R	St Justin, Martyr
02 Fri	W R	Easter feria *or* SS Marcellinus & Peter, Martyrs
03 Sat evening	R R	SS Charles Lwanga & Companions, Martyrs First Vespers and Mass of the Vigil of Pentecost *Gloria, choice of Old Testament readings, Creed, Proper Preface &* Communicantes *Double alleluia added to* Ite, missa est

JUNE 2006

04 Sun	R	**+ PENTECOST SUNDAY** *Gloria, Sequence, Creed, Proper Preface &* Communicantes *Double alleluia added to* Ite, missa est § The Church The Easter season ends. After today, the Paschal Candle is no longer kept in the sanctuary, but moved to the baptistery, where it is lit at baptisms. At funerals it is placed near the coffin, and lit, to signify that Christian death is a true Passover. From tomorrow, the recitation of the *Angelus* is resumed. § CYCLE OF PRAYER – SUMMER During Ordinary Time (Summer), i.e. up to September, we are asked to pray for these intentions: A Deeper Understanding between Christians and Jews; Those who suffer Persecution, Oppression and Denial of Human Rights; Europe; Human Life; Seafarers. Those who suffer persecution on SS John Fisher & Thomas More — 22 June Europe on St Benedict — 11 July St Bridget of Sweden — 23 July St Teresa Benedicta of the Cross — 9 August Day for Life — 1st Sunday in July — 2 July Sea Sunday — 2nd Sunday in July — 9 July The weekday Lectionary is that of Year 2 The Sunday Lectionary is that of Year B
05 Mon	R	St Boniface, Bishop & Martyr *national* *Ps Week 1*
06 Tues	G W	feria, 9th Week of the Year, *or* St Norbert, Bishop
07 Wed	G	feria
08 Thurs	G	feria
09 Fri	G W W	feria *or* St Ephraem, Deacon & Doctor or St Columba, Abbot *national*
10 Sat	G W	feria *or* Saturday Mass of the Blessed Virgin Mary

JUNE 2006			
11 Sun	W	**+ MOST HOLY TRINITY** *Gloria, Creed, Proper Preface* Announce Holyday of Obligation	
12 Mon	G	feria, 10th Week of the Year	*Ps Week 2*
13 Tues	W	St Anthony of Padua, Priest & Doctor	
14 Wed evening	G W	feria 1st Vespers and Mass of Corpus Christi	
15 Thurs	W	**+ CORPUS CHRISTI** **MOST HOLY BODY & BLOOD OF THE LORD** *Gloria, Sequence* ad lib, *Creed, Preface of the Eucharist*	
16 Fri	G W	feria *or* St Richard of Chichester, Bishop	 *national*
17 Sat	G W	feria *or* Saturday Mass of the Blessed Virgin Mary ***Anniversary of the Death of Cardinal George Basil Hume, Ninth Archbishop of Westminster, (1999).***	
18 Sun	G	+ ELEVENTH SUNDAY OF THE YEAR *Gloria, Creed, Preface of Sundays of the Year*	*Ps Week 3*
19 Mon	G W	feria *or* St Romuald, Abbot	
20 Tues	G R	feria *or* St Alban, Protomartyr	 *national*
21 Wed	W	St Aloysius Gonzaga, Religious	
22 Thurs	R	SS JOHN FISHER & THOMAS MORE, Martyrs *Gloria, Preface of Martyrs* § Those who suffer persecution, oppression and denial of human rights	*national*
23 Fri evening	W	**MOST SACRED HEART OF JESUS** *Gloria, Creed, Proper Preface* *The Vigil of the Nativity of St John the Baptist is not celebrated this year*	
24 Sat	W	**NATIVITY OF ST JOHN THE BAPTIST** *Gloria, Creed, Preface of St John the Baptist*	

JUNE/JULY 2006

Date	Colour	Celebration	
25 Sun	G	+TWELFTH SUNDAY OF THE YEAR	*Ps Week 4*
		Gloria, Creed, Preface of Sundays of the Year	
		Announce Special Collection	
		Announce Holyday of Obligation	
26 Mon	G	feria	
27 Tues	R	St John Southworth, Priest & Martyr	*diocesan*
in Cathedral	R	**ST JOHN SOUTHWORTH, Priest & Martyr**	
		Gloria, Creed, Preface of Martyrs	
28 Wed	R	St Irenaeus, Bishop & Martyr	
evening	R	First Vespers & Vigil Mass of SS Peter & Paul	
29 Thurs	R	**+ SS PETER & PAUL, Apostles**	
		Gloria, Creed, Preface of SS Peter & Paul	
30 Fri	G	feria *or*	
	R	Protomartyrs of the Holy Roman Church	

JULY 2006

Date	Colour	Celebration	
01 Sat	W	DEDICATION OF THE CATHEDRAL	
		Gloria, Preface of the Dedication of a Church II	*diocesan*
in Cathedral	W	**DEDICATION OF THE CATHEDRAL**	
		Mass of Anniversary of Dedication: in the Dedicated Church	
		Gloria, Creed, Preface of the Dedication of a Church I	
02 Sun	G	+THIRTEENTH SUNDAY OF THE YEAR	*Ps Week 1*
		Gloria, Creed, Preface of Sundays of the Year	
		Announce Special Collection, Collection for Peter's Pence	
		§ Day for Life	
03 Mon	R	ST THOMAS, Apostle	
		Gloria, Preface of Apostles	
04 Tues	G	feria *or*	
	W	St Elizabeth of Portugal	
05 Wed	G	feria *or*	
	W	St Anthony Zaccaria, Priest	
06 Thurs	G	feria *or*	
	R	St Maria Goretti, Virgin & Martyr	

JULY 2006		
07 Fri	G	feria
08 Sat	G W	feria *or* Saturday Mass of the Blessed Virgin Mary
09 Sun	G	+FOURTEENTH SUNDAY OF THE YEAR *Ps Week 2* *Gloria, Creed, Preface of Sundays of the Year* Collection for Apostleship of the Sea § Sea Sunday
10 Mon	G	feria
11 Tues	W	ST BENEDICT, Abbot, Patron of Europe *Gloria, Preface of Holy Men and Women* § Europe
12 Wed	G	feria
13 Thurs	G W	feria *or* St Henry
14 Fri	G W	feria *or* St Camillus de Lellis, Priest
15 Sat	W	St Bonaventure, Bishop & Doctor
16 Sun	G	+FIFTEENTH SUNDAY OF THE YEAR *Ps Week 3* *Gloria, Creed, Preface of Sundays of the Year*
17 Mon	G	feria
18 Tues	G	feria
19 Wed	G	feria
20 Thurs	G R	feria *or* St Apollinaris, Bishop & Martyr
21 Fri	G W	feria *or* St Lawrence of Brindisi, Priest & Doctor
22 Sat	W	St Mary Magdalene *Proper Readings*
23 Sun	G	+SIXTEENTH SUNDAY OF THE YEAR *Ps Week 4* *Gloria, Creed, Preface of Sundays of the Year* § Europe

JULY/AUGUST 2006

Date	Colour	Celebration	
24 Mon	G W	feria *or* St Charbel Makhluf, Priest	
25 Tues	R	ST JAMES, Apostle *Gloria, Preface of Apostles*	
26 Wed	W	SS Joachim & Anne, Parents of the B.V. Mary	
27 Thurs	G	feria	
28 Fri	G	feria	
29 Sat	W	St Martha *Proper Readings*	
30 Sun	G	+ SEVENTEENTH SUNDAY OF THE YEAR *Gloria, Creed, Preface of Sundays of the Year*	*Ps Week 1*
31 Mon	W	St Ignatius of Loyola, Priest	

AUGUST 2006

Date	Colour	Celebration	
01 Tues	W	St Alphonsus Liguori, Bishop & Doctor	
02 Wed	G W W	feria *or* St Eusebius of Vercelli, Bishop *or* St Peter Julian Eymard, Priest	
03 Thurs	G	feria	
04 Fri	W	St John Vianney, Priest	
05 Sat	G W	feria *or* Dedication of St Mary Major	
06 Sun	W	+ TRANSFIGURATION OF THE LORD *Gloria, Creed, Proper Preface*	
07 Mon	G R W	feria *or* St Sixtus II, Pope, & Companions, Martyrs *or* St Cajetan, Priest	*Ps Week 2*
08 Tues	W	St Dominic, Priest	

AUGUST 2006

Date	Colour	Celebration
09 Wed	R	ST TERESA BENEDICTA OF THE CROSS, Virgin & Martyr Patron of Europe *Gloria, Preface of Martyrs* § Europe
10 Thurs	R	ST LAWRENCE, Deacon & Martyr *Gloria, Preface of Martyrs*
11 Fri	W	St Clare, Virgin
12 Sat	G W W	feria *or* St Jane Frances de Chantal, Religious *transferred to this date from 12 December by the* Missale Romanum, editio typica tertia, *or* Saturday Mass of the Blessed Virgin Mary
13 Sun	G	+NINETEENTH SUNDAY OF THE YEAR *Ps Week 3* *Gloria, Creed, Preface of Sundays of the Year* Announce Holyday of Obligation
14 Mon evening	R W	St Maximilian Kolbe, Priest & Martyr First Vespers & Vigil Mass of the Assumption
15 Tues	W	**+ ASSUMPTION OF THE BLESSED VIRGIN MARY** *Gloria, Creed, Proper Preface*
16 Wed	G W	feria *or* St Stephen of Hungary
17 Thurs	G	feria
18 Fri	G	feria
19 Sat	G W W	feria *or* St John Eudes, Priest *or* Saturday Mass of the Blessed Virgin Mary
20 Sun	G	+TWENTIETH SUNDAY OF THE YEAR *Ps Week 4* *Gloria, Creed, Preface of Sundays of the Year*
21 Mon	W	St Pius X, Pope
22 Tues	W	Queenship of the Blessed Virgin Mary
23 Wed	G W	feria *or* St Rose of Lima, Virgin

AUGUST/SEPTEMBER 2006

Date	Colour	Celebration	
24 Thurs	R	ST BARTHOLOMEW, Apostle *Gloria, Preface of Apostles*	
25 Fri	G W W	feria *or* St Louis *or* St Joseph Calasanz, Priest	
26 Sat	G W W	feria *or* Blessed Dominic of the Mother of God, Priest *or* Saturday Mass of the Blessed Virgin Mary	 *national*
27 Sun	G	+TWENTY FIRST SUNDAY OF THE YEAR *Gloria, Creed, Preface of Sundays of the Year*	*Ps Week I*
28 Mon	W	St Augustine, Bishop & Doctor	
29 Tues	R	Beheading of St John the Baptist *Proper Readings, Preface of St John Baptist*	
30 Wed	G R	feria *or* SS Margaret Clitherow, Anne Line & Margaret Ward, Virgin, Martyrs	 *national*
31 Thurs	G W	feria *or* St Aidan, Bishop, & Saints of Lindisfarne	 *national*

SEPTEMBER 2006

§ CYCLE OF PRAYER – AUTUMN

During Ordinary Time (Autumn), i.e. from September to Christ the King, we are asked to pray for these intentions:
The Spread of the Gospel; The Harvest; the Fruits of Human Work, and the Reverent Use of Creation; Justice and Peace in the World; All Victims of War; Young People; Prisoners and their Families.

Racial Justice Day	Sunday 10 September	2nd Sunday in Sept
Home Mission Day	Sunday 17 September	3rd Sunday in Sept
World Mission Day	Sunday 22 October	penultimate Sunday in October
The Harvest	Sunday 24 September *or whenever harvest festivals are held*	Sunday 22–28 Sept
Harvest Fast Day	Friday 6 October	1st Friday in Oct
Remembrance Sunday	Sunday 12 November	2nd Sunday in Nov
Prisoners' Week	9 – 15 November	
Day of Prayer for Prisoners and their Dependants	Sunday 19 November	3rd Sunday in Nov
Youth Day	Sunday 26 November	Christ the King

SEPTEMBER 2006

01 Fri	G	feria
02 Sat	G W	feria *or* Saturday Mass of the Blessed Virgin Mary
03 Sun	G	+TWENTY SECOND SUNDAY OF THE YEAR *Ps Week 2* *Gloria, Creed, Preface of Sundays of the Year* Announce Special Collection
04 Mon	G W	feria *or* St Cuthbert, Bishop
05 Tues	G	feria
06 Wed	G	feria
07 Thurs	G	feria
08 Fri	W	NATIVITY OF THE BLESSED VIRGIN MARY *Gloria, 1st or 2nd Reading, Preface of the B.V. Mary*
09 Sat	G W W	feria *or* St Peter Claret, Priests *or* Saturday Mass of the Blessed Virgin Mary
10 Sun	G	+ TWENTY THIRD SUNDAY OF THE YEAR *Ps Week 3* *Gloria, Creed, Preface of Sundays of the Year* Collection for Catholic Association for Racial Justice Announce Special Collection § Racial Justice Day
11 Mon	G	feria
12 Tues	G W	feria *or* Most Holy Name of Mary
13 Wed	W	St John Chrysostom, Bishop & Doctor
14 Thurs	R	EXALTATION OF THE HOLY CROSS *Gloria, 1st or 2nd Reading, Preface of the Cross or of the Passion I*
15 Fri	W	Our Lady of Sorrows *Proper Readings, sequence ad lib, Preface of the B.V. Mary*
16 Sat	R	SS Cornelius, Pope, & Cyprian, Bishop, Martyrs

SEPTEMBER 2006

17 Sun	G	+ TWENTY FOURTH SUNDAY OF THE YEAR *Ps Week 4* *Gloria, Creed, Preface of Sundays of the Year* Collection for Agency for Evangelisation § Home Mission Day
18 Mon	G	feria
19 Tues	G R	feria *or* St Januarius, Bishop & Martyr *(The proper Calendar for England gives St Theodore as an optional memorial for today, but in the Diocese of Westminster February 3rd is an obligatory memorial for St Theodore along with SS Lawrence and Dunstan.)*
20 Wed	R	SS Andrew Kim Taegon & Companions, Martyrs
21 Thurs	R	ST MATTHEW, Apostle & Evangelist *Gloria, Preface of the Apostles*
22 Fri	G	feria
23 Sat	W	St Pio of Pietrelcina, Priest
24 Sun	G	+ TWENTY FIFTH SUNDAY OF THE YEAR *Ps Week 1* *Gloria, Creed, Preface of Sundays of the Year* § The Harvest
25 Mon	G	feria
26 Tues	G R	feria *or* SS Cosmas & Damian, Martyrs
27 Wed	W	St Vincent de Paul, Priest
28 Thurs	G R R	feria *or* St Wenceslaus, Martyr *or* SS Lawrence Ruiz & Companions, Martyrs
29 Fri	W	SS MICHAEL, GABRIEL, RAPHAEL, Archangels *Gloria, 1st or 2nd Reading, Preface of the Angels*
30 Sat	W	St Jerome, Priest & Doctor

OCTOBER 2006

OCTOBER 2006

The Rosary should be recommended to the faithful, and its nature and importance explained.

Date	Colour	Celebration	
01 Sun	G	+ TWENTY SIXTH SUNDAY OF THE YEAR *Gloria, Creed, Preface of Sundays of the Year* Annual Mass Count – 1 Announce Harvest Fast Day	*Ps Week 2*
02 Mon	W	Holy Guardian Angels *Proper Readings, Preface of the Angels*	
03 Tues	G	feria	
04 Wed	W	St Francis of Assisi	
05 Thurs	G	feria	
06 Fri	G W	feria *or* St Bruno, Priest § Harvest Fast Day	
07 Sat	W	Our Lady of the Rosary *Proper Readings, Preface of the B.V. Mary*	
08 Sun	G	+ TWENTY SEVENTH SUNDAY OF THE YEAR *Gloria, Creed, Preface of Sundays of the Year* Annual Mass Count – 2 Collect Harvest Fast Day Offerings for CAFOD	*Ps Week 3*
09 Mon	G R W	feria *or* SS Denis, Bishop, & Companions, Martyrs *or* St John Leonardi, Priest	
10 Tues	G W	feria *or* St Paulinus of York, Bishop	*national*
11 Wed	G	feria	
12 Thurs	G W	feria *or* St Wilfred, Bishop	*national*
13 Fri	W	ST EDWARD THE CONFESSOR *Gloria, Preface of Holy Men and Women*	*diocesan*
in City of *Westminster*	W	**ST EDWARD THE CONFESSOR** *Gloria, Creed, Preface of Holy Men and Women*	*diocesan*

OCTOBER 2006

Date	Colour	Celebration
14 Sat	G R W	feria *or* St Callistus, Pope & Martyr *or* Saturday Mass of the Blessed Virgin Mary
15 Sun	G	+ TWENTY EIGHTH SUNDAY OF THE YEAR *Ps Week 4* *Gloria, Creed, Preface of Sundays of the Year* Annual Mass Count – 3 Announce Special Collection
16 Mon	G W W	feria *or* St Hedwig, Religious *or* St Margaret Mary Alacoque, Virgin
17 Tues	R	St Ignatius of Antioch, Bishop & Martyr
18 Wed	R	ST LUKE, Evangelist *Gloria, Preface of Apostles II*
19 Thurs	G R W	feria *or* SS John de Brebeuf, Isaac Jogues, Priests, & Companions, Martyrs *or* St Paul of the Cross, Priest
20 Fri	G	feria
21 Sat	G W	feria *or* Saturday Mass of the Blessed Virgin Mary
22 Sun	G	+ TWENTY NINTH SUNDAY OF THE YEAR *Ps Week 1* *Gloria, Creed, Preface of Sundays of the Year* Annual Mass Count – 4 Collection for APF (Overseas Missions) § World Mission Day
23 Mon	G W	feria *or* St John of Capistrano, Priest
24 Tues	G W	feria *or* St Anthony Claret, Bishop
25 Wed	G	feria
26 Thurs	G W	feria *or* SS Chad & Cedd, Bishops *national*
27 Fri	G	feria

OCTOBER/NOVEMBER 2006

Date	Colour	Celebration
28 Sat	R	SS SIMON & JUDE, Apostles *Gloria, Preface of Apostles*
29 Sun	G	+ THIRTIETH SUNDAY OF THE YEAR *Ps Week 2* *Gloria, Creed, Preface of Sundays of the Year* Announce Special Collection Announce Holyday of Obligation
30 Mon	G	feria
31 Tues	G	feria

NOVEMBER 2006

Date	Colour	Celebration
01 Wed	W	**+ ALL SAINTS** *Gloria, Creed, Proper Preface*
02 Thurs	P or B	COMMEMORATION OF ALL THE FAITHFUL DEPARTED *Preface of Christian Death* All priests are permitted to say three Masses today, with an interval of time between one Mass and the next.
03 Fri	G W W	feria *or* St Martin de Porres, Religious *or* St Winefride, Virgin *national*
04 Sat	W	St Charles Borromeo, Bishop
05 Sun	G	+ THIRTY FIRST SUNDAY OF THE YEAR *Ps Week 3* *Gloria, Creed, Preface of Sundays of the Year* Collection for Sick & Retired Priests
06 Mon	G	feria
07 Tues	G W	feria *or* St Willibrord, Bishop
08 Wed	G	feria
09 Thurs	W	DEDICATION OF THE LATERAN BASILICA *Gloria, 1st or 2nd Reading, Preface of Dedication II* § Prisoners' Week: 9-15 November
10 Fri	W	St Leo the Great, Pope & Doctor

NOVEMBER 2006

Date	Colour	Celebration	Note
11 Sat	W	St Martin of Tours, Bishop	
12 Sun	G	+ THIRTY SECOND SUNDAY OF THE YEAR	*Ps Week 4*
		Gloria, Creed, Preface of Sundays of the Year	
		§ Remembrance Sunday	One Requiem Mass permitted
13 Mon	G	feria	
14 Tues	G	feria	
15 Wed	G	feria *or*	
	W	St Albert the Great, Bishop	
16 Thurs	W	St Edmund, Bishop	*diocesan*
17 Fri	W	St Elizabeth of Hungary, Religious *or*	
	W	St Hilda, Abbess *or*	*national*
	W	St Hugh of Lincoln, Bishop	*national*
18 Sat	G	feria *or*	
	W	Dedication of the Basilicas of SS Peter & Paul *or*	
	W	Saturday Mass of the Blessed Virgin Mary	
19 Sun	G	+ THIRTY THIRD SUNDAY OF THE YEAR	*Ps Week 1*
		Gloria, Creed, Preface of Sundays of the Year	
		Announce Special Collection	
		§ Day of Prayer for Prisoners and their Dependants	
20 Mon	G	feria	
21 Tues	W	Presentation of the Blessed Virgin Mary	
		Proper Readings, Preface of the B.V. Mary	
22 Wed	R	St Cecilia, Virgin & Martyr	
23 Thurs	G	feria *or*	
	R	St Clement I, Pope & Martyr *or*	
	W	St Columban, Abbot	
24 Fri	R	SS Andrew Dung-Lac, Priest, & Companions, Martyrs	
25 Sat	G	feria *or*	
	R	St Catherine of Alexandria, Virgin & Martyr *or*	
	W	Saturday Mass of the Blessed Virgin Mary	

NOVEMBER/DECEMBER 2006

Date	Colour	Celebration	
26 Sun	W	**+OUR LORD JESUS CHRIST, UNIVERSAL KING**	
		Gloria, Creed, Proper Preface	
		Collection for Catholic Youth Service	
		§ Youth Day	
27 Mon	G	feria	*Ps Week 2*
28 Tues	G	feria	
29 Wed	G	feria	
30 Thurs	R	ST ANDREW, Apostle	
		Patron of Scotland	*national*
		Gloria, Preface of Apostles	

DECEMBER 2006

Date	Colour	Celebration	
01 Fri	G	feria	
02 Sat	G W	feria *or* Saturday Mass of the Blessed Virgin Mary	

CYCLE OF PRAYER – ADVENT/CHRISTMAS

We are asked to pray for these intentions:
Openness to the Word of God; Migrants and Refugees; Expectant Mothers.

Migrants' Day	Sunday 3 December
Bible Sunday	Sunday 10 December 2nd Sunday of Advent
Expectant Mothers	especially on 24 December 4th Sunday of Advent

Lectionary for Sundays and Feasts: Year C

Date	Colour	Celebration	
03 Sun	P	+FIRST SUNDAY OF ADVENT	*Ps Week 1*
		Creed, Advent Preface I	
		§ Migrants' Day	
04 Mon	P	Advent feria	
05 Tues	P	Advent feria	
06 Wed	P W	Advent feria *or* St Nicholas, Bishop	

DECEMBER 2006

Date	Colour	Celebration
07 Thurs	W	St Ambrose, Bishop
08 Fri	W	**IMMACULATE CONCEPTION OF THE BLESSED VIRGIN MARY** *Gloria, Creed, Proper Preface*
09 Sat	P W	feria *or* St John Diego Cuahtlatoatzin
10 Sun	P	+ SECOND SUNDAY OF ADVENT *Ps Week 2* *Creed, Advent Preface I* § Bible Sunday
11 Mon	P W	Advent feria *or* St Damasus I, Pope
12 Tues	P W	Advent feria *or* Our Lady of Guadalupe
13 Wed	R	St Lucy, Virgin & Martyr
14 Thurs	W	St John of the Cross, Priest & Doctor
15 Fri	P	Advent feria
16 Sat	P	Advent feria
		Memorials which occur on days between 17 and 31 December may if wished be commemorated at Mass by using the collect of the saint in place of the collect of the Mass of the day.
17 Sun	RP or P	+THIRD SUNDAY OF ADVENT (Gaudete Sunday) *Ps Week 3* *Creed, Advent Preface II from today*
18 Mon	P	Advent feria
19 Tues	P	Advent feria
20 Wed	P	Advent feria
21 Thurs	P	Advent feria (St Peter Canisius)
22 Fri	P	Advent feria
23 Sat	P	Advent feria (St John of Kanty)

DECEMBER 2006/JANUARY 2007

Date	Colour	Celebration
24 Sun	P	+ FOURTH SUNDAY OF ADVENT *Ps Week 4* *Creed, Advent Preface II* Announce Holyday of Obligation
evening	W	First Vespers & Mass of the Vigil of Christmas On Christmas night, it is appropriate that before the Midnight Mass a solemn vigil be kept by celebrating the Office of Readings.
25 Mon	W	**+ NATIVITY OF THE LORD – CHRISTMAS DAY** *Gloria, Creed – genuflect at* Incarnatus, *Proper Preface &* Communicantes. All priests may celebrate three Masses today, provided that they are celebrated at their proper time.
26 Tues	R	ST STEPHEN, Protomartyr *Gloria, Preface &* Communicantes *of Christmas*
27 Wed	R	ST JOHN, Apostle & Evangelist *Gloria, Preface &* Communicantes *of Christmas*
28 Thurs	R	HOLY INNOCENTS, Martyrs *Gloria, Preface &* Communicantes *of Christmas*
29 Fri	W	FIFTH DAY IN THE OCTAVE OF CHRISTMAS *Gloria, Preface &* Communicantes *of Christmas* (St Thomas Becket) *national*
30 Sat	W	SIXTH DAY IN THE OCTAVE OF CHRISTMAS *Gloria, Preface &* Communicantes *of Christmas*
31 Sun	W	+ HOLY FAMILY OF JESUS, MARY & JOSEPH *Gloria, Creed, Preface & Communicantes of Christmas*

JANUARY 2007

Date	Colour	Celebration
01 Mon	W	**OCTAVE DAY OF CHRISTMAS** **SOLEMNITY OF MARY, MOTHER OF GOD** *Gloria, Creed, Preface of B.V. Mary I 'as we celebrate the motherhood…',* Communicantes *of Christmas*
02 Tues	W	SS Basil the Great & Gregory Nazianzen, Bishops & Doctors *Ps Week 2*
03 Wed	W W	Christmas feria *or* Most Holy Name of Jesus *Readings from this Votive Mass in Lectionary volume III*

JANUARY 2007

04 Thurs	W	Christmas feria
05 Fri	W	Christmas feria
06 Sat	W	Christmas feria
evening	W	First Vespers and Mass of the Epiphany *The* Missale Romanum, editio typica tertia, *gives texts for a Vigil Mass of the Epiphany different from those of the Mass of the day.*
07 Sun	W	**+ EPIPHANY OF THE LORD** *Gloria, Creed, Proper Preface &* Communicantes *At today's Mass, after the Gospel, the announcement may be made of moveable feasts according to the formula given in the Roman Pontifical, and on page 1247 of the* Missale Romanum, editio typica tertia

INDEX

INDEX OF ADVERTISERS

We thank our Advertisers

Please quote Westminster Year Book 2006 when contacting them

TELEPHONE DIRECTORY

Archbishop's House	020 7798 9033
Bishop Hopes	020 7798 9043
Bishop Longley	020 7931 6061
Bishop Stack	020 7798 9060
Mgr John Arnold	020 7931 6062
Mgr Ralph Brown ProtAp	020 7798 9035
Fr Martin Hayes	020 7349 5782
All Saints Pastoral Centre	01727 822010
Administration Reception	020 7798 9009
Administration Finance	020 7798 9002
Administration Personnel	020 7798 9001
Admin Planned Giving	020 7798 9004
Administration Property	020 7798 9000
Archives	020 7938 3580
Cardinal Hume Centre	020 7222 1602
Cathedral	020 7798 9055
Chancellor	020 7798 9037
Child Protection Issues	020 8969 5305
Children's Society	020 8969 5305
Clergy & Consecrated Life, Dept for	020 7798 9033
Diocesan Pastoral Board	020 7798 9008
Ecumenism & Interfaith, Dept for	020 7798 9033
Education & Formation, Dept for	020 7798 9013
Education: Parish Datechetical Support	020 8202 3611
Education: Schools Support	020 7798 9005
Hospitals Co-ordinator	020 7349 5609
Pastoral Affairs, Dept for	020 7798 9363
St Joseph's Centre	020 8202 3999
Seminary	020 7349 5600
Surveyor: Parish Building	020 8202 2695
Surveyor: School Building	020 7798 9015
The Passage	020 7828 4183
Tribunal	020 7798 9003

Vaughan House: Reception	020 7798 9009
Vocations Director	020 7798 9083
Westminster Record	020 7405 1061
Westminster Year Book	020 7798 9092
Abbots Langley	01923 265646
Acton	020 8992 2014
Acton (East)	020 8743 5732
Acton (West)	020 8992 1308
Ashford	01784 252230
Baldock	01462 893127
Barnet	020 8449 3338
Bayswater	020 7229 0487
Berkhamsted	01442 863845
Bethnal Green	020 8980 1968
Bishop's Stortford	01279 654063
Borehamwood	020 8953 1294
Borehamwood (North)	020 8953 0715
Bow	020 8980 3961
Bow Common	020 7987 3477
Brentford	020 8560 1671
Brook Green	020 7603 3832
Bunhill Row	020 7628 0326
Buntingford	01763 271471
Burnt Oak	020 8959 1971
Bushey & Oxhey	020 8950 2077
Camden Town	020 7485 2727
Carpenders Park	020 8428 2774
Chelsea (1)	020 7589 5487
Chelsea (2)	020 7352 0777
Cheshunt	01992 629878
Chipperfield	01923 265327
Chiswick	020 8994 2877
Chorleywood	01923 283616
Clapton	020 8985 2178
Clapton Park	020 8525 1929
Clerkenwell	020 7837 2094
Cockfosters	020 8449 6648
Commercial Road	020 7790 5911

Copenhagen Street	020 7837 4841
Cranford	020 8759 2160
Cricklewood	020 8452 2475
Croxley Green	01923 231969
Cuffley	01707 873308
Dollis Hill	020 8452 6158
Ealing	020 8862 2160
Eastcote	020 8866 6581
Edgware	020 8952 0663
Edmonton	020 8803 6631
Ely Place	020 7405 1061
Enfield	020 8363 2569
Farm Street	020 7493 7811
Feltham	020 8890 2367
Finchley (Church End)	020 8346 2459
Finchley (East)	020 8883 4234
Finchley (North)	020 8446 0224
French Church	020 7437 9363
Fulham	020 7385 4040
Fulham Road	020 7352 6965
Garston	01923 673239
German Church	020 7247 9529
Golders Green	020 8455 1300
Grahame Park	020 8205 6830
Greenford	020 8578 1363
Grove Park	020 8994 6861
Gunnersbury	020 8992 5037
Hackney	020 8985 2496
Hammersmith	020 8748 3788
Hampstead	020 7435 6678
Hampton Hill	020 8977 1415
Hampton-on-Thames	020 8979 3596
Hanwell	020 8567 4056
Harefield	01895 822365
Harpenden	01582 712245
Harringay	020 8348 1378
Harrow-on-the-Hill	020 8422 2513
Harrow (North)	020 8868 7531
Harrow (South)	020 8864 5455
Harrow Road	020 7286 2170
Hatfield	01707 262439
Hatfield (South)	01707 262121
Haverstock Hill	020 7485 5491
Hayes	020 8573 2065
Headstone Lane	020 8428 3260
Hemel Hempstead (Boxmoor & West)	01442 391759
Hemel Hempstead (East)	01442 255471
Hemel Hempstead (North)	01442 259141
Hendon	020 8202 0560
Hendon (West)	020 8202 5143
Hertford	01992 582109
Heston	020 8570 1818
Highbury	020 7226 0257
Highgate	020 7272 2320
Hillingdon	01895 234577
Hitchin	01462 459126
Hoddesdon	01992 440986
Holloway	020 7607 3594
Homerton	020 8985 1495
Hounslow	020 8570 1693
Hoxton	020 7739 5006
Isleworth	020 8560 1431
Islington	020 7226 3277
Italian Church	020 7837 1528
Kensal New Town	020 8969 2660
Kensal Rise	020 8964 4040
Kensington (1)	020 7937 4778
Kensington (2)	020 7937 9866
Kentish Town	020 7485 4023
Kenton	020 8204 3550
Kilburn	020 7624 1701
Kilburn West	020 7624 2188
Kingsbury Green	020 8204 2834
Kingsland	020 7254 4378
Knebworth	01438 813303
Laxton Place	020 7387 3833
Letchworth	01462 683504
Limehouse	020 7987 3563

Lincoln's Inn Fields	020 7405 0376
Lithuanian Church	020 7739 8735
London Airport (Heathrow)	020 8745 4261
London Colney	01727 822218
London Colney All Saints Pastoral Centre	01727 822010
Maiden Lane	020 7836 4700
Manor House	020 8802 9910
Marylebone	020 7723 5101
Mile End	020 8980 1845
Mill End	01923 779890
Mill Hill	020 8959 1021
Millwall	020 7987 4114
Moorfields	020 7247 8390
Much Hadham	01279 842354
Muswell Hill	020 8883 5607
Neasden	020 8451 0367
New Barnet	020 8449 1961
New Southgate	020 8368 1638
Northfields	020 8567 5421
Northwood	01923 825639
Notting Hill	020 7727 7968
Ogle Street	020 7636 2883
Old Hall Green	01920 821113
Oratory	020 7589 4811
Osterley	020 8560 4737
Paddington	020 7286 2672
Palmers Green	020 8886 9568
Parsons Green	020 7736 1068
Perivale	020 8997 3164
Pimlico	020 7834 6965
Pinner	020 8866 0098
Polish (Ealing)	020 8567 1746
Polish (Islington)	020 7226 9944
Polish (Shepherds Bush)	020 8743 8848
Ponders End	020 8804 2149
Poplar	020 7987 4523
Potters Bar	01707 654359
Puckeridge	01920 821113
Queensway	020 7229 8153
Radlett	01923 856165
Redbourn	01582 792270
Rickmansworth	01923 773387
Royston	01763 243117
Ruislip	01895 632739
Ruislip (South)	020 8845 2186
St Albans	01727 853585
St Albans (South)	01727 850066
St Charles Square	020 8969 6844
St John's Wood	020 7286 3214
St Margaret's-on-Thames	020 8892 3902
Shenley	01923 857005
Shepherds Bush	020 8743 5196
Shepperton	01932 563116
Soho Square	020 7437 2010
Somers Town	020 7387 1971
Southall	020 8574 3300
Spanish Place	020 7935 0943
Staines	01784 452381
Stamford Hill	020 8800 2121
Stanmore	020 8954 1299
Stanwell	01784 255973
Stephendale Road	020 7736 4864
Stevenage (Bedwell)	01438 351243
Stevenage (Old Town)	01438 226857
Stevenage (Shephall)	01438 352182
Stoke Newington	020 8800 5250
Stonebridge	020 8965 3313
Stroud Green	020 8340 3394
Sudbury	020 8904 2552
Sunbury-on-Thames	01932 783507
Swiss Cottage	020 7435 1388
Teddington	020 8977 2986
Tollington Park	020 7272 3415
Tottenham	020 8808 3554
Tower Hill	020 7488 4654
Tring	01442 823161
Twickenham	020 8892 4578
Ukrainian Cathedral	020 7629 1534

Underwood Road	020 7247 7833
University Chaplaincy	020 7387 6370
Upper Holloway	020 7272 8195
Uxbridge	01895 233193
Waltham Cross	01992 623156
Wapping	020 7481 2202
Ware	01920 462140
Warwick Street	020 7437 1525
Watford	01923 224085
Watford (North)	01923 223175
Wealdstone	020 8427 1955
Welwyn Garden	01707 322579
Welwyn Garden (East)	01707 323234
Welwyn Garden (Digswell)	01707 327434
Wembley	020 8902 0081
Wembley Park	020 8904 2306
Wembley/Preston Road	020 8904 6031
West Drayton	01895 442777
West Green	020 8888 5518
Westminster Cathedral	020 7798 9055
Wheathampstead	01582 832114
Whetstone	020 8445 0838
White City	020 8743 8334
Whitton	020 8894 9923
Willesden	020 8965 4935
Willesden Green	020 8451 4677
Wood Green	020 8888 2390
Yeading	020 8845 1919

Name	Telephone Number

Personal Telephone Numbers

Name	Telephone Number

Notes